CHANGING BRAINS

This book celebrates the pioneering work and contributions of Helen J. Neville, who conducted seminal neuroimaging work using electroencephalography (EEG) and functional magnetic resonance imaging (fMRI) to illustrate the role that experience plays in shaping the brain.

Bringing together her former students, collaborators, and colleagues, the book presents essays and original empirical research that pay tribute to Helen Neville's groundbreaking work. The chapters discuss her contributions to our knowledge of neuroplasticity in perception, attention, and language, and how they inspired more recent developments in these and related areas, such as work on deafness (changes in sign language processing with age and the effects of cochlear implants on language development), the early stages of reading, memory consolidation during sleep, and the connection between attentional and memory systems. The book also discusses her strong commitment to rigorous science that could be translated into real-world practice through social interventions to improve neurodevelopmental outcomes. It additionally includes short poems by Marta Kutas interspersed between chapters that are inspired by Helen's work and highlight her contributions, values, and ideas.

The book showcases Helen Neville's legacy to the field of neuroscience and is a must-read for all students and researchers of neuroplasticity and developmental cognitive neuroscience.

Aaron J. Newman is Professor at Dalhousie University, Chair of the Department of Psychology & Neuroscience, and Director of the NeuroCognitive Imaging Lab. His research program in cognitive neuroscience focuses on how the brain organization for language, hearing, and vision can be altered by experience.

Giordana Grossi is Professor of Psychology at the State University of New York at New Paltz and Director of the Brain and Cognition Lab. Her empirical work, which employs both behavioral and electrophysiological measures, explores aspects of automaticity and expertise in visual word recognition in both monolinguals and bilinguals.

CHANGING BRAINS

Essays on Neuroplasticity in Honor of Helen J. Neville

Edited by Aaron J. Newman and Giordana Grossi

Routledge
Taylor & Francis Group

NEW YORK AND LONDON

Designed cover image: © Getty

First published 2023
by Routledge
605 Third Avenue, New York, NY 10158

and by Routledge
4 Park Square, Milton Park, Abingdon, Oxon, OX14 4RN

Routledge is an imprint of the Taylor & Francis Group, an informa business

ISBN: 9780367358679 (hbk)
ISBN: 9780367358693 (pbk)
ISBN: 9780429342356 (ebk)

DOI: 10.4324/9780429342356

Typeset in Bembo
by Apex CoVantage, LLC

TABLE OF CONTENTS

FIGURES

CONTRIBUTORS

Annika Andersson
Department of Swedish, Linnaeus University, Sweden.
Annika Andersson teaches second language acquisition at Linnaeus University in Sweden. She researches first and second languages in children and adults by combining demographic and proficiency measures with event-related potentials to measure phonological, semantic, and syntactic processing with the aim of understanding the factors involved in achieving language proficiency.

Daphné Bavelier
Faculty of Psychology and Science of Education, University of Geneva, Switzerland.
Bavelier trained as a cognitive neuroscientist in Neville's laboratory (1992–1997) and collaborated with Helen on the first functional MRI study on the neural bases of American Sign Language. Bavelier's work still focuses on how the brain adapts to changes in experience (e.g., deafness and playing video games).

David P. Corina
Department of Linguistics and Center for Mind and Brain, University of California, Davis, USA.
David P. Corina, Ph.D., is Professor in the Departments of Linguistics and Psychology and Director of the Cognitive Neurolinguistics Laboratory at the Center for Mind and Brain at U.C. Davis. His work investigates the neural processing of signed and spoken languages.

Matthew W.G. Dye
National Technical Institute for the Deaf, Rochester Institute of Technology, Rochester, USA.

Matthew W.G. Dye is Director of the SPACE Center at the National Technical Institute for the Deaf where he oversees a research program that seeks to characterize the perceptual and cognitive abilities of deaf individuals. His research is funded by NIH, NSF, and private foundations.

Julia Föcker
School of Psychology, University of Lincoln, UK.
Julia Föcker obtained her Ph.D. at the University of Hamburg, Germany, and completed her postdoctoral fellowship at the University of Rochester, USA, and the University of Geneva, Switzerland. She was previously Assistant Professor at the Ludwig-Maximilians-University Munich. Her research focuses on neural plasticity after video game experience and visual deprivation.

Giordana Grossi
Department of Psychology, State University of New York, New Paltz, USA.
Giordana Grossi is Professor of Psychology at SUNY New Paltz. She was a postdoctoral fellow in Helen Neville's lab from 1997 to 2001. Her empirical work, which employs both behavioral and electrophysiological measures, explores aspects of automaticity and expertise in visual word recognition in both monolinguals and bilinguals.

Amanda Hampton Wray
Department of Communication Science and Disorders, University of Pittsburgh, USA
Amanda Hampton Wray, Ph.D., CCC-SLP, is Assistant Professor of Communication Science and Disorders at the University of Pittsburgh. She completed postdoctoral training with Helen Neville at the University of Oregon. Her research examines the development of brain functions mediating language and attention in individuals with typical development and with communication disorders.

Peter C. Hauser
National Technical Institute for the Deaf, Rochester Institute of Technology, Rochester, NY, USA.
Peter C. Hauser is Director of the Language Acquisition and Assessment Laboratory (LAA) at NTID; his research aims to understand how different individuals learn a signed language and to create theory-based sign language proficiency with evidence of psychometric validity and reliability.

Randolph F. Helfrich
Center for Neurology, University of Tübingen, Germany.
Randolph F. Helfrich is a clinician-scientist in neurology and heads the Human Intracranial Cognitive Neurophysiology lab at the University of Tübingen. In his research, he employs electrophysiology to understand the neural basis of goal-directed and flexible human behavior.

Steven A. Hillyard

Department of Neuroscience, University of California, San Diego, USA.
Steven A. Hillyard is a pioneer in the use of electrophysiological and neuroimaging techniques to study the neural bases of perceptual and cognitive processes in the human brain. He collaborated with Helen Neville in studies of selective attention and brain plasticity in blind and deaf individuals.

Elizabeth A. Hirshorn

Department of Psychology, State University of New York, New Paltz, USA.
Elizabeth A. Hirshorn is Assistant Professor of Psychology at SUNY New Paltz where she oversees the Diversity in Language Lab. She researches differences in routes to successful reading due to external factors such as writing system or individual differences in reading procedures due to deafness or other cognitive factors.

Elif Isbell

Department of Psychological Sciences, University of California, Merced, USA.
Dr. Isbell is Assistant Professor at the University of California Merced. She received her Ph.D. under Helen Neville's mentorship at the University of Oregon. Her research focuses on the neurodevelopment and plasticity of children's cognitive control, within the broader context of children's socioeconomic and cultural backgrounds.

Wayne Khoe

Department of Neuroscience, University of California, San Diego, USA.
Wayne Khoe is a cognitive neuroscientist who has studied the neural mechanisms of memory, visual perception, and selective attention in humans using both behavioral and electrophysiological techniques.

Robert T. Knight

Departments of Psychology and Neuroscience, University of California, Berkeley, USA.
Dr. Knight has received many awards, among which are the Distinguished Career Contribution Award from the Cognitive Neuroscience Society and the Howard Crosby Warren Medal for Distinguished Career Contributions to Psychological Research. His laboratory records intracranial EEG to understand the role of the prefrontal cortex in goal-directed behavior.

Marta Kutas

Departments of Cognitive Science and Neuroscience, University of California, San Diego, USA.
Marta Kutas is Distinguished Professor in the Departments of Cognitive Science and Neurosciences and the Director of the Center for Research in Language at the University of California, San Diego. Kutas was fortunate to have met Helen Neville in 1978 and to collaborate with her on several projects.

Todd LaMarr
Humanities Department, American River College, Sacramento, USA.
Todd LaMarr is Professor of Early Childhood Education at American River College. Before joining the College, he researched language and brain development of deaf children with cochlear implants, and early sign language development of Deaf and hearing native signing toddlers at UC Davis and Stanford University, respectively.

Laurel A. Lawyer
Department of Language and Linguistics, University of Essex, UK.
Laurel A. Lawyer is Senior Lecturer in Psycholinguistics, Member of the Centre for Research in Language Development throughout the Lifespan, and Director of the L+PLUS Lab at the University of Essex. Her research focuses on lexical and syntactic processing in spoken and signed languages, in adults and school-aged children.

Mairéad MacSweeney
University College London, England, UK.
Mairéad MacSweeney is the Director of the Deafness, Cognition and Language Research Centre at University College London. She is also the leader of the Visual Communication Research Group at the UCL Institute of Cognitive Neuroscience. She is a Wellcome Senior Research Fellow.

Debra L. Mills
School of Human and Behavioural Sciences, Bangor University, Wales.
Professor Mills studies the effects of experience on brain plasticity and cognition across the lifespan. Her research uses a combined behavioral and electrophysiological approach to study brain and language development as well as investigate links across genes, brain, and social cognition in neurodevelopmental disorders such as Williams Syndrome.

Matin Mortazavi
Department of Psychiatry and Psychotherapy, LMU Klinikum, Munich, Germany.
Matin Mortazavi is a researcher of neuroscience interested in brain plasticity and its relation to neuroinflammation and degeneration.

Aaron J. Newman
Department of Psychology and Neuroscience, Dalhousie University, Canada.
Aaron J. Newman is Professor at Dalhousie University, where he is Chair of the Department of Psychology and Neuroscience and Director of the Neuro-Cognitive Imaging Lab. Dr. Newman's research program in cognitive neuroscience focuses on how brain organization for language, hearing, and vision can be altered by experience.

Lucinda O'Grady Farnady
Laboratory for Language and Cognitive Neuroscience, San Diego State University, USA.
Lucinda O'Grady Farnady is a native signer and has been involved in sign language research for over 20 years. She works as a researcher in the Laboratory for Language and Cognitive Neuroscience, and assists researchers on a variety of projects. She provides Deaf community outreach, and assists in subject recruitment.

Eric Pakulak
Department of Child and Youth Studies, Stockholm University, Sweden.
Eric Pakulak is Assistant Professor in the Department of Child and Youth Studies at Stockholm University, Sweden. His research interests are the neuroplasticity of brain systems important for language and self-regulation in the context of early adversity and the development and implementation of evidence-based training programs for families.

Svenna Pedersen
Salk Institute, San Diego, USA.
Svenna Pedersen grew up in a third-generation-signing Deaf family and is an American Sign Language (ASL) professor at several universities and colleges. Her passion for ASL and Deaf culture has allowed her to immerse herself in the research field of studying how sign language impacts the brain.

Michael I. Posner
Department of Psychology, University of Oregon, USA.
Michael I. Posner studied how mental operations, particularly those related to attention, are carried out by neural networks. He continues research as Professor Emeritus of Psychology at the University of Oregon and Adjunct Professor at Weill Medical College. He has received many honors including the National Medal of Science by President Obama.

Mary K. Rothbart
Department of Psychology, University of Oregon, USA.
Mary K. Rothbart has done research on individual differences in temperament, emotion, attention, and social development. She has developed widely used measures in these areas and contributed to programs of parent training. She has received lifetime awards in the areas of infancy, child development, personality, and psychology as a science.

Elizabeth Sacchi
Binghamton University, USA.
Elizabeth Sacchi, Ph.D., is a cognitive neuroscientist with experience in using reading ability to predict neural representations of text. She is currently Clinical Data Scientist in Cambridge, MA.

Courtney Stevens
Department of Psychology, Willamette University, USA.
Courtney Stevens, Ph.D., is Professor of Psychology at Willamette University. Her research examines the effects of experience on cognitive and brain development, with an emphasis on the development of selective attention and its relationship to other cognitive skills.

Ted Supalla
Department of Neurology, Georgetown University, USA.
Ted Supalla, Ph.D., is a Professor of Neurology, Linguistics, and Psychology at Georgetown University Medical Center; he runs the Sign Language Research Lab, a part of the Center on Brain Plasticity and Recovery. He has published extensively on the structure of American Sign Language and other sign languages of the world.

Kurt Winsler
Center for Mind and Brain, University of California, Davis, USA.
Kurt Winsler is a Ph.D. student at the Center for Mind and Brain at the University of California–Davis. His research is focused on human visual perception and applied statistical modeling.

FOREWORD: BEING A SCIENTIST IN THE NEVILLE TRADITION

Ten things I learned from Helen

Debra L. Mills

Helen Neville had a profound influence on everyone fortunate enough to spend time in her lab. If all scientists conducted research the way Helen did, there would not be a crisis regarding replicability nor would there be a problem with understanding the implications of findings across levels of analysis. The time spent under Helen Neville's mentorship shaped the foundation of my expertise in event-related potential (ERP) methods, how I approach questions as a scientist, how I write a paper, the connections I have with so many of the top scientists in the field, how I teach my students, run my lab, give a talk, and much more.

A long-time friend and mentor, I had the pleasure of knowing Helen Neville for over 30 years. My time in Helen's lab started in the 1980s at the Salk Institute and continued to the mid-1990s at the University of California, San Diego. Her lab had everything that an aspiring post-doc could hope for. Helen was a highly critical thinker and not easily impressed. So, when she praised your work, it was powerful. The lab atmosphere was vibrant, stimulating, highly rigorous, and full of creative ideas. There were often famous scientists visiting, including more than one Nobel laureate, and even an astronaut. From our office window, we watched whales breaching in January, the occasional mountain lion saunter past in the brush, and once saw a movie starring Richard Gere being filmed in the parking lot below. In fact, it was so idyllic, I wasn't the only post-doc to spend a decade or more with her. Helen was beloved by her post-docs, students, and staff alike. In addition to being a brilliant scientist, Helen was a lot of fun and could be a wild and crazy person. And at least when I was in her lab, her ability to find creative parking spaces, legal or not, was legendary.

To say that Helen was a dynamic speaker is somewhat of an understatement. She delivered well over 100 distinguished lectures and invited addresses all over the world. Often when I would try to contact Helen, she was in some exotic

DOI: 10.4324/9780429342356-1

place such as giving the keynote speech at the Symposium for Queen's 60th Birthday in Stockholm, in India with the Dalai Lama, or having an audience with the Pope. As a Ph.D. student, I had the opportunity to hear Helen speak for the first time in a graduate seminar led by Professor Liz Bates. Although I had always been interested in neuropsychology (as it was called then), I was a die-hard behaviorist at the time. After Helen's talk, I told Liz, "That's it – this is what I'm going to do in my life!" Liz said, "Oh, Helen has that effect on everyone – *that woman* could read the phone book and keep everyone on the edge of their seats. Don't worry, it will pass." Thank goodness, this is one time I didn't listen to Liz. I was still a Ph.D. student when I started a "post-doc" in Helen's lab. My true education as a scientist started there.

The focus of this chapter is to share some of the main lessons I learned from Helen Neville.

Ten things I learned from Helen

1. Choose your words carefully for meaning

In addition to being a dynamic speaker, Helen wrote beautifully. Helen's papers will always provide a source of inspiration for how to phrase an idea. The first time I wrote a draft of an ERP paper, I tried to emulate Helen's eloquent prose and used my most erudite and sophisticated vocabulary. I thought it sounded pretty good. Helen's feedback was "What does this sentence mean? It doesn't mean anything. Choose your words carefully for meaning." This last phrase is something I write on just about every student's draft of a paper. Helen taught me to choose words for specific meaning rather than trying to sound smart. She then told me something surprising. She said, "I *suffer* for my sentences." Being precise and concise takes work. It is comforting to know that even Helen had to write and rewrite sentences to find the right words.

2. Carefully check your data (especially when it makes sense and things are going well)

The first year I was in Helen's lab, there was a technical problem that led to intermittent errors in the log files from an experiment. Helen stopped all testing in the lab until the problem was diagnosed and fixed and all data collected across *all* paradigms had been checked. She took accuracy very seriously, and there was no complacency surrounding errors. After my first ERP paper as first-author had been accepted for publication in the *Journal of Cognitive Neuroscience*, I noticed an error in one of the text files used to average the ERPs. The error changed the electrode locations and created an asymmetry that wasn't really there. I was horrified at the mistake and was absolutely terrified to tell Helen. I briefly thought of not saying anything and just leaving science altogether. When I got the courage to tell her, she was incredibly understanding and very happy that I found the error before the paper went into print. She said this happens, just tell the editor and adjust the results and discussion accordingly. I did, and the editor was very understanding too. Helen cared about the findings, not the publications. "Quick and dirty" publication of an interesting finding was not an option. When we published findings from one or two age groups, she needed to know what happened before and after that developmental period. Helen didn't focus on finding results that confirmed her hypotheses, but she cared about finding the correct answers.

3. Carefully look at your data for individual differences

Finding my first statistically significant differences in ERP amplitudes and latencies between experimental conditions in the predicted time windows at the predicted locations was thrilling. When I showed Helen the statistics output, instead of sharing my excitement she asked "How many infants show this effect?" It was a question she always asked. To this day I start looking at data by creating a scatterplot to look at the individual data and count how many participants show the effect. Reporting a finding that is due to a small number of participants who show a large effect, is very different from reporting findings that are consistent at the individual level.

4. Understand what the data mean

Of course, starting with a rigorous experimental design is the key to understanding what the results mean. There are well-established ERP paradigms to elicit known components, but sometimes when asking a new question there isn't already an ERP paradigm. My first ERP study with infants examined differences in brain activity to known words, unknown words, and backward words in 20-month-olds. Way back in the late 1980s, we didn't really know what blinks and other artifacts might look like in infants. Helen had me score videotapes of the infants on each trial and then compare those findings to the electroencephalography (EEG) observed for each auditory stimulus. I also remember sitting side by side with Helen looking at the EEG on individual trials trying to guess whether the child did or did not know the meaning of the word. Helen stressed that ERP effects had to be understood in relation to the cognitive functions they represent. ERP differences in amplitude and latency don't mean anything by themselves. You can't go backward from the ERP effect and infer a change in cognition.

5. Post hoc ergo propter hoc (NOT)

A point related to *understand what the data mean*, is not to interpret correlations as casual. The lab T-shirts for Helen's Brain Development Lab at the University of

Oregon had the logo "Post hoc ergo propter hoc" enclosed in a big red prohibition circle (NOT). The translation from Latin is "after this, therefore because of this." Don't assume that temporal order, or any form of correlation, implies causality. The story behind how that phrase ended up on the lab T-shirts is for someone in the Oregon lab to tell.

6. We don't study ERPs

One bit of best practice I adopted from Helen's lab is to have regular individual meetings with Ph.D. students to informally discuss updates on individual studies. The meetings with Helen, I remember, mostly took place in her office at the Salk Institute overlooking the Pacific Ocean, often with her dog under the desk. They were usually insightful, but I have to admit I was also a little terrified of making mistakes. Early in my post-doc, when Helen asked me to summarize the main findings of a study, I made the "mistake" of focusing the discussion on the development of a particular ERP component. Helen made it clear that we don't study ERPs. We are interested in larger questions about brain and language development, and particularly in the extent to which experience with language could shape brain organization. She explained that ERPs are a tool for measuring brain activity. ERP component amplitudes and latencies are simply a different kind of dependent measure. They don't mean anything by themselves. She said that some researchers have conducted studies about what modulates the amplitudes and latencies of different components, which is important to know, but that is not what this lab is about. I make this a strong point with my own research students as well as in class when lecturing on ERPs. Having recently co-authored a systematic review of the development of the N400, I know this is an important question, but still feel a small twinge of disapproval.

7. What does this study tell us about the brain?

Some lab meetings included discussion of recent ERP papers. Back in the 1980s, infant ERP papers were not as methodologically rigorous as they are now. It was relatively easy to come up with critical remarks. I remember Helen getting riled up when a journal article title included "ERP correlates of . . .. " When asked why was *that* so bad, she said ERPs are not "neural correlates." ERPs are not "correlated" with brain activity. They are a *direct index* of neural activity. ERPs are not just a fancy way of measuring reaction time. If you use ERPs, the study needs to tell you something about the brain. Saying an ERP effect is "neural evidence" of X, isn't the same as making a statement about brain organization or development. In order to have important results that say something about the brain, we must start with asking important questions and using the appropriate experimental design.

8. Ask important questions

Helen didn't see the point in asking small questions. Her studies were paradigm-shifting from the beginning. Her Ph.D. dissertation extended Eric Lenneberg's critical periods hypothesis to study the effects of altered early auditory experience on brain plasticity in congenitally deaf children. She went on to study brain plasticity and sensitive periods for language throughout her career and was one of the world's leaders in the field. Helen had many areas of interest. I was fortunate to be involved in the developmental questions. She was a leader in developmental cognitive neuroscience asking how the brain becomes specialized for language. Her questions guided our developmental research. She wanted to know how specializations for language arise. Are these specializations apparent at birth or do they develop? If they develop, what is the nature of the mechanism underlying this development? Does it stem from the maturation of different brain regions, which then allow the development of specific cognitive abilities, or do these specializations arise as a function of experience and learning? Helen did not approach these questions from an either/or perspective and did not frame the question with the intent of confirming a particular hypothesis. To this end, she often collaborated with people from different theoretical positions to examine the extent to which a variety of different factors affect functional specializations. This type of research isn't fast nor are there always immediate applications to the "real world." But it is the best kind of science.

9. Go to the Hillyard and Kutas lab meetings

This heading refers to the advice to get out of your comfort zone and learn everything you can from the resources available to you. My Ph.D. was focused on cognitive development and applied behavior analysis. If I wanted to become a cognitive neuroscientist through my post-doc, I had a lot of work to do. Helen said she felt personally responsible for my training in ERP methods, but wanted me to be exposed to other ways of thinking too. Fortunately, Helen had strong connections with two of the most prominent ERP labs in the world, also at the University of California, San Diego (UCSD): Steven A. Hillyard and Marta Kutas. I took Helen's advice and can't even begin to describe how important those experiences were. Being pushed to get out of my comfort zone taught me not only a lot about ERPs but also to grow a thick skin and feel at home when challenged. Helen's connections with other giants in the field and her willingness to make sure her lab member met them were invaluable in setting up the careers of people in her lab.

10. How to bounce back when things get tough

I'm not going to go into the specifics of how things got tough for Helen during my time in her lab. I will say that she was a model of resilience. She would bounce back and do something phenomenal. Not only that, when things got tough for me, she went above and beyond to support me even though I had been out of her lab for over 10 years. She welcomed me back into her lab, provided training on fMRI analysis, and even offered me a temporary job. I didn't take it, but it was very reassuring to know I had the option to go "home." From that experience I got to know the people in the Brain Development Lab at Oregon and feel part of a large extended academic family. I secretly refer to us as "The spawn of the Neville." So, when the going gets tough, brush yourself off and do something phenomenal in Helen's honor.

INTRODUCTION

Aaron J. Newman and Giordana Grossi

Used with permission from the University of Oregon

This book celebrates and honors the career and seminal contributions of the late Helen J. Neville (1946–2018), Ph.D., Professor Emerita, and the Robert and Beverly Lewis Endowed Chair in Cognitive Neuroscience, Department of Psychology, University of Oregon. Over her more than 40-year career, Helen published 128 peer-reviewed articles and book chapters, was cited over 10,000

DOI: 10.4324/9780429342356-2

times, and has an *h*-index of 81 (according to Google Scholar, accessed June 8, 2022). She was the recipient of many honors and awards, including the election to the National Academy of Arts and Science (2007) and the National Academy of Science (2014). Other notable awards include the William James Fellow Awards from the Association for Psychological Science (2012) and the Foundation Ipsen Neuronal Plasticity Award (2011). She was regularly invited to give keynote addresses at academic conferences (e.g., Cognitive Development Society Biennial Meeting in 2005; International Mind, Brain, and Education Society meeting in 2011), and at events on brain development that demonstrated her stature as a scholar, like the Symposium for the Queen of Sweden's 60th Birthday in Stockholm and an audience with the Pope.

Helen conducted pioneering neuroimaging work on neuroplasticity with humans, carefully connecting neuroimaging data with behavior and cognition – first using electroencephalography (EEG), and then functional magnetic resonance imaging (fMRI) when the technique was developed in the 1990s. As Drs Michael I. Posner and Mary K. Rothbart write in this volume, "The idea that brain structure changes with experience took a long time to gain acceptance in neuroscience. It is now well established, however, thanks in part to the studies of Helen Neville of deaf persons and the primate studies of Michael Merzenich on how experience shapes sensory systems. The combination of human and animal work convinced cellular neuroscientists of structural change and provided evidence that sensory alterations could shape important aspects of perceived experience in humans."

One of the remarkable strengths of Helen's work was that although she worked primarily at the level of non-invasive, lab-based studies of humans, she constantly and passionately worked to connect her work in humans to both more fine-grained levels of cellular and molecular neuroscience, and interventions at the community and societal levels. She connected her work with research in animals on underlying chemical, cellular, and physiological mechanisms of neuroplasticity and brain development to better understand how the changes observed in her research came about. She also engaged in societal-level work with economists and community organizations to implement and test interventions to encourage positive brain development. In the latter phase of her career, Helen's work was primarily focused on developing and testing interventions to improve neurodevelopmental outcomes of children from low socioeconomic status families. In recognition of the importance of this work and Helen's legacy, all proceeds from the sales of this book will be donated to Head Start of Lane County, an organization that Helen and her lab worked with in developing and validating these interventions, and that carries on this work today.

Biographical background

Helen was born in 1946 in Unity, Saskatchewan, Canada, although she grew up in Vancouver, British Columbia. She received her B.A. from the University of

British Columbia and a master's degree from Simon Fraser University (where she also met her first husband, Philip). As a child Helen was described as full of curiosity, enthusiasm, questions, eagerness to 'help', teach and be an older sister role model to her three younger siblings, and then a "wild" teen and young adult, getting into all manner of adventures and trouble. According to Helen, following completion of her master's degree, she headed off to Montreal to "join the revolution," and ended up working in a lab at the University of Sussex in Brighton, England. Around that time she read Eric Lenneberg's seminal work on the biological foundations of language, and the theory of a critical period for language acquisition. Inspired by this work, she wrote to Lenneberg, who accepted her as a Ph.D. student at Cornell University. Fascinated by brain development and desiring to study it in vivo in humans, upon completion of her doctorate Helen moved to the University of California, San Diego (UCSD) for a postdoctoral fellowship in the lab of Steven A. Hillyard, a leading expert in the event-related potential (ERP) neuroimaging technique. San Diego was (and still is) a hotbed of research involving ERPs, and Helen found an intellectual home there, first establishing the Neuropsychology Laboratory at the Salk Institute and then the Laboratory of Brain Development at UCSD, conducting seminal ERP studies on attention, language, and neuroplasticity. In 1995, she joined the Department of Psychology at the University of Oregon, where she established the Brain Development Lab and stayed until the end of her career. At the University of Oregon, Helen was instrumental in building on the university's existing strength in neuroscience, in particular in establishing the Robert and Beverly Lewis Center for Neuroimaging, an on-campus MRI research center, and the construction of the Lewis Integrative Science Building.

Personally, Helen was a force of nature. She was passionate about many things, including science, social justice, music, and the arts. She was persistent and unwavering in her pursuit of knowledge, and never shied away from asking hard questions or criticizing others – especially if she felt they were cutting corners, scientifically, or bending the truth. She demanded the highest standards of her own work, as Debra L. Mills details in the Foreword. She embodied the adage of "work hard, play hard" and would return from scientific meetings with equal measures of excitement for new scientific knowledge and the artistic and cultural wonders of wherever she had visited. Helen imbued these values and passion in her trainees as well. She could be a fearsome figure when presenting new data to her, asking cutting questions, providing earnest feedback, and pushing her trainees to ever-greater levels of scientific rigor and critical thinking. But on the other hand, she was fiercely supportive and defensive of her trainees and provided them with every opportunity she could, to travel and grow scientifically and as individuals. She also frequently invited her trainees out to barbecues and parties at the beautiful house and property where she lived with her son, Justin, and her many dogs and cats outside of Eugene, Oregon. Indeed, some of us remember going up before the house was built to help haul logs from the property to be milled for the house's trim!

Outreach and impact

Helen's impact went beyond the classroom and the halls of academia. She shared her passion for understanding reality through rigorous science with the general public in multiple ways. She started an energetic outreach program and visited local schools regularly. During these visits, Helen and her team would give presentations about the brain and its malleability, and engage students with fun and age-tailored hands-on activities. Famous was her collection of animal and human brains, which students delighted in touching and holding. In addition, Helen's lab was a regular presence at the Brain Awareness week on the University of Oregon campus. The lab also started organizing, in 2007, a Psychology/Neuroscience Camp as part of the Summer Academy to Inspire Learning (SAIL), a program aimed to introduce first-year high school students to college life and increase their chances to attend college later on.

Her commitment to translating reliable scientific knowledge into programs promoting healthy cognitive and brain development culminated with the writing and production of Changing Brains, an educational and not-for-profit DVD aimed to introduce parents, educators, and policymakers to evidence-based information about the effects of experience on the development of different brain systems. These videos remain available on the YouTube platform by searching for "Changing Brains." Helen's later work, described in the chapters by Hampton Wray and Isbell and by Pakulak and Stevens, involved developing and testing interventions to improve attentional abilities and, more generally, educational and social outcomes among children from families of lower socioeconomic status. To do this, the Brain Development Lab partnered with Head Start of Lane County (HSLC) to deliver and evaluate interventions, and ultimately translate these into practice that HSLC continues to implement.

About this book

The idea for this book took shape in early 2018, amid the planning for the celebration of Helen's retirement in May of that year. We, as many others, felt fortunate to have trained or worked with Helen and wanted to share our gratitude with her by acknowledging the role that she had in our careers and lives. We delighted Helen by presenting the plan for the book to her at the retirement celebration, which also served as a reunion of many of her past trainees and collaborators. Sadly, Helen passed away later that year. The completion of this book was subsequently delayed by the COVID-19 pandemic. We want to thank all contributors for their patience, perseverance, and dedication during such a challenging time.

The book presents a set of essays, including reviews, opinion pieces, reflections, and original empirical research by Helen's former students, collaborators, and colleagues. Topics center around the impact and legacy of Helen's work in neuroplasticity, including both basic and applied research, and her strong mandate to rigorously train scientists and leaders. Interspersed between chapters, Marta Kutas' poems, inspired by Helen's work, playfully remind us of Helen's ground-breaking ideas, rigorous approach to science, deference to empirical evidence, and commitment to translate her work into educational practices to counteract the negative effects of adversities on brain development.

The first two chapters pertain to perception and attention. Hampton Wray and Isbell (Chapter 1) chart the trajectory of Helen's work on selective attention and showcase her rigorous research program: from studies on typically developing children to children exhibiting difficulties in oral and written communication, and finally to the development of intervention programs during early childhood to improve long-term outcomes. The authors end their review by highlighting some of the new directions that Helen's mentees have taken based on her work, including the study of selective attention in children who stutter or suffer from hearing impairment, and the development of selective attention as shaped by the child's auditory environment (in the home, neighborhood, and classroom).

Föcker and colleagues (Chapter 2) provide an example of empirical research investigating the malleability of attentional networks and functions in video game players. Previous work has documented enhanced attentional control in video game players within the visual modality. In the study, the authors ask whether changes also occur across modalities and, if so, at what level. By adopting a variation of the classic dichotic listening paradigm in focused and divided conditions, Föcker and colleagues found behavioral advantages in auditory discrimination in video game players, relative to non-players; in addition, the modulation of late, not early, event-related potential (ERP) components suggested that cross-modal effects of video game playing occurred at the level of enhanced decision-making, not during perceptual encoding.

Helen contributed immensely to our understanding of how experience shapes the development of cognitive and neural systems involved in linguistic processing. Five chapters are dedicated to language. Andersson and Newman (Chapter 3) review electrophysiological research on phonological, semantic, and syntactic processing in second language (L2) learners. While investigations of the factors associated with L2 proficiency have traditionally focused on age of acquisition (AoA), Andersson and Newman argue for a more comprehensive approach including proficiency and cross-linguistic influence. The authors organize their review around two principles central to Helen's approach: the importance of individual variability, and the necessity of relating electrophysiological effects to behavior to understand their functional significance in terms of brain development.

Corina and colleagues (Chapter 4) explore age-related changes in linguistic skills in deaf signers. Age-related changes in language production are well documented for oral but not sign languages; the investigation of the latter might cast light on similarities and modality and language-specific factors that may uniquely affect sign language use in aging signers. The authors surveyed a large cohort of adult deaf signers on an American Sign Language (ASL) sentence repetition task. In this task, participants are asked to repeat verbatim ASL sentences gradually increasing in length and complexity. Overall, performance decreased with increasing age and AoA, with the two effects being independent. The analysis of errors revealed a clear pattern, across all signers, as most were errors of omission; in addition, they were more frequent with verbs and pronouns compared to other grammatical classes. Corina and colleagues interpret these errors as reflecting moments of processing overload and capacity limitations; in addition, they suggest that delayed primary language acquisition may prevent the rapid automatic encoding of language and exacerbate this pattern later in life beyond the effects of normal aging.

Two chapters are dedicated to the neurophysiological changes associated with the development of reading expertise, more specifically written word recognition. Grossi and Sacchi (Chapter 5) discuss the literature on the posterior N1, a negative ERP elicited over occipito-temporal sites and involved in processing visual stimuli. Literacy training is associated with two major changes in N1 amplitude: the development of tuning to print, operationalized as a difference in amplitude between print and control stimuli (e.g., non-alphanumeric symbols or false fonts), and a shift in scalp distribution from bilateral to left-lateralized. The pattern of lateralization varies with other experiential factors, such as the specific type of writing system, the specific reading strategy, and bilingualism, thus reflecting the individual's specific experiences. Interestingly, similar changes in N1 amplitude and lateralization are observed in adults learning to read, showing that the neural systems involved in visual word recognition retain a remarkable degree of plasticity during adulthood.

Hirshorn and colleagues' chapter (Chapter 6) focuses on reading in deaf readers. Learning to read relies on print-to-sound decoding; however, deaf readers can achieve reading proficiency without auditory input and often limited use of spoken language. This fMRI study investigates the activation pattern of the visual word form area (VWFA), a ventral region of the left temporo-occipital cortex involved in written word recognition. Activation in this region is larger for words than control stimuli (e.g., false fonts) in proficient hearing readers. In addition, some studies have reported a functional gradient in terms of word selectivity within the occipito-temporal region, with posterior regions more tuned to basic visual features and anterior regions (including the VWFA) more tuned to orthographic regularities. By testing three groups of participants matched on reading comprehension but varying in speech-based knowledge (deaf native signers, hearing individuals, and oral deaf individuals with greater speech-based phonological knowledge than deaf signers), Hirshorn and colleagues document two main findings: (1) The VWFA was not word-selective in deaf native signers with low speech-based phonological knowledge; (2) Speech-based phonological knowledge was associated with a reduction of responses to visual control stimuli along a posterior to anterior gradient in the occipito-temporal cortex, pointing to the role of speech-based phonological processing in shaping the tuning of the VWFA to print. These findings cast doubts on the necessity of word selectivity in the VWFA to attain reading proficiency, as previously suggested by research on hearing readers; instead, they indicate the existence of alternative routes for developing skilled reading, whose exploration might reveal to be promising for deaf readers and hearing individuals with deficits in phonological processing.

In Chapter 7, Newman and MacSweeney review Helen's research involving deaf people, particularly with respect to neuroplasticity, attention, and sign language. Deafness and the use of sign language presented unique opportunities to study neuroplasticity in humans to understand how unimodal sensory deprivation and/or the use of a visual language affects brain development. Helen's work was among, if not the first, to use neuroimaging (first EEG, then fMRI) to study this topic. Her work demonstrated very specific differences in visual attentional abilities between deaf and hearing people, specifically that deaf people showed greater sensitivity to motion when attending to the visual periphery. This was accompanied by enhanced ERPs to those stimuli, and an altered scalp topography suggestive of a takeover of auditory or multimodal processing areas for visual functions in deaf people. Later fMRI work was consistent with these findings and provided more precise spatial localization of those effects. Helen's work also demonstrated that native learners of sign language showed engagement of the same classical left hemisphere brain regions as spoken languages, while at the same time engaging other areas, including in the right hemisphere, associated with visual–spatial processing. After reviewing this work, Newman and MacSweeney consider its implications in light of more recent research, particularly in the context of questions about children born deaf. They highlight the value and importance of providing deaf children with exposure to sign language from birth, even if it is used imperfectly, and even if the child has or will receive a cochlear implant to restore hearing.

Chapter 8, by Helfrich and Knight, reviews work on the role of sleep in neuroplasticity. After providing a context for how ideas linking sleep and memory formation developed during the last 100 years, the authors discuss evidence suggesting that oscillations present during non-rapid eye movement (REM) sleep (reflecting hierarchically nested and coupled activity in the neocortex, thalamus, and hippocampus) provide a functional substrate for memory consolidation. Some of this evidence comes from research on humans, intracranial recordings in the hippocampus, and non-invasive electrophysiological studies. In these and other animal studies, synchronization of oscillatory activity seems to foster memory consolidation. At the end of their chapter, Helfrich and Knight discuss the promises of electrical brain stimulation to ameliorate memory problems due to aging (including changes in sleep patterns) and neurodegenerative diseases.

In Chapter 9, Pakulak and Steven discuss Helen's commitment to using evidence-based knowledge to address the disadvantages created by social inequality. This commitment became more urgent with time and pervades her later work and public engagements. After discussing basic research on the effects of selective attention on cognitive functions, the authors detail the development of the two-generation intervention program, the results of an intense collaboration with psychologists and educators which involves the children's parents (hence the name). Tested in an experiment in which preschoolers enrolled in a Head Start program were randomly assigned to one of three groups, this eight-week intervention was found to improve outcomes in multiple domains, including cognitive measures and neural indices of selective attention, relative to the other interventions. At the end of the chapter, Pakulak and Stevens discuss other interdisciplinary collaborations and educational initiatives that exemplify Helen's legacy in trying to make the world a better place.

This legacy also resonates in the final chapter of the book. Posner and Rothbart (Chapter 10) review their recent work aimed to improve the functioning of attentional neural networks and their connections to memory through low-frequency brain stimulation or behavioral interventions. The authors organize their chapter around three "lessons" learned from Helen, that is, three principles that guided her research: the integration of knowledge from human and animal studies, to probe the neurophysiological mechanisms underlying brain development and plasticity; the importance of comparing developmental changes in infants and children with the changes occurring later in life, to gain an understanding of whether brain development and plasticity rely on similar or nonidentical processes; and the goal of translating basic research into interventions to improve the human condition.

We are delighted to have so many varied contributions. They highlight the broad scope and impact of Helen's contributions to scientific knowledge and training. We are forever indebted to our colleagues for their support of this project, and to Helen for her irreplaceable (and irrepressible!) influence.

Interlude 1

THANKS, YOU GUYS!

Marta Kutas

Which cognitive and brain functions are fixed,
which modifiable, pliable with experience
is the BIG question HJN asked, and tasked herself to answer,
so that along the way she could refer, defer to data,
and use it as she felt she should to make a tangible difference
in people's lives as she knew she could,
keeping her mind open to experimental findings,
not just blindly binding her conclusions to theoretical preconceptions.
Although, from the outset, her scientific approach
met with reluctant reception not to mention reproach
as several senior scientists scoffed at the idea of brain plasticity,
as a biologically plausible, viable possibility.

Brain changes post-birth, how could that possibly be?

No! Certain they were that the brain was genetically hard-wired.
Molded and fired by evolutionary pressures into an immutable shape
from which there was no easy, experiential escape.
Its development effectively set on a predetermined course.
The source of neural sensitivities and functional organization(s)
driven by genetic expression; regional profession
determined by DNA sequences.

DOI: 10.4324/9780429342356-3

How could we ever explain an ever-changing brain
with non-stable preferences?
Couldn't she see?

But in fact, Neville did not agree, and wouldn't let it be, eloquently,
and indeed presciently, arguing for neuroplasticity,
experience-based modifiability,
compensatory functional reorganization,
new connections, new configurations,
with concomitant changes in perception,
because all definitely was not frozen in place by
9 months post conception.

1

DEVELOPMENT AND PLASTICITY OF SELECTIVE AUDITORY ATTENTION IN EARLY CHILDHOOD

Amanda Hampton Wray and Elif Isbell

Helen Neville's research has profoundly impacted many fields across cognitive neuroscience, as evidenced by the diversity of content in the chapters of this book. One of the fields profoundly changed by Dr. Neville's work was the neurophysiology of attention. Building on her earlier work comparing central to peripheral attention in visual and auditory modalities (e.g., Bavelier et al., 2000, 2001; Neville & Lawson, 1987a, 1987b, 1987c; Stevens & Neville, 2006), later in her career Dr. Neville focused on the development and plasticity of selective attention in children. This chapter reviews her work on selective attention, her innovative basic science and intervention research, and future directions for continuing and expanding (or extending) what she started.

The importance of selective attention

Selective attention is defined as actively focusing on relevant stimuli in the presence of distracting, competing stimuli. For the purpose of this chapter, we will focus on voluntary selective attention, the ability that allows one to intentionally attend to a specific channel, stimulus, or input stream. The study of attention retains an important place in fields like cognitive neuroscience and hearing science, and in the study of disorders from infancy across the lifespan. The importance of attentional skills in daily life cannot be overstated. Attention plays a critical role in the development of early cognitive skills, such as joint engagement, which support early word learning as well as the ongoing development of language and self-regulation skills (e.g., Jones et al., 2003; Posner & Rothbart, 2007; Stevens & Bavelier, 2012). Attention is also foundational for academic success, as classrooms and other learning environments require active engagement with a specific stimulus – the teacher – while ignoring distractions, such as ambient

DOI: 10.4324/9780429342356-4

noise in the room as well as other students (e.g., McClelland et al., 2013; McClelland & Cameron, 2011; Posner et al., 2006; Rhoades et al., 2011; Stevens & Bavelier, 2012; Stipek & Valentino, 2015).

Neural mechanisms of selective attention

Three general mechanisms are proposed to support selective attention: signal enhancement, external and internal distractor/noise suppression, and selective read-out (i.e., modulation of the efficiency with which sensory information is used to inform decisions) (Serences & Kastner, 2014). In this chapter, we discuss the first two mechanisms and the ways in which they directly modify the quality of sensory representations.

Researchers have employed neuroimaging methods while participants completed selective attention tasks to better understand the neural mechanisms underlying selective attention (e.g., Serences & Kastner, 2014). Among these methods, electroencephalography (EEG) and event-related brain potentials (ERPs; averaged EEG signal time-locked to specific stimuli) provide information about neural processes with an exquisite temporal resolution, on the order of milliseconds. EEG/ERPs are non-invasive, making it a highly accessible methodology, ideal for acquiring neural data from both adults and children (Luck, 2014; Nunez, 1995).

Early selective attention studies focused on adults. In pioneering studies, one of Dr. Neville's mentors, Steven A. Hillyard, conducted carefully controlled experiments in which auditory stimuli presented in attended and unattended conditions were identical, with the only difference between conditions being the direction of attention. This setup allowed for direct assessment of the effects of attention on sensory processes, regardless of presentation ear, pitch, or timing (Hillyard et al., 1973). Auditory stimuli reliably elicit a series of ERP components beginning ~50 ms after stimulus presentation, the P1–N1–P2 complex. P1 is a positive component peaking between 40 and 60 ms and is followed by a negative component, N1, which peaks between 80 and 120 ms. A second positivity, P2, peaks between 140 and 170 ms (Ponton et al., 2000). This series of components is posited to reflect auditory cortical activity (P1, N1) as well as higher-level cognitive processes (N1, P2) (e.g., Hansen & Hillyard, 1980; Ponton et al., 2000). Effects of attention are consistently observed on the P1–N1–P2 complex, most pronounced for P1 and N1. In a series of studies, Hillyard and colleagues determined that directing attention toward a stimulus results in increased amplitude of early ERP components, indicating increased allocation of neural resources for processing attended stimuli (for review of early findings, see Hillyard & Kutas, 1983). This increased, or enhanced, neural response reflects increased activity from distributed attention networks, such as frontal networks, and plays a role in distinguishing the target input stream from competing information (e.g., Knight et al., 1998). In contrast, when attention is directed away from a stimulus, early ERP amplitudes are significantly reduced. This diminished early neural response reflects suppression of the non-target, or unattended signal, and is believed to allow for further differentiation between target and non-target input streams (e.g., Hansen & Hillyard, 1980; Hillyard & Anllo-Vento, 1998; Hillyard et al., 1973; Hink et al., 1977). Signal enhancement and distractor suppression are measured relative to each other in this seminal selective attention paradigm, which precludes direct conclusions about the distinctiveness of these mechanisms. However, in later neuroimaging studies, neural responses elicited by target and distractor stimuli were assessed separately while the perceptual load associated with targets was systematically manipulated. These studies suggested that the effects of enhancement and suppression on neural responses are intermixed yet distinct (see Serences & Kastner, 2014, for a comprehensive review).

Over the past three decades extensive research in this area has further clarified the neural processes engaged in selective attention and demonstrated that, in adults, neural processes are modulated by selective attention as early as 50 ms post-stimulus (Giuliano et al., 2014; Ross et al., 2010). Despite extensive research on selective attention in adults (for a review, see Serences & Kastner, 2014), the development and functioning of these skills in childhood remained less clear.

Measuring selective auditory attention in children

Selective attention skills appear to emerge within the first six months of life (e.g., Gomes et al., 2000) and continue to develop rapidly throughout the preschool period. Before age 3 years, young children are able to attend to highly engaging stimuli, while by age 5 years, children are better able to selectively engage with target stimuli while at least partially ignoring distractors (e.g., Gomes et al., 2000; Posner & Rothbart, 2007). Both signal enhancement and distractor suppression skills continue to develop and become more refined throughout adolescence (Gomes et al., 2000; Karns et al., 2015; Posner & Rothbart, 2007; Rueda et al., 2004). Dr. Neville and colleagues aimed to directly evaluate the ways in which selectively attending to information affects neural processing in children, and the developmental trajectory of these processes, as behavioral measures alone provide limited insights into neural processes.

Coch and colleagues (2005) developed a child-friendly version of Hillyard's selective auditory attention task. In this selective auditory attention task, two child-oriented stories are played simultaneously, one from a speaker to the right of the child, and one from a speaker to the left. Each story is read by a different narrator, one male and one female. Children are instructed to listen to the story from one speaker and ignore the other story. The stories are designed to help children engage in the task and tap into their selective attention skills. To further support attending to only one story, images related to the target story are displayed on the computer screen. Additionally, an arrow on the image points toward the to-be-attended speaker (e.g., pointing to the left; Figure 1.1) to further reinforce the direction of attention. For additional methodological details, see Hampton Wray et al. (2017).

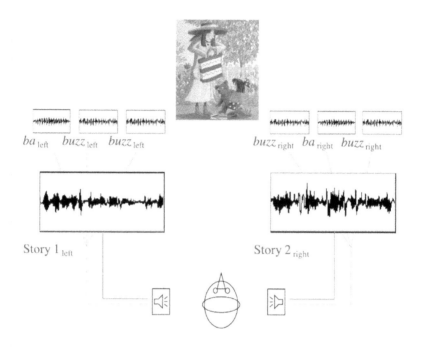

FIGURE 1.1 Schematic representation of the experimental design. Children are instructed to listen to one story and ignore the other. Event-related brain potentials are elicited by the identical linguistic (/ba/) and non-linguistic (/bzz/) probes embedded in both the attended and ignored stories.

Source: Adapted from Stevens et al. (2009).

In order to evaluate the impact of selective attention on neural processing, EEG is time-locked to auditory probes embedded in both the attended and unattended stories. The probes in each story are identical such that the only difference between them is whether the child is attending to or ignoring information coming from that speaker. Two 100 ms probes are presented: a linguistic /ba/syllable and a non-linguistic /bzz/ syllable. The /bzz/ syllable was created by manipulating (spectrally rotating and reordering) 4–6 ms segments of the /ba/. Probes are presented at interstimulus intervals (ISIs) of 200, 500, or 1000 ms in one of the two channels (never simultaneously) in a pseudo-random order.

At the beginning of each story, a sample of the narrator's voice for the attended story is played. Children are instructed to listen carefully to this voice and ignore the other voice. A research assistant sits next to the child to help ensure children are engaged in the task and remain still throughout. At the end of each story, the research assistant asks three questions about the attended story to ensure the child was listening to the correct story. Questions have two choices, and a response of "I don't know" is recorded as incorrect. Children must get a minimum of six questions correct to be included in EEG analyses.

Seminal studies of selective auditory attention in children and adults

Using the paradigm described earlier, Coch and colleagues (2005) evaluated ERPs in 6- to 8-year-old children and adults. In adults, both probe types elicited the P1–N1–P2 complex (see earlier), although some differences were observed between probe types. Across both probe types, N1, but not P1 or P2, amplitudes were modulated by attention, with larger N1 amplitudes elicited by stimuli from the speaker on the attended compared to the unattended side (i.e., the attention effect). Attention effects elicited by non-linguistic stimuli were largest over anterior and medial electrode sites, while attention effects elicited by linguistic stimuli were most prominent over posterior and medial sites. Together, these findings supported the validity of this paradigm, as they replicated the previous effects of selective attention on the N1 in adults.

In contrast to the P1–N1–P2 complex observed in adults, 6- to 8-year-old children exhibited a single, broad positivity between 100 and 300 ms post-stimulus onset elicited by both probe types. This positivity was larger for stimuli on the attended compared to the unattended side, and most prominent over anterior and medial sites for both linguistic and non-linguistic probe types. These findings revealed that both adults and 6- to 8-year-olds exhibit effects of selective attention on early neural responses, though with differences in waveform morphology. Such findings align with theories of protracted development of selective attention into later childhood and adolescence (Coch et al., 2005).

Using the same paradigm, Sanders and colleagues (2006) extended this work to preschool-age children, 3–5 years of age, and compared them to school-age children (6–8 years) and adults. ERP patterns observed in adults and 6- to 8-year-olds were similar to those of Coch and colleagues (2005) described earlier. Preschool-age children exhibited similar effects of attention on neural responses as older children: a broad positivity between 100 and 200 ms post-stimulus onset, larger in response to attended compared to unattended stimuli, with an anterior and medial distribution, and larger over the right hemisphere for both probe types. However, while the attention effect in older children resolved by ~200 ms, the effect in younger children persisted until ~450 ms. This study, combined with findings from Coch and colleagues (2005), revealed that children as young as 3 years could successfully employ selective attention, even in complex acoustic environments.

To further explore the development of neural mechanisms of selective attention, Karns and colleagues (2015) compared how selective attention modulates auditory processes for linguistic and non-linguistic probes across a broader developmental range, including preschool-age children (3- to 5-year-olds), 10-year-olds, 13-year-olds, 16-year-olds, and university students. For both the linguistic and non-linguistic probes, P1 latency decreased with age. The non-linguistic N1, which appeared around age 13, did not differ in latency among younger and older adolescents and young adults. However, the linguistic N1 decreased in latency with increasing age. P2 was primarily observed for the non-linguistic probes and also decreased in latency with increasing age. These results suggested that the neural systems for auditory processing go through age-related changes that are specific to the properties of the auditory stimuli (e.g., linguistic versus non-linguistic).

Furthermore, Karns and colleagues (2015) found a notable interplay between age and how selective attention modulates auditory evoked potentials from early childhood through young adulthood. Consistent with previous findings (Coch et al., 2005; Sanders et al., 2006), young children showed modulation of the auditory ERPs between 100 and 200 ms as a larger positive amplitude for the attended versus unattended conditions, both for the linguistic and non-linguistic probes. For older age groups, attentional modulation varied between probe types and ERP components. For the linguistic probes, attention robustly increased the late N1 amplitude by age 10. For the non-linguistic probes, amplitudes of the auditory evoked potentials were modulated in both the P1 and P2 windows for 13-year-olds and adults and within the P1 window for 10-year-olds. However, attentional modulation of auditory ERPs was weak or absent for non-linguistic probes among the 16-year-olds in this study. Overall, these results suggest that, while the modulation of auditory processing by selective attention was evident as early as preschool age, the development of neural mechanisms of selective attention was not observed uniformly across probe types and age groups. The authors concluded that these results call into question the common practice of combining data from wide age groups, as there may be intricate differences in ERP morphology and latency even between groups relatively close in age.

Vulnerability of selective auditory attention in children

The protracted developmental time course of selective attention suggests the potential for neuroplasticity in the system (for review, see Stevens & Neville, 2014). Neuroplasticity is a "double-edged sword": systems that confer high degrees of plasticity, especially for extended developmental periods, are susceptible, or vulnerable, to reduced stimulation or input, either as a function of individual capacity or environmental input. But these systems are also highly malleable, making them strong targets for intervention programs. Work by Dr. Neville and others has demonstrated both the vulnerability and malleability of neural systems for selective attention.

Selective auditory attention in children with developmental language disorder

Previous studies had suggested that children with atypical language and reading development (e.g., children with developmental language disorder (DLD) and dyslexia) also exhibited reduced skills in attention, as well as other aspects of executive function and self-regulation (e.g., Asbjørnsen & Bryden, 1998; Facoetti et al., 2003; Leonard, 2000; Neville et al., 1993; Sperling et al., 2005; Thomson et al., 2005). Given that selective attention is believed to serve as a foundation for the development of other cognitive skills, including language, it is important to understand the nature of neural processes for selective attention in children with DLD. Stevens et al. (2006) examined neural processes for selective attention in 3- to 8-year-olds with specific language impairment, also known as DLD, and children with typical language development matched for age and non-verbal intelligence quotient (IQ). Findings revealed the expected attention effect in children with typical development. However, children with DLD did not exhibit modulation of neural responses with attention; neural responses elicited by attended and unattended stimuli were comparable. This pattern suggests that children with DLD exhibit deficits in the neural processes for selective attention. These deficits, or poor early attentional filtering in children with DLD, may have cascading effects on processing speech and language, especially in complex acoustic environments (Stevens et al., 2006).

Selective auditory attention in children from lower socioeconomic status (SES) backgrounds

In the last two decades, a growing body of research revealed lower academic outcomes and graduation rates among individuals growing up in lower SES households compared to their peers from higher SES backgrounds, despite performing within the normal range on standardized measures of non-verbal IQ and language abilities (e.g., Baydar et al., 1993; Duncan et al., 1994; Hackman et al., 2010; Shonkoff et al., 2012; Walker et al., 1994). SES reflects one's position in society and is believed to be a proxy variable for other factors, including parental nurturance, neighborhood characteristics, family resources, and household stress (e.g., Shonkoff et al., 2012). Negative effects from these factors are believed to result in excessive stress responses, including increased levels of stress hormones (such as cortisol), which in turn negatively affect brain development. The impacts of these neural changes are then observed in short- and long-term behavioral and physiological differences as a function of SES (e.g., Shonkoff, 2011).

To investigate whether selective attention skills differed as a function of SES, Stevens and colleagues (2009) used the selective auditory attention paradigm described earlier to evaluate differences in ERP patterns between groups of

3- and 8-year-olds whose mothers had higher versus lower levels of maternal education, which has been widely used as a proxy for SES (for a recent review, see Davis-Kean et al., 2021). Children from both groups exhibited an effect of selective attention on neural processes. However, children in the lower maternal education group exhibited a significantly smaller attention effect than their peers in the higher maternal education group. These differences were driven by larger responses to unattended probes in the lower maternal education group compared to the higher maternal education group. In other words, children from households with higher SES (as measured by maternal education) displayed better suppression of distracting stimuli (probes in the unattended story) than children from lower SES households. These findings were among the first to illustrate differences in early stages of auditory selective attention, within 100 ms of hearing a sound, in children from higher compared to lower SES backgrounds, and laid the groundwork for future studies on plasticity in this system in children.

In a follow-up study, Stevens and colleagues (2015) extended their seminal work to evaluate the effects of stimulus presentation rate on neural processes for auditory attention. In the selective attention paradigm described earlier, the probe stimuli were presented at ISIs of 200, 500, or 1000 ms. The shorter versus longer ISIs allow for examining the auditory neural refractory period, reflected by the reduced amplitude of neural responses when stimulus presentation rates are rapid. This reduction is thought to reflect temporal aspects of the activity of neural generators (e.g., Budd et al., 1998; Coch et al., 2005). The auditory neural refractory period was compared in 3- to 8-year-old children from higher and lower SES backgrounds. Findings revealed, overall, a similar reduction in neural response amplitudes to rapidly presented stimuli and, therefore, a comparable auditory neural refractory period between groups. However, differences were observed as a function of attention. Children from higher SES backgrounds showed more rapid recovery for stimuli in the attended versus unattended stories, with reduced neural responses only to 200 ms ISI probes in the attended stories, but reduced responses to probes at both 200 and 500 ms ISI in the unattended stories. In contrast, children from lower SES backgrounds exhibited similar recovery rates for stimuli in both attended and unattended stories. Neural responses were reduced for 200 ms ISI probes for both attended and unattended conditions, while amplitude responses were similar for 500 and 1000 ms ISI probes in both attended and unattended stories. Together, these findings suggest top-down regulation of auditory processing interacts with stimulus presentation rate. Children from higher SES backgrounds showed more sustained attenuation of neural responses to unattended stimuli. Suppression of unattended information in children from lower SES backgrounds was less effective, most notably at rapid presentation rates. These findings support models of cascading consequences of selective attention, with effects especially pronounced for rapidly presented information in unattended channels (Stevens et al., 2015).

While this and other studies of selective auditory attention have revealed reduced distractor suppression skills in children from lower compared to higher SES backgrounds (D'Angiulli et al., 2008; Neville et al., 2013; Stevens et al., 2009, 2015), it was not clear whether these differences reflected a delay in the developmental trajectory of selective attention skills or divergent developmental trajectories in children from lower SES backgrounds. Hampton Wray and colleagues (2017) aimed to further elucidate the developmental trajectory of selective attention skills in young children from lower SES backgrounds. Using the same selective attention paradigm described earlier, neural indices of selective attention were evaluated in 4-year-olds from higher and lower SES backgrounds. Children from lower SES backgrounds were then followed for one year, from age 4 to 5 years, to characterize the development of selective auditory attention during this period of rapidly developing attention skills. At age 4, children from higher SES backgrounds exhibited a significant attention effect, while no attention effect was observed in 4-year-olds from lower SES backgrounds, consistent with previous findings (Isbell et al., 2016a; Neville et al., 2013; Sanders et al., 2006; Stevens et al., 2009). From age 4 to 5 years, children from lower SES backgrounds exhibited a significant increase in the attention effect, marked by greater signal enhancement (increased neural responses elicited by attended stimuli), with no change in distractor suppression. Post hoc analyses comparing the attention effect in 4-year-olds from higher SES backgrounds to 5-year-olds from lower SES backgrounds revealed that while neural responses elicited by attended stimuli were similar in amplitude, 5-year-olds from lower SES backgrounds continued to exhibit larger neural responses elicited by unattended stimuli than 4-year-olds from higher SES backgrounds (Hampton Wray et al., 2017).

These findings suggest significant development of neural processes for selective auditory attention in children from lower SES backgrounds from age 4 to 5 years, marked by increased signal enhancement. Children from lower SES backgrounds appear to have delayed development of signal enhancement skills compared to peers from higher SES backgrounds. Distractor suppression skills, in contrast, were still reduced in 5-year-olds from lower SES backgrounds compared to 4-year-olds from higher SES backgrounds, suggesting a divergent developmental trajectory in distractor suppression in young children from lower SES backgrounds. Previous studies have also found reduced distractor suppression skills in older children and adolescents from lower SES backgrounds (D'Angiulli et al., 2008, 2012; Stevens et al., 2009), suggesting this may be an area of persistent difference between children from lower versus higher SES backgrounds. It is important for future research to evaluate the development of selective auditory attention in children from both higher and lower SES backgrounds, at both younger and older ages to further specify the nature of these developmental trajectories (Hampton Wray et al., 2017).

Individual differences in selective auditory attention in children

Another way to increase understanding of selective attention skills is to examine factors that contribute to differences between individuals. The study of individual differences is important as it can contribute to our knowledge of which children are at greater risk under socioeconomic adversity, which neurobiological and contextual factors act as protective factors, and which training and education programs would work the best for whom. Although SES-related differences had been documented in the development of brain structures and functioning, including selective attention (Noble et al., 2015; Stevens et al., 2009), relatively little work had examined individual variability among children from lower SES backgrounds. Dr. Neville's research group addressed this gap by studying individual differences in neural mechanisms of selective attention in children from lower SES backgrounds (Isbell et al., 2016a, 2016b, 2017).

In an initial study, Isbell and colleagues (Isbell et al., 2016a) examined individual differences in neural mechanisms of selective attention in preschool-age children (3- to 5-year-olds) from lower SES backgrounds, particularly in relation to non-verbal cognition. According to the executive control of attention framework, the domain-general ability to control attention is a critical element of higher-order cognitive abilities (Engle & Kane, 2004). In line with this framework, a larger selective attention effect (as indexed by greater P1 amplitude for the attended compared to the unattended conditions) was linked to better visual working memory performance in adults in a study by Dr. Neville's research group (Giuliano et al., 2014). Building on this work, Isbell and colleagues hypothesized stronger neural mechanisms of selective attention to be associated with better non-verbal cognitive skills. To test this hypothesis, they assessed the neural mechanisms of selective attention in a relatively large sample of children who attended Head Start, a preschool program for children living in households at or below the poverty level. The effect of attention on neural processing was measured using the auditory selective attention task (described earlier) and indexed by the difference between ERPs elicited in the attended versus unattended conditions. Non-verbal cognition was assessed via subscales of a non-verbal intelligence test, including tests of fluid reasoning, working memory, and quantitative reasoning. Findings revealed that larger differences in amplitudes between attended and unattended conditions between 100 and 200 ms were linked to better non-verbal cognition. Importantly, this study emphasized notable individual variability in neural indices of selective attention in children from lower SES backgrounds.

This study was followed up with investigations of the neurobiological mechanisms underlying such individual differences (Isbell et al., 2016b, 2017). Based on the structural and functional connections between serotonergic systems and the prefrontal cortex (Lesch & Waider, 2012), and the role of the prefrontal cortex in auditory selective attention (Bidet-Caulet et al., 2015; Knight et al., 1981), the researchers reasoned that serotonergic functioning would be linked to neural mechanisms of selective attention. Serotonergic functioning was indexed by the allelic variations of the 5-HTTLPR polymorphic region in the gene SLC6A4, which is involved in serotonin transportation and reuptake (Iurescia et al., 2015). In individuals of Northern European ancestry, there are two predominant allelic variations of 5-HTTLPR: the short allele and the long allele (Heils et al., 1996). Although the short allele of 5-HTTLPR has been generally associated with lower transcriptional activity of the serotonin transporter gene, the precise neurobiological mechanisms through which these allelic variations contribute to brain development and functioning have yet to be determined (Iurescia et al., 2015).

The participants in these studies were a subsample of the preschool-age children included in the previous work by Isbell and colleagues (Isbell et al., 2016a) and for whom genetic data were available. In the first study, children who carried at least one copy of the short allele of 5-HTTLPR (i.e., "short carriers") were found to have larger selective attention effects compared to children who did not carry this allele (i.e., "long homozygotes"). This finding suggested that carrying the short allele of 5-HTTLPR conferred an advantage in selective attention in children from lower SES backgrounds (Isbell et al., 2016b).

In a follow-up study, interactions between this neurobiological mechanism and the dual-generation intervention developed by Dr. Neville and colleagues (discussed later and detailed in the chapter in this book by Pakulak and Stevens) were evaluated in a preliminary dataset (Isbell et al., 2017). The participants in this study consisted of preschool-age children who were randomly assigned to either the dual-generation intervention group or the control group, and who had both pre-test and post-test ERP data as well as 5-HTTLPR data. Children in the intervention versus control groups were compared based on the 5-HTTLPR allelic variations. At pre-test, as would be expected from a random assignment, there were no main effects of group assignment, and there was a main effect of the allele frequencies of 5-HTTLPR polymorphism, such that the children who carried one short allele had larger attention effects. At post-test, there was a main effect of intervention, which was qualified by an interaction between allele frequencies of 5-HTTLPR polymorphism and intervention. Specifically, among the children who were in the control group, "long homozygotes" continued to show reduced effects of selective attention on neural responses relative to the short-allele carriers. However, within the intervention group, "long homozygotes" no longer showed reduced effects of attention compared to their peers with at least one short allele. These results suggested that an effective intervention could modify the links between serotonergic functioning, as indexed by the 5-HTTLPR allele frequencies, and neural mechanisms of selective attention in young children from lower SES backgrounds. These results should be considered preliminary given the relatively small sample sizes and reconsidered with new advances in genetic research beyond candidate gene methods.

Autonomic nervous system activity and selective auditory attention

Giuliano and colleagues (Giuliano et al., 2018a, 2018b) extended this line of research to examine links between the activity of the peripheral nervous system and selective attention. Their research addressed the dearth of empirical evidence for the theorized interconnectedness between the neural and peripheral structures regulating physiology, cognition, and behavior. The selective auditory attention task developed by Dr. Neville and colleagues provided a great medium for testing such links, as the task indexed neural mechanisms of selective attention without requiring any motor responses, which had been shown to confound the interpretation of autonomic nervous system measures (Bush et al., 2011).

In a study with adults, the aim was to delineate how parasympathetic and sympathetic autonomic nervous system activity related to concurrent neural measures of selective attention (Giuliano et al., 2018a). The participants were community members, specifically parents of children who attended Head Start, and were recruited as part of a larger study testing the efficacy of a dual-generation intervention, Creating Connections, which was implemented across entire Head Start preschools (O'Neil et al., 2019). The neural measure was the modulation of early auditory evoked potentials (P1 and N1) during the auditory selective attention task. High-frequency heart rate variability (HF-HRV), a measure of the regulatory role of the parasympathetic nervous system, and cardiac pre-ejection period (PEP), a measure of sympathetic nervous system activity, were collected during a baseline task and the selective auditory attention task. Higher HF-HRV at rest (baseline) and greater HF-HRV withdrawal from baseline to task have been linked to stronger cognitive-behavioral performance and inhibitory control in children (e.g., Calkins et al., 2007). Higher sympathetic nervous system activity (measured by PEP) at rest is also associated with stronger self-regulation skills, though understanding of the relationships between sympathetic nervous system activity and neural processes, especially in children, is limited (Beauchaine et al., 2013). Giuliano and colleagues found that adults with higher resting levels of HF-HRV and shorter resting levels of PEP exhibited larger modulations of the N1 component elicited by the selective attention task. These results suggested that both parasympathetic and sympathetic activity may independently relate to neural systems supporting selective attention.

This study was followed up by the examination of the associations between parasympathetic and sympathetic activity and selective attention in preschool-age children, especially in relation to socioeconomic adversity (Giuliano et al., 2018b). Socioeconomic adversity was central to this work, as previous research had linked it to both autonomic function and selective attention (Skowron et al., 2014; Stevens et al., 2009). Participants were children from predominantly lower SES backgrounds who attended Head Start at the time of the study. A cumulative socioeconomic risk index was computed for each child, taking into consideration low household income, single parenthood, and low maternal education as the primary risk factors. Similar to previous work with adults (Giuliano et al., 2018a), HF-HRV and PEP were measured both at baseline and during the selective auditory attention task. Findings showed that, even within a group of children from predominantly lower SES backgrounds, greater cumulative socioeconomic risk was linked to less suppression of the auditory response to distractor stimuli (i.e., worse distractor suppression). Greater socioeconomic risk was also linked to longer PEP both during baseline and the selective attention task. Contrary to their previous findings with adults (Giuliano et al., 2018a), in this sample of young children from predominantly lower SES backgrounds, HF-HRV was not associated with either signal enhancement or distractor suppression indices of selective attention. However, heightened sympathetic nervous system activity, as indexed by shorter PEP, was associated with better distractor suppression (smaller neural responses to distractor stimuli). Furthermore, the socioeconomic risk was indirectly linked to larger ERP responses elicited by distractor sounds through PEP. These results indicate that increased cardiovascular arousal both at rest and in response to task demands could be a potential biological cost for achieving better cognitive performance in children from lower SES backgrounds.

Training selective auditory attention in children

As discussed earlier, neural systems with high plasticity that are vulnerable to the effects of the environment also have the potential for malleability, making them excellent targets for intervention programs (for review, see Stevens & Neville, 2014). Building on the research revealing differences in multiple neural systems, including language, auditory processing, and attention, in children with DLD (Neville et al., 1993; Stevens et al., 2006), Stevens and colleagues assessed the effects of attention on neural processes in children with DLD before and after an intensive rapid auditory processing training aimed at mitigating DLD symptoms (Stevens et al., 2008). Children with and without DLD, aged 6–8 years, completed an auditory training program, Fast ForWord (Tallal, 2004). The training was completed in 30 sessions across six weeks, with each session lasting 2 h and containing 100 min of dedicated training. Training sessions included attending to speech and non-speech sounds in small-group settings with an expert interventionist. A group of children with typical development served as a no-training comparison group. They completed the selective attention paradigm described earlier within 30 days before and upon completion of the training program. The no-training group completed both sessions in similar time periods.

Children with and without DLD in the training groups exhibited increased receptive, but not expressive, language skills post-intervention compared to the no-training group. Consistent with previous findings (Stevens et al., 2006), children without DLD (both training and no-training groups) exhibited an attention effect at pre-test, a pattern not observed in children with DLD. At post-test, both children with and without DLD who completed training exhibited increased effects of attention on neural processes, while no changes were observed in the no-training group. These changes were driven by increased neural responses to attended stimuli, or increased signal enhancement, with no changes observed in distractor suppression from pre- to post-testing. These findings revealed that intensive auditory training can increase the effects of selective attention on neural processes in children with DLD, as well as in peers without DLD. Furthermore, they highlighted the potential for training and intervention programs to effect change on early neural processes for selective attention in children (Stevens et al., 2008) and laid the groundwork for future intervention research.

Stevens and colleagues extended this work to assess a supplemental reading intervention for children at risk for reading difficulties (Stevens et al., 2013). While it is unlikely that attention accounts for all the difficulties experienced by children at risk for, or with, reading difficulties, attention skills have been posited to play a key role in a child's response to intervention (e.g., Al Otaiba & Fuchs, 2006; Chenault et al., 2006; Torgesen et al., 1999). The authors examined the effects of selective attention on neural responses in two groups of kindergarteners (5-year-olds). Children in one group had poor early literacy skills (sound and letter naming) and were considered at risk for reading difficulties, while children in the other group had age-expected early literacy skills and were not considered at risk. Children in the at-risk group received supplemental reading instruction, an extended version of the Early Reading Intervention (Kame'enui & Simmons, 2003) consisting of 45 min of training in phonemic awareness, letter knowledge, word reading, spelling, and sentence reading. Sessions occurred outside of the school day, five days per week for eight weeks. All children completed behavioral and neurophysiological testing within 30 days before and upon completion of the training period.

In behavioral measures of reading skills, assessed via subtests of the Dynamic Indicators of Basic Early Literacy Skills (DIBELS; Good & Kaminski, 2003), children in the at-risk for reading difficulties group exhibited lower scores than the on-track group at pre-test. However, the at-risk group caught up after intervention, with both groups performing comparably on the DIBELS subtests at post-test. Children in the at-risk group also tended to have reduced effects of attention on neural processing compared to the on-track group at pre-test. At post-test, significant increases in the amplitude of the attention effect were observed in the at-risk group, while the on-track group did not show changes from pre- to post-test. Although the sample size was small (eight children in the at-risk group and six children in the on-track group), these findings suggest that early neural processes affected by attention may differ in children at risk for reading difficulties, which may have cascading effects on other language skills, learning in a classroom environment, and receiving maximal benefits of intervention programs (e.g., Al Otaiba & Fuchs, 2006; Chenault et al., 2006; Stevens et al.,

2013; Stevens & Bavelier, 2012; Torgesen et al., 1999). Importantly, early and intensive intervention programs can enhance early neural processes for selective attention, as well as reading skills. Effective reading and/or language interventions may work, at least in part, by improving selective attention (Stevens et al., 2013).

Following these studies, Dr. Neville embarked on her most substantial and significant intervention work (Neville et al., 2013). She developed a novel intervention to train selective attention skills, which were previously found to be vulnerable in children with typical development growing up in lower SES environments. Using neural processes for selective attention as a neurobiological index of change, she and her colleagues revealed that leveraging the family environment by working directly with children and parents resulted in the most significant changes in behavior as well as neural processes for attention in preschool-age children from lower SES backgrounds (Neville et al., 2013). This profound body of research, including specifics about the dual-generation intervention and assessment of the intervention, is described in detail in the chapter in this book by Pakulak and Stevens. This body of work employed training programs designed for specific populations to target and improve auditory selective attention skills. The success and impact of the intervention research conducted by Dr. Neville's research group cannot be overstated and continues to have an impact and influence around the world.

Helen Neville's influence on new research programs

As demonstrated throughout this book, Dr. Neville had a significant impact on many fields across cognitive neuroscience and developmental science. The foundations laid by Dr. Neville continue to expand in exciting and innovative ways, highlighted by some new research directions by her mentees.

Dr. Hampton Wray is extending her research on selective attention to populations with communication disorders, including children who stutter and children with hearing impairment, to characterize relationships between neural systems for attention and language. Dr. Isbell is extending her previous work to the examination of associations between neighborhood, household, and classroom auditory environments and the neurodevelopment of selective attention. Dr. Giuliano is continuing his work in early adversity, examining how family interactions during moments of stress and frustration may shape profiles of autonomic nervous system activity and how the autonomic nervous system can act as a source of individual differences in neurocognitive development, specifically selective attention in children. Dr. Pakulak is extending his research program to examine the effects of integrating training and support between the classroom and home environments on selective attention and associated skills in cross-national and cross-cultural comparisons, including in his now-home country of Sweden, as well as in Argentina, Columbia, Canada, and the United States.

Conclusion

The groundbreaking research of Dr. Neville into the neural mechanisms of selective attention in children revealed the developmental trajectory of selective auditory attention skills. These findings laid the groundwork for an improved understanding of the vulnerability of selective auditory attention in children with different types of language-based disorders, including DLD and reading difficulties, and in children with typical development growing up in lower SES households. Importantly, she also showed that, although selective auditory attention is vulnerable in these populations, it is also malleable, or changeable. Her work on the development and plasticity of selective attention has left a profound mark at the intersections of developmental cognitive neuroscience, education science, and intervention sciences; researchers for years to come will continue to build on her innovative work.

References

Al Otaiba, S., & Fuchs, D. (2006). Who are the young children for whom best practices in reading are ineffective?: An experimental and longitudinal Study. *Journal of Learning Disabilities, 39*(5), 414–431. https://doi.org/10.1177/00222194060390050401

Asbjørnsen, A. E., & Bryden, M. (1998). Auditory attentional shifts in reading-disabled students: Quantification of attentional effectiveness by the Attentional Shift Index. *Neuropsychologia, 36*(2), 143–148. https://doi.org/10.1016/S0028-3932(97)00090-0

Bavelier, D., Brozinsky, C., Tomann, A., Mitchell, T., Neville, H., & Liu, G. (2001). Impact of early deafness and early exposure to sign language on the cerebral organization for motion processing. *The Journal of Neuroscience, 21*(22), 8931–8942.

Bavelier, D., Tomann, A., Hutton, C., Mitchell, T., Corina, D., Liu, G., & Neville, H. (2000). Visual attention to the periphery is enhanced in congenitally deaf individuals. *Journal of Neuroscience, 20*(17), 1–6.

Baydar, N., Brooks-Gunn, J., & Furstenberg, F. F. (1993). Early warning signs of functional illiteracy: Predictors in childhood and adolescence. *Child Development, 64*, 815–829.

Beauchaine, T. P., Gatzke-Kopp, L., Neuhaus, E., Chipman, J., Reid, M. J., & Webster-Stratton, C. (2013). Sympathetic- and parasympathetic-linked cardiac function and prediction of externalizing behavior, emotion regulation, and prosocial behavior among preschoolers treated for ADHD. *Journal of Consulting and Clinical Psychology, 81*, 481–493. http://dx.doi.org/10.1037/a0032302

Bidet-Caulet, A., Buchanan, K. G., Viswanath, H., Black, J., Scabini, D., Bonnet-Brilhault, F., & Knight, R. T. (2015). Impaired facilitatory mechanisms of auditory attention after damage of the lateral prefrontal cortex. *Cerebral Cortex, 25*(11), 4126–4134. https://doi.org/10.1093/cercor/bhu131

Budd, T. W., Barry, R. J., Gordon, E., Rennie, C., & Michie, P. T. (1998). Decrement of N1 auditory event-related potential with stimulus repetition: Habituation vs. refractoriness. *International Journal of Psychophysiology, 31*, 51–68.

Bush, N. R., Alkon, A., Obradović, J., Stamperdahl, J., & Boyce, W. T. (2011). Differentiating challenge reactivity from psychomotor activity in studies of children's psychophysiology: Considerations for theory and measurement. *Journal of Experimental Child Psychology, 110*(1), 62–79. https://doi.org/10.1016/j.jecp.2011.03.004

Calkins, S. D., Graziano, P. A., & Keane, S. P. (2007). Cardiac vagal regulation differentiates among children at risk for behavior problems. *Biological Psychology*, *74*, 144–153.

Chenault, B., Thomson, J., Abbott, R. D., & Berninger, V. W. (2006). Effects of prior attention training on child dyslexics' response to composition instruction. *Developmental Neuropsychology*, *29*(1), 243–260. https://doi.org/10.1207/s15326942dn2901_12

Coch, D., Sanders, L. D., & Neville, H. J. (2005). An event-related potential study of selective auditory attention in children and adults. *Journal of Cognitive Neuroscience*, *17*(4), 605–622.

D'Angiulli, A., Herdman, A., Stapells, D., & Hertzman, C. (2008). Children's event-related potentials of auditory selective attention vary with their socioeconomic status. *Neuropsychology*, *22*(3), 293–300. https://doi.org/10.1037/0894-4105.22.3.293

D'Angiulli, A., Weinberg, J., Oberlander, T. F., Grunau, R. E., Hertzman, C., & Maggi, S. (2012). Frontal EEG/ERP correlates of attentional processes, cortisol and motivational states in adolescents from lower and higher socioeconomic status. *Frontiers in Human Neuroscience*, *6*. https://doi.org/10.3389/fnhum.2012.00306

Davis-Kean, P. E., Tighe, L. A., & Waters, N. E. (2021). The role of parent educational attainment in parenting and children's development. *Current Directions in Psychological Science*, *30*(2), 186–192.

Duncan, G. J., Brooks-Gunn, J., & Klebanov, P. K. (1994). Economic deprivation and early childhood development. *Child Development*, *65*(2), 296. https://doi.org/10.2307/1131385

Engle, R. W., & Kane, M. J. (2004). Executive attention, working memory capacity, and a two-factor theory of cognitive control. In B. Ross (Ed.), *Psychology of learning and motivation* (vol. 44, pp. 145–199). New York: Academic Press. https://doi.org/10.1016/S0079-7421(03)44005-X

Facoetti, A., Lorusso, M. L., Paganoni, P., Cattaneo, C., Galli, R., Umiltà, C., & Mascetti, G. G. (2003). Auditory and visual automatic attention deficits in developmental dyslexia. *Cognitive Brain Research*, *16*(2), 185–191. https://doi.org/10.1016/S0926-6410(02)00270-7

Giuliano, R. J., Karns, C. M., Bell, T. A., Petersen, S., Skowron, E. A., Neville, H. J., & Pakulak, E. (2018a). Parasympathetic and sympathetic activity are associated with individual differences in neural indices of selective attention in adults. *Psychophysiology*, *55*(8), e13079. https://doi.org/10.1111/psyp.13079

Giuliano, R. J., Karns, C. M., Neville, H. J., & Hillyard, S. A. (2014). Early auditory evoked potential is modulated by selective attention and related to individual differences in visual working memory capacity. *Journal of Cognitive Neuroscience*, *26*(12), 2682–2690. https://doi.org/10.1162/jocn_a_00684

Giuliano, R. J., Karns, C. M., Roos, L. E., Bell, T. A., Petersen, S., Skowron, E. A., Neville, H. J., & Pakulak, E. (2018b). Effects of early adversity on neural mechanisms of distractor suppression are mediated by sympathetic nervous system activity in preschool-aged children. *Developmental Psychology*, *54*(9), 1674–1686. https://doi.org/10.1037/dev0000499

Gomes, H., Molholm, S., Christodoulou, C., Ritter, W., & Cowan, N. (2000). The development of auditory attention in children. *Frontiers in Bioscience*, *5*, 108–120.

Good, R. H., & Kaminski, R. (2003). *DIBELS: Dynamic indicators of basic early literacy skills* (6th ed.). Longmont, CO: Sopris West.

Hackman, D. A., Farah, M. J., & Meaney, M. J. (2010). Socioeconomic status and the brain: Mechanistic insights from human and animal research. *Nature Reviews Neuroscience*, *11*, 651–659.

Hampton Wray, A., Stevens, C., Pakulak, E., Isbell, E., Bell, T., & Neville, H. (2017). Development of selective attention in preschool-age children from lower socioeconomic status backgrounds. *Developmental Cognitive Neuroscience, 26,* 101–111. https://doi.org/10.1016/j.dcn.2017.06.006

Hansen, J. C., & Hillyard, S. A. (1980). Endogenous brain potentials associated with selective attention. *Electroencephalography and Clinical Neurophysiology, 49,* 277–290.

Heils, A., Teufel, A., Petri, S., Stober, G., Riederer, P., Bengel, D., & Lesch, K. P. (1996). Allelic variation of human serotonin transporter gene expression. *Journal of Neurochemistry, 66*(6), 2621–2624. https://doi.org/10.1046/j.1471-4159.1996.66062621.x

Hillyard, S. A., & Anllo-Vento, L. (1998). Event-related brain potentials in the study of visual selective attention. *Proceedings of the National Academy of Sciences, 95*(3), 781–787. https://doi.org/10.1073/pnas.95.3.781

Hillyard, S. A., Hink, R. F., Schwent, V. L., & Picton, T. W. (1973). Electrical signs of selective attention in human brain. *Science, 182*(4108), 177–180.

Hillyard, S. A., & Kutas, M. (1983). Electrophysiology of cognitive processing. *Annual Review of Psychology, 33,* 33–61.

Hink, R. F., Van Voorhis, S. T., Hillyard, S. A., & Smith, T. S. (1977). The division of attention and the human auditory evoked potential. *Neuropsychologia, 15*(4–5), 597–605.

Isbell, E., Hampton Wray, A., & Neville, H. J. (2016a). Individual differences in neural mechanisms of selective auditory attention in preschoolers from lower socioeconomic status backgrounds: An event-related potentials study. *Developmental Science, 19*(6), 865–880. https://doi.org/10.1111/desc.12334

Isbell, E., Stevens, C., Hampton Wray, A., Bell, T., & Neville, H. J. (2016b). 5-HTTLPR polymorphism is linked to neural mechanisms of selective attention in preschoolers from lower socioeconomic status backgrounds. *Developmental Cognitive Neuroscience, 22,* 36–47. https://doi.org/10.1016/j.dcn.2016.10.002

Isbell, E., Stevens, C., Pakulak, E., Hampton Wray, A., Bell, T. A., & Neville, H. J. (2017). Neuroplasticity of selective attention: Research foundations and preliminary evidence for a gene by intervention interaction. *Proceedings of the National Academy of Sciences, 114*(35), 9247–9254. https://doi.org/10.1073/pnas.1707241114

Iurescia, S., Seripa, D., & Rinaldi, M. (2015). Role of the 5-HTTLPR and SNP promoter polymorphisms on serotonin transporter gene expression: A closer look at genetic architecture and in vitro functional studies of common and uncommon allelic variants. *Molecular Neurobiology, 53*(8), 5510–5526. https://doi.org/10.1007/s12035-015-9409-6

Jones, L. B., Rothbart, M. K., & Posner, M. I. (2003). Development of executive attention in preschool children. *Developmental Science, 6*(5), 498–504. https://doi.org/10.1111/1467-7687.00307

Kame'enui, E., & Simmons, D. (2003). *Early reading intervention.* Glenview, IL: Scott, Foresman.

Karns, C. M., Isbell, E., Giuliano, R. J., & Neville, H. J. (2015). Auditory attention in childhood and adolescence: An event-related potential study of spatial selective attention to one of two simultaneous stories. *Developmental Cognitive Neuroscience, 13,* 53–67. https://doi.org/10.1016/j.dcn.2015.03.001

Knight, R. T., Hillyard, S. A., Woods, D. L., & Neville, H. J. (1981). The effects of frontal cortex lesions on event-related potentials during auditory selective attention. *Electroencephalography and Clinical Neurophysiology, 52,* 571–582.

Knight, R. T., Scabini, D., & Woods, D. L. (1998). Prefrontal cortex gating of auditory transmission in humans. *Brain Research, 504,* 338–342.

Leonard, L. B. (2000). *Children with specific language impairment*. Cambridge, MA: The MIT Press.

Lesch, K.-P., & Waider, J. (2012). Serotonin in the modulation of neural plasticity and networks: Implications for neurodevelopmental disorders. *Neuron, 76*(1), 175–191. https://doi.org/10.1016/j.neuron.2012.09.013

Luck, S. J. (2014). *An introduction to the event-related potential technique* (2nd ed.). Cambridge, MA: The MIT Press.

McClelland, M. M., Acock, A. C., Piccinin, A., Rhea, S. A., & Stallings, M. C. (2013). Relations between preschool attention span-persistence and age 25 educational outcomes. *Early Childhood Research Quarterly, 28*(2), 314–324. https://doi.org/10.1016/j.ecresq.2012.07.008

McClelland, M. M., & Cameron, C. E. (2011). Self-regulation and academic achievement in elementary school children. *New Directions for Child and Adolescent Development, 2011*(133), 29–44. https://doi.org/10.1002/cd.302

Neville, H. J., Coffey, S. A., Holcomb, P. J., & Tallal, P. (1993). The neurobiology of sensory and language processing in language-impaired children. *Journal of Cognitive Neuroscience, 5*(2), 235–253.

Neville, H. J., & Lawson, D. (1987a). Attention to central and peripheral visual space in a movement detection task: An event-related potential and behavioral study. II. Congenitally deaf adults. *Brain Research, 405*, 268–283.

Neville, H. J., & Lawson, D. (1987b). Attention to central and peripheral visual space in a movement detection task. III. Separate effects of auditory deprivation and acquisition of a visual language. *Brain Research, 405*, 284–294.

Neville, H. J., & Lawson, D. (1987c). Attention to central and peripheral visual space in movement detection task: An event-related potential and behavioral study. I. Normal hearing adults. *Brain Research, 405*, 253–267.

Neville, H. J., Stevens, C., Pakulak, E., Bell, T. A., Fanning, J., Klein, S., & Isbell, E. (2013). Family-based training program improves brain function, cognition, and behavior in lower socioeconomic status preschoolers. *Proceedings of the National Academy of Sciences, 110*(29), 12138–12143. https://doi.org/10.1073/pnas.1304437110

Noble, K. G., Houston, S. M., Brito, N. H., Bartsch, H., Kan, E., Kuperman, J. M., Akshoomoff, N., Amaral, D. G., Bloss, C. S., Libiger, O., Schork, N. J., Murray, S. S., Casey, B. J., Chang, L., Ernst, T. M., Frazier, J. A., Gruen, J. R., Kennedy, D. N., Van Zijl, P., Mostofsky, S., Kaufmann, W. E., Kenet, T., Dale, A. M., Jernigan, T. L., & Sowell, E. R. (2015). Family income, parental education and brain structure in children and adolescents. *Nature Neuroscience, 18*(5), 773–778. https://doi.org/10.1038/nn.3983

Nunez, P. L. (1995). *Neocortical dynamics and human EEG rhythms* (1st ed.). New York: Oxford University Press.

O'Neil, L. V., Pakulak, E., Stevens, C., Bell, T. A., Fanning, J. L., Gaston, M., Gomsrun, M., Hampton Wray, A., Holmes, K. B., Klein, S., Longoria, Z., Reynolds, M. M., Snell, K., Soto, A., & Neville, H. (2019). Creating connections between researchers and educators. *Journal of Cognition and Development, 20*(2), 110–133. https://doi.org/10.1080/15248372.2018.1515078

Ponton, C. W., Eggermont, J. J., Kwong, B., & Don, M. (2000). Maturation of human central auditory system activity: Evidence from multi-channel evoked potentials. *Clinical Neurophysiology, 111*, 22–236.

Posner, M. I., & Rothbart, M. K. (2007). *Educating the human brain*. Washington, DC: American Psychological Association.

Posner, M. I., Sheese, B. E., Odludaş, Y., & Tang, Y. (2006). Analyzing and shaping human attentional networks. *Neural Networks*, *19*(9), 1422–1429. https://doi.org/10.1016/j. neunet.2006.08.004

Rhoades, B. L., Warren, H. K., Domitrovich, C. E., & Greenberg, M. T. (2011). Examining the link between preschool social – emotional competence and first grade academic achievement: The role of attention skills. *Early Childhood Research Quarterly*, *26*(2), 182–191. https://doi.org/10.1016/j.ecresq.2010.07.003

Ross, B., Hillyard, S. A., & Picton, T. W. (2010). Temporal dynamics of selective attention during dichotic listening. *Cerebral Cortex*, *20*(6), 1360–1371. https://doi.org/10.1093/ cercor/bhp201

Rueda, M. R., Fan, J., McCandliss, B. D., Halparin, J. D., Gruber, D. B., Lercari, L. P., & Posner, M. I. (2004). Development of attentional networks in childhood. *Neuropsychologia*, *42*(8), 1029–1040. https://doi.org/10.1016/j.neuropsychologia.2003.12.012

Sanders, L. D., Stevens, C., Coch, D., & Neville, H. J. (2006). Selective auditory attention in 3- to 5-year-old children: An event-related potential study. *Neuropsychologia*, *44*(11), 2126–2138. https://doi.org/10.1016/j.neuropsychologia.2005.10.007

Serences, J. T., & Kastner, S. (2014). A multi-level account of selective attention. In A. C. (Kia) Nobre & S. Kastner (Eds.), *The Oxford handbook of attention* (pp. 76–104). New York: Oxford University Press. https://doi.org/10.1093/oxfordhb/9780199675111.013.022

Shonkoff, J. P. (2011). Protecting brains, not simply stimulating minds. *Science*, *333*, 982–983.

Shonkoff, J. P., & Garner, A. S. (2012). The committee on psychosocial aspects of child and family health, committee on early childhood, adoption, and dependent care, and section on developmental and behavioral pediatrics, Siegel, B. S., Dobbins, M. I., Earls, M. F., . . . Wood, D. L. The lifelong effects of early childhood adversity and toxic stress. *Pediatrics*, *129*(1), e232–e246. https://doi.org/10.1542/peds.2011-2663

Skowron, E. A., Cipriano-Essel, E., Gatzke-Kopp, L. M., Teti, D. M., & Ammerman, R. T. (2014). Early adversity, RSA, and inhibitory control: Evidence of children's neurobiological sensitivity to social context: Early adversity, RSA, and inhibitory control. *Developmental Psychobiology*, *56*(5), 964–978. https://doi.org/10.1002/dev.21175

Sperling, A. J., Lu, Z.-L., Manis, F. R., & Seidenberg, M. S. (2005). Deficits in perceptual noise exclusion in developmental dyslexia. *Nature Neuroscience*, *8*(7), 862–863. https:// doi.org/10.1038/nn1474

Stevens, C., & Bavelier, D. (2012). The role of selective attention on academic foundations: A cognitive neuroscience perspective. *Developmental Cognitive Neuroscience*, *2*, S30–S48. https://doi.org/10.1016/j.dcn.2011.11.001

Stevens, C., Fanning, J., Coch, D., Sanders, L., & Neville, H. (2008). Neural mechanisms of selective auditory attention are enhanced by computerized training: Electrophysiological evidence from language-impaired and typically developing children. *Brain Research*, *1205*, 55–69. https://doi.org/10.1016/j.brainres.2007.10.108

Stevens, C., Harn, B., Chard, D. J., Currin, J., Parisi, D., & Neville, H. (2013). Examining the role of attention and instruction in at-risk kindergarteners: Electrophysiological measures of selective auditory attention before and after an early literacy intervention. *Journal of Learning Disabilities*, *46*(1), 73–86. https://doi.org/10.1177/0022219411417877

Stevens, C., Lauinger, B., & Neville, H. (2009). Differences in the neural mechanisms of selective attention in children from different socioeconomic backgrounds: An event-related brain potential study. *Developmental Science*, *12*(4), 634–646. https://doi. org/10.1111/j.1467-7687.2009.00807.x

Stevens, C., & Neville, H. (2006). Neuroplasticity as a double-edged sword: Deaf enhancements and dyslexic deficits in motion processing. *Journal of Cognitive Neuroscience, 18*(5), 701–714.

Stevens, C., & Neville, H. (2014). Specificity of experiential effects in neurocognitive development. In M. S. Gazzaniga & G. R. Mangun (Eds.), *The cognitive neurosciences* (5th ed., pp. 129–142). London: The MIT Press.

Stevens, C., Paulsen, D., Yasen, A., & Neville, H. (2015). Atypical auditory refractory periods in children from lower socio-economic status backgrounds: ERP evidence for a role of selective attention. *International Journal of Psychophysiology, 95*(2), 156–166. https://doi.org/10.1016/j.ijpsycho.2014.06.017

Stevens, C., Sanders, L., & Neville, H. (2006). Neurophysiological evidence for selective auditory attention deficits in children with specific language impairment. *Brain Research, 1111*(1), 143–152. https://doi.org/10.1016/j.brainres.2006.06.114

Stipek, D., & Valentino, R. A. (2015). Early childhood memory and attention as predictors of academic growth trajectories. *Journal of Educational Psychology, 107*(3), 771–788. https://doi.org/10.1037/edu0000004

Tallal, P. (2004). Improving language and literacy is a matter of time. *Nature Reviews Neuroscience, 5*(9), 721–728. https://doi.org/10.1038/nrn1499

Thomson, J. B., Chenault, B., Abbott, R. D., Raskind, W. H., Richards, T., Aylward, E., & Berninger, V. W. (2005). Converging evidence for attentional influences on the orthographic word form in child dyslexics. *Journal of Neurolinguistics, 18*(2), 93–126. https://doi.org/10.1016/j.jneuroling.2004.11.005

Torgesen, J. K., Wagner, R. K., Rashotte, C. A., Lindamood, P., Rose, E., Conway, T., & Garvan, C. (1999). Preventing reading failure in young children with phonological processing disabilities: Group and individual responses to instruction. *Journal of Educational Psychology, 91*(4), 579–593.

Walker, D., Greenwood, C., Hart, B., & Carta, J. (1994). Prediction of school outcomes based on early language production and socioeconomic factors. *Child Development, 65*(2), 606. https://doi.org/10.2307/1131404

Interlude 2

A BIG FAT P3

Marta Kutas

The brain responds sometimes like a mental finger
or perhaps as more of a mental zinger
when the mind (or is it the brain?) is caught by surprise
at least according to the P3 ERP cognitive brain wave enterprise
stimulus reception, perception, and then evaluation
apparently an electrophysiological manifestation
of neural classification.

DOI: 10.4324/9780429342356-5

2

ALLOCATION OF AUDITORY SPATIAL SELECTIVE ATTENTION IN ACTION VIDEO GAME PLAYERS

Julia Föcker, Matin Mortazavi, Wayne Khoe, Steven A. Hillyard, and Daphné Bavelier

Introduction

Auditory attention in action video game players (AVGPs)

Action video game play fosters a number of key cognitive skills, including attention (Castel et al., 2005; Chisholm & Kingstone, 2012; Green & Bavelier, 2003; Schubert et al., 2015), multitasking and task-switching (Belchior et al., 2013; Cain et al., 2012; Cardoso-Leite & Bavelier, 2014; Rupp et al., 2016; Strobach et al., 2012), perception (Bejjanki et al., 2014; Berard et al., 2015; Buckley et al., 2010; Li et al., 2009, 2010), visual short-term memory (Pavan et al., 2019; Sungur & Boduroglu, 2012; Waris et al., 2019), and spatial cognition (Feng et al., 2007), to mention a few. Some of those improvements have even been observed from an early age, such as in children aged 5–12 years who showed enhanced performance in tracking multiple moving objects (Dye & Bavelier, 2010; Trick et al., 2005), visuo-haptic integration (Nava et al., 2019), spatial cognition (Subrahmanyam & Greenfield, 1994), executive functions (Al-Gabbani et al., 2014) and in specific populations such as patients with low vision in one eye, also called amblyopia (Gambacorta et al., 2014; Vedamurthy et al., 2015), or with dyslexia (Franceschini et al., 2013). However, most studies have focused on adults, with beneficial effects of action video game play being most clearly evident for goal-directed, top-down attention and for spatial cognition (see Bediou et al., 2018 for an overview; also see Sala et al., 2018).

Interestingly, those beneficial effects have been mainly reported in the visual domain, as only a few studies have included other modalities in their experimental designs (Chopin et al., 2019). In a cross-modal study, Donohue and co-authors (2010) asked AVGPs and non-video game players (NVGPs) to indicate whether a sound or a light flash occurred first or whether these two stimuli were

DOI: 10.4324/9780429342356-6

simultaneously presented. AVGPs were more accurate in this cross-modal simultaneity judgment task compared to NVGPs. As AVGPs tended to outperform NVGPs predominantly when the auditory stimulus came after the visual stimulus, it was argued that more efficient processing of visual stimuli in AVGPs may limit the attentional dwell time associated with such processing, which would allow AVGPs to focus their visual attention faster and more accurately to a spatial location, thereby resulting in a more accurate estimation of the time of occurrence of the subsequent auditory stimulus. Thus, while this study indicates an enhanced ability in AVGPs to determine the temporal sequence of multisensory stimuli, it does not directly point to an auditory processing advantage.

In a study of auditory decision-making (Green et al., 2010), target sounds were presented either to the left ear or to the right ear while white noise was played in both ears. Participants were asked to indicate the ear in which the sound had been presented. AVGPs were faster compared to NVGPs at indicating the ear to which the sound had been presented, especially at low signal-to-noise ratios. A similar pattern was observed in initially naïve participants who received 50 h of action video game training, suggesting a causal relationship between action video game play and improved auditory decision-making (Green et al., 2010). These results are in contrast to those of another study, in which participants were trained for only 20 h on an action video game and were asked to detect as fast as possible a target tone either in the left ear or in the right ear while pressing another button when no sound was presented (Oei & Patterson, 2015). In this discriminative reaction time task, there were no behavioral improvements observed in AVGPs compared to NVGPs. It remains unclear whether 20 h of action video game training might not be sufficient to establish improved auditory perceptual functions, or if this particular task might be less amenable to change via action video game play (for a discussion of this point, see Chopin et al., 2019).

Improved attentional control in AVGPs

More effective attentional control has been proposed to be a common underlying mechanism to explain the variety of improved task performance skills in AVGPs (Bavelier & Green, 2019). Improved attentional control includes the ability to focus on task-relevant items while ignoring distracting events. At the behavioral level, AVGPs are better able to suppress irrelevant distractors than NVGPs as exemplified by their faster response to targets located among distractors (Chisholm, 2010; Chisholm & Kingstone, 2012; Clark et al., 2011; Green & Bavelier 2003, 2006; West et al., 2013) and by preserving speed as additional distractors are presented (Chisholm et al., 2010). Reduced attentional and oculomotor capture effects in AVGPs are also consistent with an enhanced top-down control over the allocation of spatial attention (Chisholm et al., 2010; Chisholm & Kingstone, 2012). At the neural level, one might expect to find a corresponding enhancement of the to-be-attended, task-relevant inputs, suppression of irrelevant inputs, or both in AVGPs. Using steady-state visual evoked potentials (SSVEPs) to track the fate of irrelevant, potentially distracting information, Mishra et al. (2011) reported stronger neural suppression of distracting information in AVGPs as compared to NVGPs. AVGPs displayed a larger SSVEP amplitude difference between neural signals evoked to the attended and the unattended (distractor) stream than NVGPs; importantly, while the two groups showed matched neural signals evoked by the attended stream, AVGPs showed reduced neural response to the unattended (distractor) stream.

Studies using event-related potentials (ERPs) examined whether early markers of attentional selection in AVGPs and NVGPs may explain such greater suppression in AVGPs. Surprisingly, so far, early visual selection of relevant stimuli at the level of the visual cortex appears comparable in AVGPs and NVGPs (Föcker et al., 2019; Krishnan et al., 2013; Wu et al., 2012). For example, in one such ERP study, fast flickering visual stimuli (Gabor patches) were presented in the left and right visual fields, while a cue indicated participants to attend either to the left or to the right visual field or distribute their attention across both fields (Föcker et al., 2019). Participants were asked to detect rare target Gabor patches that differed in orientation from the more frequently presented standard patches and to ignore all stimuli at the unattended location. AVGPs and NVGPs showed comparable attentional modulation of early posterior ERP components P1 (at 115–160 ms) and N1 (at 170–215 ms), which are generated in the visual cortex. However, AVGPs displayed an enhanced anterior visual N1 (at 125–175 ms) compared to NVGPs when attention was focused on one visual stream; this enhancement was absent when attention was distributed across both visual streams.

This suggested attention-dependent processing differences between the two groups in the parietal cortex where the anterior N1 is generated (Di Russo et al., 2002, 2003; Föcker et al., 2019). This pattern accords with fMRI studies suggesting that the attentional advantages noted in AVGPs may be largely mediated by widespread changes in the connectivity between areas of the fronto-parietal network of attention (Bavelier et al., 2012; Föcker et al., 2018; Gong et al., 2015, 2016). Indeed, this network has been repeatedly associated with top-down allocation of attention and the ability to suppress distractions (Scolari et al., 2015; Suzuki & Gottlieb, 2013).

The present study

The present study focuses on auditory attention and how its underlying brain mechanisms may be modified in AVGPs, by combining ERP recordings with behavioral assessments. The study design paralleled that of the visual attention study by Föcker et al. (2019) wherein rapid sequences of Gabor patches were presented in the left and right visual hemifields. As outlined earlier, in that study participants were instructed to attend to one of the visual fields (focused attention) or both (divided attention) and to detect Gabor patches having a specific orientation at the attended location(s). The present auditory version of this experiment compared AVGPs and NVGPs as they listened to dichotic streams of tones and performed a frequency discrimination task. At the start of each trial, a visual arrow cue directed the participant's attention either to the left or to the right ear stream (focused attention) or both ears (divided attention). The task was to report detections of occasional target tones having a slightly different frequency from the more frequent standard tones in the attended ear(s).

The neural correlates of auditory spatial attention in selective listening tasks, like the present one, have been studied extensively in humans (Hillyard et al., 1995; Näätänen, 1992). Attending to a sound source in space is indexed by modulations of a negative ERP beginning 60–80 ms after the onset of the stimulus (the N1 component), which is greater in amplitude in response to sounds at attended than at unattended locations. Even earlier attention effects (as early as 20–50 ms after stimulus onset) have been reported under some conditions (Woldorff & Hillyard, 1991; see Luck, 2014 for an overview). The auditory N1 is followed by a positive-going component that peaks at about 200 ms (P2 or P200), which is not consistently modified by attention (Tong et al., 2009). A second negative peak (the mismatch negativity or MMN) is typically elicited by sounds that deviate from a sequence of repetitive standard sounds in parameters such as intensity, duration, or frequency (Näätänen, 1992; Scherg et al., 1989; Squires et al., 1975). The MMN (peaking between 160 and 220 ms) indexes the integrity of auditory sensory memory (Naatanen et al., 2007) and may be enhanced by attention (Woldorff et al., 1998).

Longer latency endogenous ERP components such as the N2 and P3 (or P300) families of components have been associated with higher cognitive processes such as stimulus categorization, decision, and working memory operations (Polich & Kok, 1995). The negative-going N2 peaks at around 200–350 ms and has been linked specifically with stimulus discrimination and categorization processes (Anderer et al., 1996; Falkenstein et al., 1993; Luck, 2014; Patel & Azzam, 2005; Simson et al., 1977; Squires et al., 1975). The P3b, a task-dependent member of the P3 family, is generally elicited 300–500 ms after the onset of a task-relevant stimulus with a maximal amplitude over parietal areas. It has been extensively studied in the classic auditory oddball paradigm in which participants have to respond to rare (target) sounds in a sequence of frequent non-target (standard) sounds (Polich & Kok, 1995). Larger P3b amplitudes have been associated with greater stimulus relevance, attentional resource allocation, and decision confidence (Hillyard & Picton, 1987; Polich, 2004). Several visual ERP studies have shown an enhanced amplitude of the P3b in response to visual target stimuli in AVGPs, an effect that has been attributed to more effective target processing and decision-making processes (Mishra et al., 2011; Wu et al., 2012). The P3b component is often preceded by an enhanced N2 wave, which is modulated by many of the same factors that affect the P3b (Näätänen & Picton, 1986; Patel & Azzam, 2005).

In line with previous reports of enhanced attentional control using visual stimuli, we expected AVGPs to outperform NVGPs in this auditory target detection task, under both the focused and divided attention conditions. Moreover, we hypothesized that, as in the visual modality in which posterior N1 amplitudes did not differ between gamers and non-gamers as a function of spatial attention, early auditory ERP indexes of attentional filtering, such as the anterior N1, would be comparable in the two groups. We anticipated that only later ERP indices of target processing and decision-making (e.g., N2 and P3b) might show group differences indicative of a more efficient selection of task-relevant auditory targets in AVGPs.

Methods

Participants

A total of 30 right-handed male young adults from the University of California, San Diego community (mean age = 21.0, SD = 2.7; range 18–28 years) were classified as AVGPs or NVGPs according to their response to a questionnaire asking about video game play of different genres during the previous 12 months (Green & Bavelier, 2007). AVGPs (n = 15) played a minimum of 3–5 h/week of first or third person shooter video games (M = 7.0 h, SD = 2.5); NVGPs (n = 15) had no experience with action video games and played a maximum of 20 min/week of any other type of video game (M = 0.15 h, SD = 0.97). All participants reported having normal or corrected-to-normal vision and hearing. All participants were paid $15.00/h for their participation. The study was approved by the Committee on Human Subjects Protection of the UCSD Medical School.

Experimental design

The experiment was conducted in a darkened sound attenuated chamber with an ambient background noise of 32 dB. Participants viewed a 21-inch video monitor having a gray background (1.8 cd/m^2) at a distance of 100 cm. Visual stimuli were limited to a fixation cross (0.5° of visual angle) and attention-directing arrow cues (1.5° of visual angle) presented at fixation. Auditory stimuli were delivered from a pair of headphones (Audio-Technica Model ATH-M50) at 68 dB SL. Each auditory stimulus was a 30 ms duration tone burst including 5 ms rise and fall times. Standard tones had frequencies of 1000 and 3100 Hz, presented, respectively, to the left and right ears. Left ear targets consisted of 970 and 1030 Hz tone bursts. Right ear targets consisted of 3050 and 3250 Hz tone bursts (see Figure 2.1). We presented different tone frequencies to the two ears in order to increase the selectivity of attention. Early research found that separating the attended and unattended streams of tones by both spatial (ear

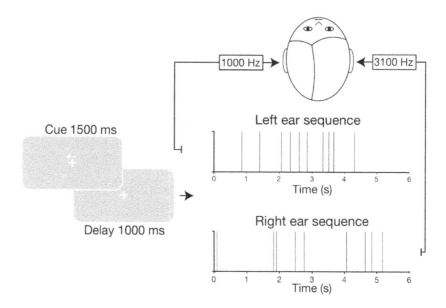

FIGURE 2.1 Experimental paradigm.

of entry) and frequency cues resulted in greater modulation of the attention-sensitive N1 component than when identical frequencies were presented to the two ears (Schwent et al., 1976).

At the start of each trial, an arrow cue was presented for 1500 ms that directed the subject's attention either to the left, right, or both auditory streams. Following a 1000 ms delay, independent sequences of tone bursts at an average rate of about 2/s were presented to each ear. Specifically, following a Bernoulli process, the probability of a stimulus presentation was 0.06 in each ear at successive intervals of 30 ms, ensuring that each stimulus event was temporally independent of the preceding and subsequent events (James et al., 2005). The probability of tones being presented simultaneously to both ears was <0.01 and responses to such concurrent stimuli were excluded in the subsequent ERP analysis.

Participants were informed that single arrow cues predicted with 100% certainty the stream containing the target (i.e., targets were not presented in the unattended ear's stream of tones). In contrast, double arrow cues indicated that targets were equally likely to occur in either of the auditory streams. Target tones were randomly interspersed in the attended sequence(s) between 3 and 10 s after cue onset and could be either higher or lower in frequency than the standard tones. Targets were presented in only 77% of the trials. The stimulus sequence self-terminated if a target did not appear by 10 s. Participants were instructed to press the response button when a target was detected. Whether or not the target was detected, the stimulus sequence continued for another 1.5 s past the target. A response was categorized as a "hit" if executed within this 1500 ms time window. Failure to respond in this interval was classified as a "miss." Finally, the tone sequences ended immediately when subjects responded to a non-target; these incorrect responses were classified as "false alarms."

ERP data acquisition and analysis

Scalp potentials were recorded from 60 tin electrodes mounted in a custom cap that were distributed evenly over the scalp (Electro-Cap International), with the electrode locations approximating those of the 10–20 system. The scalp recordings were referenced to the right mastoid during recording. Scalp and mastoid electrode impedances were maintained below 5 KΩ. Vertical eye movements were recorded by means of an electrode placed below the left eye and referenced to the right mastoid. Horizontal eye movements were recorded with a bipolar montage at the left and right outer canthi. Electroencephalographic (EEG) activity was amplified with an online 0.1–80 Hz band-pass filter (SA Amps – Model SAH BA 64). The electro-oculographic activity was amplified with an online 0.01–80 Hz band-pass filter. Data were digitized at a sampling rate of 250 Hz with a gain of 10,000. Automated artifact rejection was used in the time windows −100 to 500 ms for standards and −100 to 600 ms for targets to reject trials offline to eliminate blinks, muscle potentials, or amplifier blocking. After artifact removal, the remaining ERPs were algebraically re-referenced to the average of the left and right mastoid signals and low-pass filtered to attenuate signals at and above 57 Hz.

For the ERP analyses, each component's mean amplitude was measured in each individual subject over specified time windows (see Results section) at electrode sites where the component was most prominent in the grand-average ERP waveform of the entire sample.

A mixed-design repeated measure omnibus analysis of variance (ANOVA) was performed on the mean amplitudes of the different ERP components. ERPs to standard stimuli were analyzed at midline-anterior electrode sites where the early attention-sensitive N1 component had maximal amplitudes. Factors specified in the ANOVA model included *Group* (AVGPs versus NVGPs), *Attention* (Focused, Divided, and Unattended), and *Electrode* (Fz, FCz, and Cz). ERPs to target stimuli were analyzed at midline-posterior electrode sites, where the N2 and P3b components had maximal amplitudes. Factors included in the ANOVA were *Group* (AVGPs versus NVGPs), *Attention* (Focused and Divided), and *Electrode* (Pz, POz, and Oz). Greenhouse-Geisser corrections were made as needed to counter violations of sphericity.

Behavioral data analysis

Correct responses to the targets (i.e., hits) and incorrect responses to the standards (i.e., false alarms) were used to calculate the perceptual sensitivity measure d'

(Green & Swets, 1966). A d' was calculated for each participant and attention condition and submitted to an ANOVA with the between-participants factor *Group* (AVGPs versus NVGPs) and the within-participants factor *Attention* (Focused versus Divided). Participants were encouraged to prioritize accuracy over speed of responding. For technical reasons, reaction times were not available for analysis.

Results

Behavioral results

AVGPs distinguished standards from targets more accurately than NVGPs as revealed by their higher d' scores [main effect of *Group*: $F(1,28) = 11.79$, $p < 0.001$, $\eta_p^2 = 0.30$]. Moreover, the interaction between the factors *Group* and *Attention* was significant [$F(1,28) = 5.36$, $p = 0.02$, $\eta_p^2 = 0.16$], indicating a lesser performance decline from the focused to the divided attention condition in AVGPs as compared to NVGPs (see Figure 2.2).

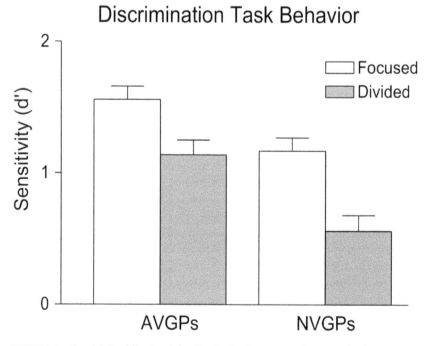

FIGURE 2.2   Sensitivity (d' prime) for discriminating targets from standards in AVGPs and NVGPs.

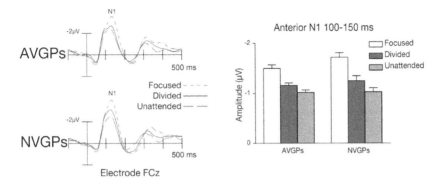

FIGURE 2.3   *Left:* Grand-averaged ERPs to auditory standard tones recorded when the left or the right ear was attended or unattended (during focused attention) and when attention was divided between the two ears recorded from electrode FCz in the two groups. *Right:* Bar graphs of the mean N1 amplitudes in the two groups.

ERPs to standard tones – N1 at anterior sites (100–150 ms)

The omnibus ANOVA on the mean N1 amplitude over 100–150 ms including the factors *Group* (AVGP versus NVGP), *Attention* (Focused, Divided, and Unattended), and *Electrode* (Fz, FCz, and Cz) revealed a significant main effect of *Attention* [$F(2,56) = 52.71$, $p < 0.001$, $\eta_p^2 = 0.65$]. ERPs to the focused attention stream showed a more pronounced N1 negativity compared to the divided and unattended streams in both groups (see Figure 2.3). No other main effects or interactions were statistically significant; in particular, there were no *Group* effects or interactions (all $ps > 0.12$).

ERPs to target tones – N1/MMN at anterior sites (150–200 ms)

The ERP to the target tones showed broad anterior negativity over the latency window of 80–200 ms, which appears to be the overlapping combination of the anterior N1 and the MMN that is typically elicited by deviant sounds in a repetitive sequence (Näätänen, 1992; Scherg et al., 1989; Squires et al., 1975). The analysis interval of 80–200 ms was chosen post hoc on the basis of visual inspection. An omnibus ANOVA with the factors *Group* (AVGP versus NVGP), *Attention* (Focused and Divided), and *Electrode* (Fz, FCz, and Cz) revealed that the anterior N1/MMN was larger under the focused attention condition compared to the divided attention in both groups [main effect of *Attention*: $F(1,28) = 4.86$, $p = 0.03$, $\eta_p^2 = 0.15$]. No other effects were statistically significant, including no *Group* effects or interactions (all $ps > 0.05$) (see Figure 2.4).

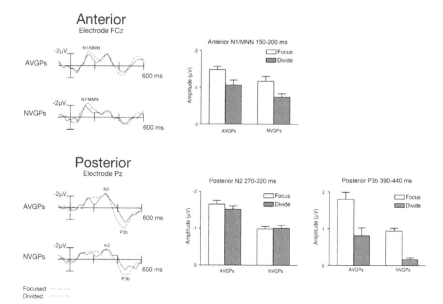

FIGURE 2.4 *Left:* Grand-averaged ERPs to auditory targets recorded in the focused and divided conditions at the anterior electrode FCz and the posterior electrode Pz in the two groups. *Right:* Upper bar graphs show the mean amplitudes of the anterior N1/MMN elicited by target tones in AVGPs and NVGPs. Lower bar plots show the amplitudes of the posterior N2 and P3 elicited by targets in the two groups. AVGPs show more pronounced N2 and P3 amplitudes compared to NVGPs for both divided and focused conditions.

ERPs to target tones – N2 at posterior sites (270–320 ms)

For the N2 amplitude at posterior sites, the omnibus ANOVA with the factors *Group* (AVGP versus NVGP), *Attention* (Focused and Divided), and *Electrode* (Pz, POz, and Oz) revealed a significant main effect of *Group*: $F(1,28) = 6.02$, $p = 0.02$, $\eta_p^2 = 0.18$, but no significant main effect of *Attention* or interaction between *Attention* and *Group* ($p > 0.05$). The main effect of the *Group* resulted from a more pronounced anterior N2 negativity in AVGPs compared to NVGPs (see Figure 2.4).

ERPs to target tones – P3b at posterior sites (390–440 ms)

An omnibus ANOVA with the factors *Group* (AVGP versus NVGP), *Attention* (Focused and Divided), and *Electrode* (Pz, POz, and Oz) showed a highly significant main effect of *Attention* [$F(1,28) = 17.26$, $p < 0.001$, $\eta_p^2 = 0.38$] resulting from an enhanced posterior P3b for the focused attention condition compared to the divided attention condition. A significant main effect of *Group* [$F(1,28) = 4.42$, $p < 0.04$, $\eta_p^2 = 0.14$] was also observed, showing a more pronounced P3b positivity in AVGPs compared to NVGPs. There was no significant interaction between *Group* and *Attention* ($p > 0.05$) (Figure 2.4).

Discussion

The goal of the present study was to assess whether the attentional advantages noted in AVGPs in the visual modality generalized to the auditory modality. Using an attentionally demanding auditory discrimination task, we found that AVGPs outperformed NVGPs in detecting auditory target stimuli and distinguishing them from auditory standards. These results suggest that similar to the visual modality (Föcker et al., 2019; Mishra et al., 2011), AVGPs show better performance in auditory spatial selective attention compared to NVGPs. The superior performance of AVGPs is in line with the results of another study showing faster auditory location discrimination performance in AVGPs compared to NVGPs (Green et al., 2010; also see Stewart et al., 2020, who did not find any group differences). While in the task of Green et al. (2010) bottom-up auditory information (i.e., the tone itself) guided attention to a specific location, the present study showed for the first time better top-down auditory selective attention in AVGPs, whether engaged by focusing or dividing attention to streams of tones at different locations in space.

At the neural level, we observed that the early N1 ERP component (100–150 ms) was strongly modulated by spatial selective attention, in line with previous literature (reviewed in Hillyard et al., 1995; Näätänen, 1992). ERPs to auditory standards showed a more pronounced N1 negativity in the focused attention as compared to the divided and unattended conditions. Similarly, targets elicited larger N1 negativity (that was combined with an overlapping mismatch negativity; see Scherg et al., 1989) at anterior electrode sites in the focused attention compared to the divided attention condition. However, the attentional modulation of this anterior N1 component, generally considered to index early attentional filtering of auditory information (Hillyard et al., 1995), did not differ between groups.

In line with our hypotheses, the later N2 and P3b components elicited by auditory targets did show enhanced amplitudes in AVGPs compared to NVGPs. The main neural differences between AVGPs and NVGPs occurred during auditory target processing starting at about 270 ms. A more pronounced negativity in the time range of the auditory N2 was observed in AVGPs compared to NVGPs when they detected rare target tones. It has been proposed that the auditory N2 reflects neural processes involved in the discrimination, identification, and categorization of task-relevant stimuli, for instance in the context of an oddball design in which a rare target stimulus follows the presentation of more frequent standard stimuli (Anderer et al., 1996; Falkenstein et al., 1993; Luck, 2014; Patel & Azzam,

2005; Simson et al., 1977; Squires et al., 1975). These ERP findings thus converge with the behavioral evidence suggesting that AVGPs have a superior ability to make rapid discriminations and categorizations of task-relevant stimuli in the auditory modality.

The ERPs of AVGPs and NVGPs also differed in the time range of the P3b, with AVGPs showing an enlarged positivity to target tones. An enhanced P3b in AVGPs as compared to NVGPs has also been reported in the visual domain when rapid sequences of alphanumeric stimuli were presented in the left, right, or center of the screen and participants were asked to detect rare target letters (Mishra et al., 2011; Wu et al., 2012; also see Föcker et al., 2019). In the oddball paradigm, the P3b has been linked to the discrimination and classification of unpredictable stimuli and the decisions made as to their relevance (for reviews, see Hillyard & Picton, 1987; Picton, 1992; Polich, 1998, 2007). In situations that call for rapid-fire decisions, the P3b has been shown to track the rate of decision-making as fast as 3/s (Woods et al., 1980). The enhanced P3b observed here also parallels the behavioral results, which showed higher sensitivity in AVGPs for detecting rare and unpredictable targets at the attended location. Wu et al. (2012) and Mishra et al. (2011) also reported an enhanced P3b in AVGPs as compared to NVGPs. We can only speculate as to why enhanced P3b amplitudes were not observed in AVGPs in Föcker et al. (2019), whose study had a design similar to the one adopted here. Different stimulus materials, stimulus probabilities, or task difficulties might have affected the degree of modulation of the P3b amplitude (see Luck & Hillyard, 2014). In any case, the P3b results of the present study support the overall hypothesis of enhanced perceptual decision-making processes in AVGPs (Donohue et al., 2010; Schubert et al., 2015).

In summary, the present study, when considered in the context of the existing literature on the beneficial impact of action video game play on attentional control, suggests that these attentional benefits extend to auditory spatial attention. We found that AVGPs outperformed NVGPs in detecting auditory targets within the to-be-attended auditory stream. Electrophysiological data showed comparable early attentional filtering in AVGPs and NVGPs, with the two groups only differing in later processing stages, as indexed by modulation of the N2 and the P3b ERP components. As reviewed earlier, this pattern of results parallels what has been observed in the visual modality where neural markers of early attentional selection were found to be comparable in AVGPs and NVGPs. Together, these findings suggest that early attentional selection in modality-specific cortex, one of the best documented neural mechanisms of attention, may not underlie the superior attentional control observed in AVGPs. Rather, a more efficient late selection, indexed by the N2 and P3b components, appears more compatible with the existing data. Furthermore, a recent brain imaging study has shown that the temporo-parietal junction, one of the most prominent neural sources of the P3b, is preferentially activated in gamers and is related to the selective suppression of irrelevant visual stimuli (Föcker et al., 2018). Although it remains to be fully tested, this pattern of results would be consistent with AVGPs having a superior ability to flexibly allocate attention to rapid stimulus sequences and to identify and select relevant stimuli through decisional mechanisms at a relatively late processing stage.

Finally, we acknowledge our indebtedness to the pioneering research of Helen Neville on the plasticity of auditory and visual processing after early deprivation such as blindness and deafness. Her studies paved the way for a new avenue of research investigating the influence of enriched environments (such as video gaming) on brain plasticity for functions of attention and learning. Here we showed that adults who play action video games display improved auditory spatial attention skills, suggesting that an "enriched" environment, such as playing action video games, might boost perceptual and cognitive functions even after the closure of time windows in which the brain functions have been suggested to be highly plastic (Bavelier et al., 2010). As discussed in Bavelier and Green (2019), enhanced attentional control may facilitate brain plasticity and learning. As Helen Neville taught us, understanding when and how this facilitation occurs will be key to developing evidence-based, translational approaches such as boosting attentional control through properly titrated video game play activities. To this end, it remains critical to go beyond the cross-sectional work such as the one presented here and compare different training regimes administered at different ages in order to identify the mechanisms that causally link action video game play to its neural impact on attention, and more broadly on brain plasticity and learning.

Funding

This work was supported by the Swiss National Fund 100014_140676, the German Research Foundation (DFG, FO 786), and the U.S. Office of Naval Research (N00014-07-1-0937).

References

Al-Gabbani, M., Morgan, G., & Eyre, J. A. (2014). Positive relationship between duration of action video game play and visuospatial executive function in children. In *2014 IEEE 3rd international conference on serious games and applications for health (SeGAH), Rio de Janeiro, Brazil* (pp. 1–4). New York: IEEE.

Anderer, P., Semlitsch, H. V., & Saletu, B. (1996). Multichannel auditory event-related brain potentials: Effects of normal aging on the scalp distribution of N1, P2, N2 and P300 latencies and amplitudes. *Electroencephalography and Clinical Neurophysiology, 99*(5), 458–472.

Bavelier, D., Achtman, R. L., Mani, M., & Föcker, J. (2012). Neural bases of selective attention in action video game players. *Vision Research, 61*, 132–143.

Bavelier, D., Levi, D. M., Li, R. W., Dan, Y., & Hensch, T. K. (2010). Removing brakes on adult brain plasticity: From molecular to behavioral interventions. *Journal of Neuroscience, 30*(45), 14964–14971.

Bavelier, D., & Green, C. S. (2019). Enhancing attentional control: Lessons from action video games. *Neuron, 104*(1), 147–163.

Bediou, B., Adams, D. M., Mayer, R. E., Tipton, E., Green, C. S., & Bavelier, D. (2018). Meta-analysis of action video game impact on perceptual, attentional, and cognitive skills. *Psychological Bulletin*, *144*(1), 77.

Bejjanki, V. R., Zhang, R., Li, R., Pouget, A., Green, C. S., Lu, Z. L., & Bavelier, D. (2014). Action video game play facilitates the development of better perceptual templates. *Proceedings of the National Academy of Sciences*, *111*(47), 16961–16966.

Belchior, P., Marsiske, M., Sisco, S. M., Yam, A., Bavelier, D., Ball, K., & Mann, W. C. (2013). Video game training to improve selective visual attention in older adults. *Computers in Human Behavior*, *29*(4), 1318–1324.

Berard, A. V., Cain, M. S., Watanabe, T., & Sasaki, Y. (2015). Frequent video game players resist perceptual interference. *PloS One*, *10*(3), e0120011.

Buckley, D., Codina, C., Bhardwaj, P., & Pascalis, O. (2010). Action video game players and deaf observers have larger Goldmann visual fields. *Vision Research*, *50*(5), 548–556.

Cain, M. S., Landau, A. N., & Shimamura, A. P. (2012). Action video game experience reduces the cost of switching tasks. *Attention, Perception, & Psychophysics*, *74*(4), 641–647. https://doi.org/10.3758/s13414-012-0284-1

Cardoso-Leite, P., & Bavelier, D. (2014). Video game play, attention, and learning: How to shape the development of attention and influence learning? *Current Opinion in Neurology*, *27*(2), 185–191.

Castel, A. D., Pratt, J., & Drummond, E. (2005). The effects of action video game experience on the time course of inhibition of return and the efficiency of visual search. *Acta Psychologica*, *119*, 217–230.

Chisholm, J. D., Hickey, C., Theeuwes, J., & Kingstone, A. (2010). Reduced attentional capture in action video game players. *Attention, Perception, & Psychophysics*, *72*(3), 667–671.

Chisholm, J. D., & Kingstone, A. (2012). Improved top-down control reduces oculomotor capture: The case of action video game players. *Attention, Perception, & Psychophysics*, *74*(2), 257–262.

Chopin, A., Bediou, B., & Bavelier, D. (2019). Altering perception: The case of action video gaming. *Current Opinion in Psychology*, *29*, 168–173.

Clark, K., Fleck, M. S., & Mitroff, S. R. (2011). Enhanced change detection performance reveals improved strategy use in avid action video game players. *Acta Psychologica*, *136*(1), 67–72.

Di Russo, F., Martínez, A., & Hillyard, S. A. (2003). Source analysis of event-related cortical activity during visuo-spatial attention. *Cerebral Cortex*, *13*, 486–499.

Di Russo, F., Martínez, A., Sereno, M. I., Pitzalis, S., & Hillyard, S. A. (2002). Cortical sources of the early components of the visual evoked potential. *Human Brain Mapping*, *15*, 95–111.

Donohue, S. E., Woldorff, M. G., & Mitroff, S. R. (2010). Video game players show more precise multisensory temporal processing abilities. *Attention, Perception, & Psychophysics*, *72*(4), 1120–1129.

Dye, M. W., & Bavelier, D. (2010). Differential development of visual attention skills in school-age children. *Vision Research*, *50*(4), 452–459.

Falkenstein, M., Hohnsbein, J., & Hoormann, J. (1993). Late visual and auditory ERP components and choice reaction time. *Biological Psychology*, *35*(3), 201–224.

Feng, J., Spence, I., & Pratt, J. (2007). Playing an action video game reduces gender differences in spatial cognition. *Psychological Science*, *18*(10), 850–855.

Föcker, J., Cole, D., Beer, A. L., & Bavelier, D. (2018). Neural bases of enhanced attentional control: Lessons from action video game players. *Brain and Behavior, 8*(7), e01019. https://doi.org/10.1002/brb3.1019

Föcker, J., Mortazavi, M., Khoe, W., Hillyard, S. A., & Bavelier, D. (2019). Neural correlates of enhanced visual attentional control in action video game players: An event-related potential study. *Journal of Cognitive Neuroscience, 31*(3), 377–389.

Franceschini, S., Gori, S., Ruffino, M., Viola, S., Molteni, M., & Facoetti, A. (2013). Action video games make dyslexic children read better. *Current Biology, 23*(6), 462–466. https://doi.org/10.1016/j.cub.2013.01.044

Gambacorta, C., Huang, S., Vedamurthy, I., Nahum, M., Bayliss, J., Bavelier, D., & Levi, D. (2014). Action video games as a treatment of amblyopia in children: A pilot study of a novel, child-friendly action game. *Journal of Vision, 14*(10), 665–665. https://doi.org/10.1167/14.10.665

Gong, D., He, H., Liu, D., Ma, W., Dong, L., Luo, C., & Yao, D. (2015). Enhanced functional connectivity and increased gray matter volume of insula related to action video game playing. *Scientific Reports, 5*, 9763.

Gong, D., He, H., Ma, W., Liu, D., Huang, M., Dong, L., & Yao, D. (2016). Functional integration between salience and central executive networks: A role for action video game experience. *Neural Plasticity, 2016*, 1–9.

Green, C. S., & Bavelier, D. (2003). Action video game modifies visual selective attention. *Nature, 423*(6939), 534.

Green, C. S., & Bavelier, D. (2006). Effect of action video games on the spatial distribution of visuospatial attention. *Journal of Experimental Psychology: Human Perception and Performance, 32*(6), 1465.

Green, C. S., & Bavelier, D. (2007). Action-video-game experience alters the spatial resolution of vision. *Psychological Science, 18*(1), 88–94.

Green, C. S., Pouget, A., & Bavelier, D. (2010). Improved probabilistic inference as a general learning mechanism with action video games. *Current Biology, 20*(17), 1573–1579.

Green, D. M., & Swets, J. A. (1966). *Signal detection theory and psychophysics* (vol. 1, pp. 1969–2012). New York: Wiley & Sons, Inc.

Hillyard, S. A., Mangun, G. R., Woldorff, M. G., & Luck, S. J. (1995). Neural systems mediating selective attention. In M. S. Gazzaniga (Ed.), *The cognitive neurosciences* (pp. 665–681). Cambridge, MA: The MIT Press.

Hillyard, S. A., & Picton, T. W. (1987). Electrophysiology of cognition. In F. Plum (Ed.), *Handbook of physiology section 1: The nervous system. Volume V. Higher functions of the brain, part 2* (pp. 519–584). Bethesda, MD: American Physiological Society.

James, A. C., Ruseckaite, R., & Maddess, T. E. D. (2005). Effect of temporal sparseness and dichoptic presentation on multifocal visual evoked potentials. *Visual Neuroscience, 22*(1), 45–54.

Krishnan, L., Kang, A., Sperling, G., & Srinivasan, R. (2013). Neural strategies for selective attention distinguish fast-action video game players. *Brain Topography, 26*(1), 83–97.

Li, R., Polat, U., Makous, W., & Bavelier, D. (2009). Enhancing the contrast sensitivity function through action video game training. *Nature Neuroscience, 12*(5), 549. https://doi.org/10.1038/nn.2296

Li, R., Polat, U., Scalzo, F., & Bavelier, D. (2010). Reducing backward masking through action game training. *Journal of Vision, 10*(14), 33–33. https://doi.org/10.1167/10.14.33.

Luck, S. J. (2014). *An introduction to the event-related potential technique*. Cambridge, MA: The MIT Press.

Luck, S. J., & Hillyard, S. A. (2014). Electrophysiology of visual attention in humans. In M. S. Gazzaniga & G. R. Mangun (Eds.), *The cognitive neurosciences* (4th ed., pp. 187–196). Cambridge, MA: The MIT Press.

Mishra, J., Zinni, M., Bavelier, D., & Hillyard, S. A. (2011). Neural basis of superior performance of action videogame players in an attention-demanding task. *Journal of Neuroscience, 31*(3), 992–998.

Näätänen, R. (1992). *Attention and brain function.* Mahwah, NJ: Lawrence Erlbaum Associates.

Näätänen, R., Paavilainen, P., Rinne, T., & Alho, K. (2007). The mismatch negativity (MMN) in basic research of central auditory processing: A review. *Clinical Neurophysiology, 118*(12), 2544–2590.

Näätänen, R., & Picton, T. W. (1986). N2 and automatic versus controlled processes. *Electroencephalography and Clinical Neurophysiology Supplement, 38,* 169–186.

Nava, E., Föcker, J., & Gori, M. (2019). Children can optimally integrate multisensory information after a short action-like mini game training. *Developmental Science, 23*(1), e12840.

Oei, A. C., & Patterson, M. D. (2015). Enhancing perceptual and attentional skills requires common demands between the action video games and transfer tasks. *Frontiers in Psychology, 6,* 113.

Patel, S. H., & Azzam, P. N. (2005). Characterization of N200 and P300: Selected studies of the event-related potential. *International Journal of Medical Sciences, 2*(4), 147.

Pavan, A., Hobaek, M., Blurton, S. P., Contillo, A., Ghin, F., & Greenlee, M. W. (2019). Visual short-term memory for coherent motion in video game players: Evidence from a memory-masking paradigm. *Scientific Reports, 9*(1), 6027.

Picton, T. W. (1992). The P300 wave of the human event-related potential. *Journal of Clinical Neurophysiology, 9*(4), 456–479.

Polich, J. (1998). P300 clinical utility and control of variability. *Journal of Clinical Neurophysiology, 15*(1), 14–33.

Polich, J. (2004). Clinical application of the P300 event-related brain potential. *Physical Medicine and Rehabilitation Clinics, 15*(1), 133–161.

Polich, J. (2007). Updating P300: An integrative theory of P3a and P3b. *Clinical Neurophysiology, 118*(10), 2128–2148.

Polich, J., & Kok, A. (1995). Cognitive and biological determinants of P300: An integrative review. *Biological Psychology, 41*(2), 103–146.

Rupp, M. A., McConnell, D. S., & Smither, J. A. (2016). Examining the relationship between action video game experience and performance in a distracted driving task. *Current Psychology, 35*(4), 527–539.

Sala, G., Tatlidil, K. S., & Gobet, F. (2018). Video game training does not enhance cognitive ability: A comprehensive meta-analytic investigation. *Psychological Bulletin, 144*(2), 111.

Scherg, M., Vajsar, J., & Picton, T. W. (1989). A source analysis of the late human auditory evoked potentials. *Journal of Cognitive Neuroscience, 1*(4), 336–355.

Schubert, T., Finke, K., Redel, P., Kluckow, S., Müller, H., & Strobach, T. (2015). Video game experience and its influence on visual attention parameters: An investigation using the framework of the Theory of Visual Attention (TVA). *Acta Psychologica, 157,* 200–214.

Schwent, V. L., Snyder, E., & Hillyard, S. A. (1976). Auditory evoked potentials during multichannel selective listening: Role of pitch and localization cues. *Journal of Experimental Psychology: Human Perception and Performance, 2*(3), 313.

Scolari, M., Seidl-Rathkopf, K. N., & Kastner, S. (2015). Functions of the human fron-toparietal attention network: Evidence from neuroimaging. *Current Opinion in Behavioral Sciences, 1*, 32–39.

Simson, R., Vaughan, H. G., & Ritter, W. (1977). The scalp topography of potentials in auditory and visual discrimination tasks. *Electroencephalography and Clinical Neurophysiology, 42*, 528–535.

Squires, N. K, Squires, K. C., & Hillyard, S. A. (1975). Two varieties of long-latency positive waves evoked by unpredictable auditory stimuli. *Electroencephalography and Clinical Neurophysiology, 38*, 387–401.

Stewart, H. J., Martinez, J. L., Perdew, A., Green, C. S., & Moore, D. R. (2020). Auditory cognition and perception of action video game players. *Scientific Reports, 10*(1), 1–11.

Strobach, T., Frensch, P. A., & Schubert, T. (2012). Video game practice optimizes executive control skills in dual-task and task switching situations. *Acta Psychologica, 140*(1), 13–24.

Subrahmanyam, K., & Greenfield, P. M. (1994). Effect of video game practice on spatial skills in girls and boys. *Journal of Applied Developmental Psychology, 15*(1), 13–32.

Sungur, H., & Boduroglu, A. (2012). Action video game players form more detailed representation of objects. *Acta Psychologica, 139*(2), 327–334.

Suzuki, M., & Gottlieb, J. (2013). Distinct neural mechanisms of distractor suppression in the frontal and parietal lobe. *Nature Neuroscience, 16*(1), 98–104.

Tong, Y., Melara, R. D., & Rao, A. (2009). P2 enhancement from auditory discrimination training is associated with improved reaction times. *Brain Research, 1297*, 80–88.

Trick, L. M., Jaspers-Fayer, F., & Sethi, N. (2005). Multiple-object tracking in children: The "Catch the Spies" task. *Cognitive Development, 20*(3), 373–387.

Vedamurthy, I., Nahum, M., Bavelier, D., & Levi, D. M. (2015). Mechanisms of recovery of visual function in adult amblyopia through a tailored action video game. *Scientific Reports, 5*, 8482.

Waris, O., Jaeggi, S. M., Seitz, A. R., Lehtonen, M., Soveri, A., Lukasik, K. M., & Laine, M. (2019). Video gaming and working memory: A large-scale cross-sectional correlative study. *Computers in Human Behavior, 97*, 94–103.

West, G. L., Al-Aidroos, N., & Pratt, J. (2013). Action video game experience affects oculomotor performance. *Acta Psychologica, 142*(1), 38–42.

Woldorff, M. G., & Hillyard, S. A. (1991). Modulation of early auditory processing during selective listening to rapidly presented tones. *Electroencephalography and Clinical Neurophysiology, 79*(3), 170–191.

Woldorff, M. G., Hillyard, S. A., Gallen, C. C, Hampson, S. R., & Bloom, F. E. (1998). Magnetoencephalographic recordings demonstrate attentional modulation of mismatch-related neural activity in human auditory cortex. *Psychophysiology 35*(3), 283–292.

Woods, D. L., S. A. Hillyard, Courchesne, E., & Galambos, R. (1980). Electrophysiological signs of split-second decision making in man. *Science, 207*, 655–656.

Wu, S., Cheng, C. K., Feng, J., D'Angelo, L., Alain, C., & Spence, I. (2012). Playing a first-person shooter video game induces neuroplastic change. *Journal of Cognitive Neuroscience, 24*(6), 1286–1293.

Interlude 3

STRUCTURE AND CONTENT

Marta Kutas

Form and meaning are not the same
and each has a metaphorical hand
in the language processing and language learning game
Left frontal (Broca's) area rules posterior (Wernicke's) region memes
in time and space, Open to all, no if ands or buts
slotted and ordered by syntactic functions to insure the inputs keep pace
as they help make sense of a headful of potentially meaningful whats.

DOI: 10.4324/9780429342356-7

3

THE ROLES OF AGE OF ACQUISITION, PROFICIENCY, AND FIRST LANGUAGE ON SECOND LANGUAGE PROCESSING

Annika Andersson and Aaron J. Newman

It is well established that the development of a healthy brain in babies requires exposure to certain stimuli before reaching a certain age. To gain a better understanding of this process, Helen Neville focused her research on brain plasticity. When each of us met Helen in her Brain Development Lab, she was investigating how different types of stimuli were processed depending on the age of exposure. These studies included those on second language (L2) processing. The focus was to learn at what time a language needs to be acquired for the brain to process the language effectively. This line of investigation is of outmost importance as increased international mobility requires humans to acquire new languages at different ages. This chapter discusses some of the neurocognitive research on second language processing with a focus on studies utilizing event-related potentials (ERPs). Helen's research in this field has been essential for our understanding of how the brain process different subsystems of language depending on the age of acquisition (AoA).

This chapter is organized around three different subsystems of language: phonology, semantics, and syntax – and for each we focus on three factors important for second language processing: AoA, proficiency, and cross-linguistic influence (CLI). All three have been investigated in both behavioral and neurophysiological studies of L2 acquisition but to different extents. The outline of the chapter follows the order in which the subsystems are acquired in a native language: phonology, followed by vocabulary (semantics), and then syntax. We argue for a shift in ERP research from a focus on AoA as a sole factor for describing differences in processing first and second languages to a more comprehensive approach including proficiency and CLI.

Two important lessons we learned from Helen were first, that variability among individuals must always be examined to better understand the diversity

DOI: 10.4324/9780429342356-8

and the patterns that contribute to a group average, and second, that an ERP effect is not interesting in itself if we cannot relate it to behavior. In this chapter, we exemplify these lessons by including research that examined individual data and how they affected the authors' conclusions, and by beginning each subsection with a discussion of behavioral patterns in language acquisition in order to better understand what the neurophysiological processing might represent behaviorally.

Phonology

AoA affecting phonological processing

A phoneme is the smallest unit of sound in a language that affects meaning such that changing one phoneme in a word creates a different word and meaning (e.g., changing /b/ into /p/ changes the word bat to pat). The perception of phonemes is thus crucial for word learning (Kuhl et al., 2005; Lindsey et al., 2003). Phonemes are perceived categorically, meaning that we perceive them as one speech sound or another (e.g., /b/ or /p/) even though different occurrences of phonemes vary along an acoustic continuum. When we learn a second language, we must acquire a new phonological system that encompasses some phonemes shared between the first language (L1) and L2, and usually additional phonemic categories that are not present in L1. Studies indicate that sensitivity to non-native phonemes in children learning their L1 is greatly reduced already at an age of 12 months (Werker & Lalonde, 1988; Werker & Tees, 1984), thus indicating strong AoA effects on phonological processing.

Studies of categorical perception have utilized ERPs to investigate neurophysiological sensitivity to the native and non-native contrasts in adults (e.g., Rivera-Gaxiola et al., 2000) and infants (Rivera-Gaxiola et al., 2005). Adults showed ERP effects that differentiated between different phonemes for both native and non-native contrasts including a mismatch negativity (MMN), a neural response that reflects pre-attentive detection of differences in auditory input. Notably, the ERPs showed sensitivity to non-native phonemic contrasts in the absence of participants being able to consciously distinguish them. However, the effects of non-native contrasts were affected by how well the non-native phonemes could be assimilated with the native phoneme. For infants, native and non-native contrasts elicited similar ERP effects at 7 months, but no effects for non-native contrasts were found at 11 months (Rivera-Gaxiola et al., 2005). These results emphasize the influence of L1 phonology on L2 perception (Rivera-Gaxiola et al., 2005).

Hisagi et al. (2015) compared the MMN elicited when a change in phoneme is detected (in this case a vowel contrasts) in native speakers of English and two groups of Spanish learners of English who either acquired L2 early (before 5 years of age) or late (after 18 years of age). Interestingly, the MMN elicited in the two groups of learners did not differ from each other but differed from that of native speakers, who showed a larger effect, indicating that delays in AoA even within the first 5 years of life can have lasting impacts on speech perception. While the L2 MMN effect has been reported for 5- to 7-year-old children who were immersed in L2 in a school setting from the age of 3–4 (Peltola et al., 2005), this effect was not compared to that of native-speaking children, so it is difficult to know whether their MMN effect was native-like. Indeed, in a study of 5- to 6-year-olds Turkish-German bilingual born in Germany but immersed first at about 2 years of age, the MMN was lower in amplitude for vowel contrasts that existed in L2 only (Rinker et al., 2010). In sum, non-native contrasts seem to be more difficult to acquire and process in a native-like manner after 12 months of age, as indicated by both behavioral studies and neurophysiological studies.

Proficiency and phonological processing

Even though the perception of non-native phonemes changes after around 12 months of age, they can still be acquired, albeit with greater variability. In these cases, the quality and quantity of input, as well as attention to the input, becomes increasingly important for native-like perception (Flege, 2018; McCandliss et al., 2002; Snow & Hoefnagel-Hohle, 1977). The ability to master the phonology of a new language impacts learning other aspects of the language as well; several stud-ies report a positive relationship between phonology skills and vocabulary size in monolinguals, and within each language in bilinguals (e.g., López & Greenfield, 2004; Manis et al., 2004).

Specific training on non-native phonological contrasts has been shown to lead to similar brain activation for native and trained, non-native contrasts. In one study (Golestani & Zatorre, 2004), adult monolingual English speakers were trained for 5 h across two weeks in perceiving the difference between the dental consonant /d/ and the dental retroflex that does not exist in English and therefore is typically perceived as a /d/ by native English speakers (Werker & Lalonde, 1988). Golestani and Zatorre showed changes with training such that adults could recruit the same brain regions (left inferior frontal gyrus, bilateral superior temporal gyri, and fron-tal operculum) for perceiving non-native and native contrasts. Similarly, training on processing L2 lexical tones affected the amplitude of the pre-attentive MMN in an L2 phoneme discrimination task (Lu et al., 2015), as well as both the amplitude and latency of another ERP component, the P3. Notably, the P3 – which indexes detection of infrequent, attended differences in a stimulus stream – was related to experience with the language in another study (Grubb et al., 1998).

Collectively, these studies highlight the fact that while behavioral and neu-rophysiological indices of phonological processing show sensitivity to AoA, the direction of causality is not clear. Altered neural responses in L2 learners may be due to – or at least modulated by – proficiency, and specific training may mitigate both the behavioral and neural differences between L1 and L2 phoneme percep-tion. However, the extent to which specific training on phonetic contrasts gener-alizes outside of a laboratory setting to natural speech is unknown.

CLI on phonological processing

Results discussed earlier suggest that adults can perceive non-native contrasts, but the perception is affected by the native language (Rivera-Gaxiola et al., 2000). Additional evidence for CLI comes from a study that compared adults from two different L1 backgrounds, French and Japanese (Dehaene-Lambertz et al., 2000). Participants were presented with pairs of novel words, with the first in each pair containing a consonant cluster followed by the same word but with an epenthetic vowel breaking up the cluster (e.g., /ebzo/ – /ebuzo/). Critically, both words in each pair were phonotactically legal in French, but the first was phonotactically illegal in Japanese. French, but not Japanese, participants perceived the difference and showed a corresponding MMN. Both the ERP and behavioral results suggest that Japanese participants could not perceive the differences between the phonotactically legal (/ebuzo/) and the illegal (/ebzo/) phoneme clusters and instead perceived both as the legal variant. Thus, in adults, CLI seems to affect whether (Dehaene-Lambertz et al., 2000) and how (Rivera-Gaxiola et al., 2000) non-native phonemes are perceived.

Vocabulary (semantics)

Behavioral studies of vocabulary acquisition

For an adult speaker to comprehend everyday conversations within a particular language, a receptive vocabulary of approximately 20,000 lexemes (words) is considered to be needed (Nation & Waring, 1997). Vocabulary acquisition during development follows a common temporal pattern in monolingual and bilingual children: (1) receptive vocabulary before expressive vocabulary, (2) higher frequency words before lower frequency words, (3) general terms before specific terms, (4) positive polarity before negative polarity, (5) morphologically related (e.g., *bike, biking*) before lexically distinct (e.g., *car, driving*), and (6) words describing experiences before words describing beliefs (Fusté-Herrmann et al., 2006; Lindholm et al., 1979; Peña et al., 2003). However, L2 vocabulary acquisition in adults, or even older children, does not necessarily follow this pattern, given that they already have a rich vocabulary in their L1. This raises the question of the extent to which semantic representations are shared or distinct in bilinguals.

Hernandez and Li (2007) proposed that both L1 and L2 vocabularies are connected to a single shared semantic storage. Supporting this shared storage hypothesis, an intervention study that trained children (in kindergarten and second grade) in L1 vocabulary found enhancement in subsequent L2 acquisition (Escamilla & Medina, 1993). Similarly, kindergarteners have shown positive cross-linguistic relationships in their receptive and expressive vocabularies (Uchikoshi, 2006). Additional support for the shared semantic storage hypothesis comes from the fact that adults acquire an L2 vocabulary overall faster than a child (e.g., Snow & Hoefnagel-Hohle, 1978). Since adults have already acquired a vast number of concepts, the shared storage hypothesis can explain the different patterns of vocabulary acquisition in adults compared to children.

The relationship between AoA and semantic processing

Weber-Fox and Neville's (1996) seminal study of the effects of AoA on language processing has been cited well over 1000 times (according to Google Scholar, accessed March 11, 2022), showing the strong influence of Helen's work on brain development and language processing studies. This study investigated sentence processing in groups of participants differing in AoA, from native learners to those who only began learning English in their later teens. Sentences were visually presented, word by word; in some sentences, a word was not congruent with the semantic expectation (e.g., *event* in the sentence *★The scientist criticized Max's event of the theorem*). In native learners, such violations have been established to elicit an N400 ERP response, a centro-medial negativity first described by Kutas and Hillyard (1980). While the N400 is typically present for any open-class word, it is larger for words violating semantic expectations relative to felicitous words (e.g., *The scientist criticized Max's proof of the theorem*) – this difference is often referred to as the N400 effect. Weber-Fox and Neville found that the two groups who started learning English as their L2 during or after puberty (AoA 11–13 years of age, and after 16 years of age) showed differences in the peak latency of the N400 effect in comparison with that of native speakers indicating slower processing for these two groups, whereas earlier learners showed no differences from native learners on the N400.

Several other ERP studies of bilingual processing have investigated the effect of AoA on N400s during sentence processing, but largely comparing adult learners to native speakers, rather than including a range of AoAs as Weber-Fox and Neville did. Adult L2 learners tend to show reduced-amplitude and later-onset N400 effects than native speakers in sentence processing tasks (Ardal et al., 1990; Hahne, 2001; Hahne & Friederici, 2001; Moreno & Kutas, 2005; Newman et al., 2012; Ojima et al., 2005; Weber-Fox & Neville, 1996, 2001).

Factors modulating the relationship between AoA and semantic processing

In a compelling study by Ardal et al. (1990), the effects of AoA on the N400 elicited by semantically anomalous words during sentence processing were examined by comparing native language processing in monolinguals and bilinguals, as well as L2 processing in bilinguals. Consistent with later studies, N400 effect latency was longer in L2 than L1 in the bilinguals. Interestingly, N400 effect latency was longer in bilinguals' L1 than in monolinguals. The study thus suggests an influence of bilingualism on L1 processing. The difference in latency between

L1 processing in bilinguals and monolinguals could be due to any number of factors, including bilinguals' larger total vocabulary (L1 and L2 combined), the need to suppress words that are not in use in the language, or lower proficiency (smaller vocabulary size) in L1 (Sheng et al., 2013), but in either case, it could not be attributed to AoA since in both groups, according to this study, their L1 was acquired from birth. If bilingualism modulates even native language processing, then the results of studies that compare native language processing in monolinguals (as is common, especially for studies conducted in North America) to L2 processing in bilinguals confound the effects of AoA with effects of knowing more than one language.

The effect of language proficiency on N400s during sentence processing has also been investigated. Early studies of AoA effects often did not consider proficiency as a covariate in their analyses, but it is established that increasing AoA is associated with lower ultimate L2 proficiency – albeit with a wide range of proficiency between individuals, and the size of the effect being modulated by the L1. For example, English L2 learners from Asian countries showed stronger effects of AoA (Johnson & Newport, 1989) on ultimate proficiency than people whose L1 was Spanish (Birdsong & Molis, 2001), even when the same measure of English proficiency was used. A few ERP studies have looked at the effects of proficiency, however. Moreno and Kutas (2005) found that a measure of L2 vocabulary knowledge correlated with N400 latency in a group of adult L2 learners, with higher proficiency associated with shorter latency. In the work done during Newman's Ph.D. under Helen's supervision, Newman and colleagues (2012) replicated the finding of longer latencies for adult L2 learners, but they did not replicate an effect of proficiency on N400 latency. This may be because Newman and colleagues regressed out the overall difference in proficiency between groups, effectively decorrelating the influence of adult AoA from that of proficiency. This study did however find an effect of proficiency on N400 amplitude. Specifically, the L2 learners overall had smaller N400 effects than native learners, but (again after removing the effect of group) higher proficiency was associated with larger N400 effects. This correlation was found in *both* L2 learners and native learners (having used a proficiency measure that showed variance among native speakers), consistent with there being distinct effects of AoA and proficiency on semantic processing.

Taking a different approach, McLaughlin et al. (2004) examined the relationship between hours of L2 instruction and N400 effects, in a group of monolingual English speakers taking an introductory French course – thus controlling for AoA and examining exposure and, by proxy, proficiency. They likewise found a positive correlation between N400 violation effects (in this case contrasting pairs of words in a semantic priming paradigm, rather than sentence violations) and hours of instruction. In a similar vein, a longitudinal study with an impressive number of participants – 322 Japanese native-speaking children (9–12 years of age) – recorded ERPs in response to auditory English (L2) words that were either congruent or incongruent with presented pictures (Ojima et al., 2010). By recording ERPs once a year over three years, Ojima and colleagues again showed a larger N400 effect with the increasing length of exposure and proficiency. One challenge with this approach, however, is that since exposure and proficiency are correlated, it is difficult to determine whether they have separable effects.

Newman and colleagues (2012) further investigated the locus of the relationship between N400 violation effect amplitude and proficiency by comparing the N400 amplitudes between groups, separately for violation and control words. This showed that the amplitude of the N400 response to violation words was insensitive to proficiency. Rather, lower proficiency was associated with larger N400 responses to control words in semantically well-formed sentences, in both late and native learners. Other studies have also suggested that adult L2 learners show larger N400s to congruous words in sentence processing (Elgort et al., 2015; Hahne, 2001). As well, a parallel effect has been documented in L1 development; a study by Helen and colleagues (Holcomb et al., 1992) compared N400s between younger children (up to 12 years of age) and older children and young adults (15–26 years of age). Although both groups showed a typical N400 violation effect, the younger group showed a larger N400 than the older group for words that were congruent with the sentence context. Given that the amplitude of the N400 is thought to be related to semantic integration, these findings suggest that younger children and L2 learners (especially those with lower proficiency) incur a greater load in accessing word meanings and integrating them with the context.

Collectively, these studies suggest that while the N400 semantic violation effect is quite robust – with late learners reliably showing it across studies – its timing and amplitude are sensitive to both AoA and proficiency. Notably, these two factors have often been confounded and more work is needed to better understand their separable influences as well as consider the potential impact of other factors such as socioeconomic status (SES) (see chapters by Hampton Wray and Isbel, and by Pakulak and Stevens, in this volume) and the influence of different L1 backgrounds on acquiring a specific L2.

CLI on semantic processing

Although the shared storage hypothesis suggests overlapping semantic representations in L1 and L2, this is not always the case. For instance, the distinction between *cup* and *glass* in English is dependent on its material, while in Russian the equivalent distinction between *chashka* and *stakan* is based on its shape. Accordingly, a glass such as a prototypical tall glass made of glass would be overlapping in the two languages (*glass/stakan*) while a paper cup would be considered a *cup* in English while it would be considered a *stakan* in Russian due to its shape (Pavlenko & Malt, 2011). When semantics or concepts are not shared across L1 and L2, L2 learners typically experience challenges and often demonstrate CLI in behavioral studies (e.g., Jarvis & Pavlenko, 2008). In a recent ERP study, we investigated how two groups of learners acquire and process shared or unshared verbal semantics (Andersson & Gullberg, 2022). In Swedish, there are three verbs that are obligatory when one describes the position of an item with support from below, such as a glass or an orange being put on a table. When an item with a functional base is placed on its base, either *ställa* "stand" or *sätta* "set" can be used; if the item is placed off its base or does not have a functional base (e.g., an orange), the verb *lägga* "lay" is used (Viberg, 1998). The learner groups consisted of German speakers whose L1 has similar overlapping verb semantics as Swedish (German: *stellen, legen*), and English speakers whose L1 typically uses a more general term (English: *put*). Participants were presented with an image of an item being placed on a table while listening to a sentence describing the event (e.g., *Hon lägger apelsinen på bordet* – "She lays the orange on the table", **Hon sätter apelsinen på bordet* – *"She sets the orange on the table", or **Hon ställer apelsinen på bordet* – *"She stands the orange on the table"). English learners (matched with German learners on AoA and formal Swedish proficiency) rated atypical verb use as more appropriate than Swedish native speakers and German learners, who did not differ from each other. Complementing this behavioral effect, we observed distinct ERP effects: English learners tended to show a centro-medial increased positivity for atypical verb use, while Swedish native speakers and German L2 learners both showed lateral negativities. Therefore, these data suggest that when participants are matched on proficiency and AoA, there is CLI such that when L1 has similar verb semantics (German) verbs are processed in a more native-like manner than when L1 typically uses a more general term (English).

Syntax

Behavioral studies of syntax acquisition

Just as phonology is important for vocabulary acquisition, vocabulary is an important foundation for syntactic and morphosyntactic development – a certain amount of vocabulary is needed to be acquired before patterns and rules can be extracted (Bland-Stewart & Fitzgerald, 2001; Marchman & Bates, 1994). Longitudinal studies have shown a steep increase in syntactic proficiency after the acquisition of 400 words (Conboy & Thal, 2006). Thus, proficiency in syntax is not necessarily attributable to developmental age but rather to vocabulary size within each language (Bates & Goodman, 1997; Conboy & Thal, 2006; Marchman et al., 2004). However, since age is typically positively correlated with the size of the vocabulary, age should be positively correlated with the acquisition of syntax when exposure to the language is similar. Supporting this hypothesis, among a group of native Spanish-speaking children ranging from kindergarten to third grade, the time from not having any L2 proficiency to being proficient in L2 was measured and it was found that older children acquired L2-English syntax in half the time of that required by kindergartners (MacSwan & Pray, 2005). Other longitudinal studies have reported similar advantages with age (e.g., Asher & Price, 1967; Snow & Hoefnagel-Hohle, 1978). For example, adults showed better retention than 8- to 14-year-old children of complex L2 syntax as evidenced through acting out complex instructions in L2 Russian that were acquired in the study (Asher & Price, 1967). Similarly, when adults and children (3–15-year old) were tested during their first year of immersion after moving to the Netherlands, adults and older children performed better on tests of syntax such as sentence repetition and on morphological rules initially (Snow & Hoefnagel-Hohle, 1978). However, the improvement over time was slower with age.

These studies suggest that older children and adults may be superior to younger children in the initial stages of L2 syntax acquisition. At the same time, however, syntax and morphosyntax have been reported to be sensitive to AoA effects, with lower ultimate grammatical proficiency in later learners (DeKeyser, 2005; Flege et al., 1999; Johnson & Newport, 1989). Taken together, these findings suggest that the *rate* of acquisition of syntactic skills may be slower in younger individuals, but, in the long term, children who begin learning an L2 earlier achieve the highest syntactic proficiency (e.g., Birdsong, 2018; Birdsong & Molis, 2001; Neville, 1995; Newport, 1990).

Neurophysiological studies of syntax (and morphosyntax)

Processing of L1 syntax as measured by ERPs

In ERP studies of L1 processing, syntactic violations typically elicit a posterior positivity (P600) approximately 500–1000 ms after the onset of a critical word in both auditory and visual modalities; this is sometimes preceded by a left-lateralized anterior negativity (LAN) between 100 and 500 ms (Friederici et al., 1993, 1999; Gunter et al., 1999; Hahne, 2001; Hahne & Friederici, 1999; Neville et al., 1991; Yamada & Neville, 2007).

The P600 is also elicited by garden-path sentences and sentences that are syntactically correct but deviate from the most common or expected syntactic structure (Kaan et al., 2000; Kaan & Swaab, 2003; Osterhout & Holcomb, 1992, 1993; Osterhout et al., 1994). The P600 has been suggested to index reanalysis or repair of the syntactic structure of the sentence (Osterhout et al., 1994); therefore, this ERP effect is assumed to reflect controlled processes (Coulson et al., 1998; Hahne & Friederici, 1999, 2002). In contrast, the LAN preceding the P600 – which is elicited by syntactic violations but not garden-path sentences – has been related to working memory processes induced by violations that require participants to store prior information to enable an evaluation of the correctness of the structures presented (Coulson et al., 1998; King & Kutas, 1995; Kluender & Kutas, 1993). Indeed, the LAN has been found in some cases to be sustained and have a longer latency (Pakulak & Neville, 2010; Steinhauer & Drury, 2012), consistent with similar left anterior negativities observed in some studies of working memory.

In monolinguals, the biphasic response (LAN/P600) has been reported in children as young as 24 months of age; at 18 months of age, infants only exhibit a posterior positivity that is thought to represent the P600 found in adults (Brusini et al., 2016, 2017; Oberecker & Friederici, 2006; Oberecker et al., 2005). These studies used predictable syntactic violations in simple sentences with child-directed speech; when more complex sentences have been used, such as passive forms, the LAN was left-lateralized only after 13 years of age (Hahne et al., 2004; Sabisch et al., 2006). These combined results suggest that children display a response to syntactic violations that appears more mature with age, but it emerges earlier for simpler syntactic constructions. This pattern should inform what we could expect for adult L2 syntactic processing.

How AoA relates to syntactic processing

Neurocognitive studies of L2 acquisition have reported strong AoA effects for syntactic and morphosyntactic processing such that adult bilinguals consistently show less native-like processing with later (especially post-pubertal) acquisition (e.g., Hahne, 2001; Hahne & Friederici, 2001; Neville et al., 1992; Newman et al., 2001; Pakulak & Neville, 2011; Wartenburger et al., 2003; Weber-Fox & Neville, 1996, 2001). For instance, in Helen's investigations of bilingual processing of syntactic structures, native-speaking adults and bilinguals with AoA before 4 years of age displayed the LAN followed by the P600 (Weber-Fox & Neville, 1996). Adults who learned L2 later – but before puberty – showed a bilaterally distributed anterior negativity and a later, smaller, P600 effect. In participants who learned L2 after 16 years of age, the anterior negativity was largest over the right hemisphere and the P600 effect was not significant. In another study, a similar biphasic response for violations of regular L2 inflections was reported for L1 and post-pubertal L2 learners, whereas violations of irregular inflections elicited an N400 in L2 learners (Hahne et al., 2006). These findings replicate the processing pattern of children's L1 in that more difficult, and presumably less frequent, constructions are related to an ERP pattern that suggests less efficient or automatic processing (Ullman, 2020).

However, other studies have shown that, depending on syntactic complexity, adults with late AoA can seemingly process L2 in a native-like manner (Hahne et al., 2006; Rossi et al., 2006). Similarly, L2 proficiency may also modulate syntactic ERP responses. Hahne and colleagues (2006) also showed an effect of proficiency, with only the higher proficiency group showing a biphasic LAN-P600 pattern for agreement violations; the low proficiency group only showed a P600. The distribution and amplitude of the anterior effect seem more sensitive to AoA and/or proficiency than the P600 (Weber-Fox & Neville, 1996; see also Steinhauer et al., 2009 for a review on ERP effects in L2 acquisition).

How proficiency relates to syntactic processing

More recent studies have focused on exploring the role of proficiency, both in monolinguals (Pakulak & Neville, 2010) and in the early stages of L2 acquisition where AoA is controlled; these studies have been conducted with real languages (e.g., Osterhout et al., 2006), artificial languages (e.g., Friederici et al., 2002), and miniature versions of a language (e.g., a constrained set of Japanese words and syntactic rules; Mueller et al., 2005).

In a study with monolinguals, language proficiency was related to quantitative (amplitude) and qualitative (distribution) differences in the ERP effects on phrase structure violations, indicating that proficiency affects syntactic processing (Pakulak & Neville, 2010). More specifically, higher proficiency monolingual adults displayed a focal LAN that was followed by a large P600 effect extending to anterior and medial regions. In the lower proficiency group, the anterior negativity was bilaterally distributed, more sustained, and was followed by a smaller posterior P600. These differences are similar to those typically reported as AoA effects in other studies; in a review, Steinhauer et al. (2009) suggested a developmental pattern in L2 syntactic processing such that in early acquisition a posterior N400 is elicited (e.g., after 1 month of training; Osterhout et al., 2006), followed by a parietal P600 (e.g., after 4 months of training; Mueller et al., 2009; Osterhout et al., 2006). The posterior N400 has been suggested to indicate a reliance on lexical or semantic processes for processing syntax with lower proficiency (e.g., Kimppa et al., 2019). Then, after the P600 is present, a bilateral anterior negativity can become more lateralized with proficiency (Steinhauer et al., 2009).

Even though proficiency effects have been documented for syntax, differences in the ERP effects elicited by syntactic violations have been found in comparisons of monolingual and bilingual adults matched in terms of proficiency. Pakulak and Neville (2011) found that native English speakers displayed an early anterior negativity followed by a temporally focal P600 that was largest over posterior sites. Bilingual late learners of English (after 10 years of age) did not show any significant anterior negativity, and the P600 was more widely distributed. The results of this study suggested late learners may rely on more resources and different processing to achieve similar proficiency as native speakers. Arguably, when behavioral or electrophysiological differences are found, one measure may be more sensitive than the other; alternatively, it is indeed possible to reach the same proficiency with different means (Kotz, 2009).

In sum, with early AoA, learners appear to use the same neural resources to process syntax in L2 and L1 (as indexed by the biphasic LAN/P600 ERP response). With later AoA and lower proficiency, different neural activity appears to be engaged to process L2, as indicated by an absent, bilateral anterior, or posterior negativity. As proficiency increases, neural indices of L2 processing become more native-like, even in late L2 learners. This pattern seems to support Green's convergence hypothesis, which states that the processing of L1 and L2 converges with proficiency (Green, 2003).

CLI effects on syntactic processing as measured by ERPs

Cross-linguistic similarities affect L2 syntactic processing. For instance, when languages share constructions such as marking gender and number in noun phrases, learners use the same neural regions for processing L2 and L1 (Dowens et al., 2010; Sabourin & Stowe, 2008; Sabourin et al., 2006). More specifically, when grammatical constructions were similar across languages, syntactic violations in L2 elicited a biphasic ERP response similar to that recorded in native speakers, while the response was reduced to a P600 in learners with an L1 that did not share the grammatical construction. Similar results have been reported elsewhere (e.g., Alemán Bañón et al., 2014). Importantly, the native-like neural responses by learners with shared structures have been reported even when learners differ from native speakers on acceptability judgments for the structures (e.g., Foucart & Frenck-Mestre, 2012; Tokowicz & MacWhinney, 2005). Thus, neural indices of native-like processing seem not to be restricted to early AoA and higher proficiency.

In a recent study, we investigated the CLI effects on verb-second word order processing (Andersson et al., 2019). ERP indices of violations of word order in Swedish were investigated in native speakers and two groups of learners matched on proficiency and AoA: German learners whose L1 shared the syntactic feature and English learners whose L1 did not share the feature. Though all learners showed similar P600 effects as native speakers, the ERP effects differed over anterior sites. More specifically, the anterior effect in German speakers did not significantly differ from the effect elicited in native speakers, though it did for English speakers. In addition, an anterior positivity was elicited in English learners. This was similar to an anterior P600 effect reported in prior work, which was associated with syntactic complexity and interpreted as reflecting higher processing costs (e.g., Kaan & Swaab, 2003) for this learner group. Thus, in the L1 English learners, this anterior positivity may similarly reflect the greater difference between their L1 and L2 than in L1 German learners. These results reveal the importance of adding CLI as a predictor for L2 processing. Native-like processing of L2 in late learners with higher proficiency could, in some cases, be attributed to CLI (e.g., Bowden et al., 2013; for a discussion, see Steinhauer et al., 2009).

Summary

Overall, earlier studies suggested proficiency to be the strongest predictor for semantic processing, while AoA seemed to be the strongest predictor for phonological, syntactic, and morphosyntactic processing (McLaughlin et al., 2004; Neville, et al., 1992, 1997; Newman et al., 2001, 2012; Pakulak & Neville, 2011;

Weber-Fox & Neville, 1996, 2001). Importantly, however, studies that have controlled for AoA have reported proficiency to predict native-like processing for syntax as well (Alemán Bañón et al., 2018; Friederici et al., 2002; Tanner et al., 2014). In addition, in cases in which L1 and L2 share more overlapping syntactic structures (e.g., word order and gender), native-like processing of syntax and morphosyntax can seemingly be acquired even with a late AoA (Andersson et al., 2019; Díaz et al., 2016; Dowens et al., 2010, 2011; Sabourin & Stowe, 2008). As mentioned, one reason why semantic processing, in contrast to phonological and syntactic processing, has little or no relationship with AoA could be due to investigations being restricted to simple semantics.

From early claims of strong effects of AoA reflecting critical periods for language acquisition, the field now seems to be more prone to suggest that L2 acquisition is not much different from L1 acquisition, in that we use the same neural structures to process both languages (Mayberry & Kluender, 2018). When differences in L1 and L2 processing are present, they are commonly related to proficiency such that more resources are required when proficiency is low; however, these differences are not of kind. Thus, rather than restricting studies to investigating AoA effects solely, studies increasingly include proficiency measures and considerations of CLI. However, it is difficult to tear any of these predictive variables apart since early AoA affects the length of exposure, which affects proficiency. Proficiency is in turn affected by CLI as L2 acquisition is easier and faster if concepts and structures are already acquired in L1.

In addition, with early AoA, other factors such as motivation to acquire L2 and to have native-like proficiency for social integration are probably stronger than with later AoA (see Chik, 2019 for a review, see Dörnyei, 2005, 2009); at the same time, proficiency in L1 is sometimes found to be negatively related to early AoA, at least in immigrant populations who are immersed in their L2 outside of the home environment (e.g., Weber-Fox & Neville, 1996). As such, restricting our investigations of bilinguals to their processing of sequentially acquired L2 is problematic (see Bylund et al., 2020 for a similar claim). If AoA is the main variable affecting mature native-like processing (Birdsong, 2018), then L1 and L2 should be similarly processed with an early AoA, while differences should emerge with later L2 acquisition. The studies of L1 attrition provide some important predictions that will not be further discussed here (see Kasparian et al., 2016 and Steinhauer & Kasparian, 2020 for a review).

Helen's work on brain plasticity has increased our understanding of how AoA influences the processing of second languages, using both behavioral and neuro-physiological measures. Over time, the focus of her work expanded to include other mediating factors, such as proficiency and SES. These pioneering efforts have had a significant impact on the direction of the field, as documented in the studies reviewed here. With current trends in population migration, international mobility, and connectedness, an understanding of the factors that lead to optimal L2 acquisition is increasingly important. Our hope is that Helen's legacy of studying the effects of early experience on brain processing will continue to make a difference.

References

Alemán Bañón, J., Fiorentino, R., & Gabriele, A. (2014). Morphosyntactic processing in advanced second language (L2) learners: An event-related potential investigation of the effects of L1–L2 similarity and structural distance. *Second Language Research, 30*(3), 275–306. https://doi.org/10.1177/0267658313515671

Alemán Bañón, J., Fiorentino, R., & Gabriele, A. (2018). Using event-related potentials to track morphosyntactic development in second language learners: The processing of number and gender agreement in Spanish. *PloS One, 13*(7), 1–35. https://doi.org/10.1371/journal.pone.0200791

Andersson, A., & Gullberg, M. (2022). First language matters: Event-related potentials show crosslinguistic influence on the processing of placement verb semantics. *Frontiers in Psychology, 13*. https://doi.org/10.3389/fpsyg.2022.815801

Andersson, A., Sayehli, S., & Gullberg, M. (2019). Language background affects online word order processing in a second language but not offline. *Bilingualism: Language and Cognition, 22*(4), 802–825. https://doi.org/10.1017/S1366728918000573

Ardal, S., Donald, M. W., Meuter, R., Muldrew, S., & Luce, M. (1990). Brain responses to semantic incongruity in bilinguals. *Brain & Language, 39*(2), 187–205. https://doi.org/10.1016/0093-934X(90)90011-5

Asher, J. J., & Price, B. S. (1967). The learning strategy of the total physical response: Some age differences. *Child Development, 38*(4), 1220–1227. https://doi.org/10.2307/1127119

Bates, E., & Goodman, J. C. (1997). On the inseparability of grammar and the lexicon: Evidence from acquisition, aphasia and real-time processing. *Language & Cognitive Processes, 12*(5/6), 507–584. https://doi.org/10.1080/016909697386628

Birdsong, D. (2018). Plasticity, variability and age in second language acquisition and bilingualism. *Frontiers in Psychology, 9*, 81. https://doi.org/10.3389/fpsyg.2018.00081

Birdsong, D., & Molis, M. (2001). On the evidence for maturational constraints in second-language acquisition. *Journal of Memory and Language, 44*(2), 235–249. https://doi.org/10.1006/jmla.2000.2750

Bland-Stewart, L. M., & Fitzgerald, S. M. (2001). Use of Brown's 14 grammatical morphemes by bilingual Hispanic preschoolers: A pilot study. *Communication Disorders Quarterly, 22*, 171–186. https://doi.org/10.1177/152574010102200403

Bowden, H. W., Steinhauer, K., Sanz, C., & Ullman, M. T. (2013). Native-like brain processing of syntax can be attained by university foreign language learners. *Neuropsychologia, 51*(13), 2492–2511. https://doi.org/10.1016/j.neuropsychologia.2013.09.004

Brusini, P., Dehaene-Lambertz, G., Dutat, M., Goffinet, F., & Christophe, A. (2016). ERP evidence for on-line syntactic computations in 2-year-olds. *Developmental Cognitive Neuroscience, 19*, 164–173. https://doi.org/10.1016/j.dcn.2016.02.009

Brusini, P., Dehaene-Lambertz, G., van Heugten, M., de Carvalho, A., Goffinet, F., Fiévet, A.-C., & Christophe, A. (2017). Ambiguous function words do not prevent 18-month-olds from building accurate syntactic category expectations: An ERP study. *Neuropsychologia, 98*, 4–12. https://doi.org/10.1016/j.neuropsychologia.2016.08.015

Bylund, E., Hyltenstam, K., & Abrahamsson, N. (2020). Age of acquisition – not bilingual-ism – is the primary determinant of less than nativelike L2 ultimate attainment. *Bilingualism: Language and Cognition*, 1–13. https://doi.org/10.1017/S1366728920000188

Chik, A. (2019). Motivation and informal language learning. In M. Dressman & R. W. Sandler (Eds.), *The handbook of informal language learning* (pp. 13–26). Hoboken, NJ: Wiley-Blackwell. https://doi.org/10.1002/9781119472384.ch1

Conboy, B. T., & Thal, D. J. (2006). Ties between the lexicon and grammar: Cross-sectional and longitudinal studies of bilingual toddlers. *Child Development*, 77(3), 712–735. https://doi.org/10.1111/j.1467-8624.2006.00899.x

Coulson, S., King, J. W., & Kutas, M. (1998). Expect the unexpected: Event-related brain response to morphosyntactic violations. *Language & Cognitive Processes*, 13(1), 21–58. https://doi.org/10.1080/016909698386582

Dehaene-Lambertz, G., Dupoux, E., & Gout, A. (2000). Electrophysiological correlates of phonological processing: A cross-linguistic study. *Journal of Cognitive Neuroscience*, 12(4), 635–647. https://doi.org/10.1162/089892900562390

DeKeyser, R. M. (2005). What makes learning second-language grammar difficult? A review of issues. *Language Learning*, 55(Suppl. 1), 1–25. https://doi.org/10.1111/j.0023-8333.2005.00294.x

Díaz, B., Erdocia, K., de Menezes, R. F., Mueller, J. L., Sebastián-Gallés, N., & Laka, I. (2016). Electrophysiological correlates of second-language syntactic processes are related to native and second language distance regardless of age of acquisition. *Frontiers in Psychology*, 7, 133. https://doi.org/10.3389/fpsyg.2016.00133

Dörnyei, Z. (2005). *The psychology of the language learner: Individual differences in second language acquisition*. Mahwah, NJ: Lawrence Erlbaum Associates. https://doi.org/10.4324/9781410613349

Dörnyei, Z. (2009). The L2 motivational self system. In Z. Dörnyei & E. Ushioda (Eds.), *Motivation, language identity and the L2 self* (pp. 9–42). Bristol: Multilingual Matters. https://doi.org/10.21832/9781847691293-003

Dowens, M. G., Guo, T., Guo, J., Barber, H., & Carreiras, M. (2011). Gender and number processing in Chinese learners of Spanish – Evidence from event related potentials. *Neuropsychologia*, 49(7), 1651–1659. https://doi.org/10.1016/j.neuropsychologia.2011.02.034

Dowens, M. G., Vergara, M., Barber, H. A., & Carreiras, M. (2010). Morphosyntactic processing in late second-language learners. *Journal of Cognitive Neuroscience*, 22(8), 1870–1887. https://doi.org/10.1162/jocn.2009.21304

Elgort, I., Perfetti, C. A., Rickles, B., & Stafura, J. Z. (2015). Contextual learning of L2 word meanings: Second language proficiency modulates behavioural and event-related brain potential (ERP) indicators of learning. *Language, Cognition and Neuroscience*, 30(5), 506–528. https://doi.org/10.1080/23273798.2014.942673

Escamilla, K., & Medina, M. (1993). English and Spanish acquisition by limited-language-proficient Mexican Americans in a three-year maintenance bilingual program. *Hispanic Journal of Behavioral Sciences*, 15(1), 108–120. https://doi.org/10.1177/07399863930151006

Flege, J. E. (2018). It's input that matters most, not age. *Bilingualism: Language and Cognition*, 1–2. https://doi.org/10.1017/S136672891800010X

Flege, J. E., Yeni-Komshian, G. H., & Liu, S. (1999). Age constraints on second-language acquisition. *Journal of Memory and Language*, 41(1), 78–104. https://doi.org/10.1006/jmla.1999.2638

Foucart, A., & Frenck-Mestre, C. (2012). Can late L2 learners acquire new grammatical features? Evidence from ERPs and eye-tracking. *Journal of Memory & Language, 66*, 226–248. https://doi.org/10.1016/j.jml.2011.07.007

Friederici, A. D., Pfeifer, E., & Hahne, A. (1993). Event-related brain potentials during natural speech processing: Effects of semantic, morphological and syntactic violations. *Cognitive Brain Research, 1*(3), 183–192. https://doi.org/10.1016/0926-6410(93)90026-2

Friederici, A. D., Steinhauer, K., & Frisch, S. (1999). Lexical integration: Sequential effects of syntactic and semantic information. *Memory & Cognition, 27*(3), 438–453. https://doi.org/10.3758/BF03211539

Friederici, A. D., Steinhauer, K., & Pfeifer, E. (2002). Brain signatures of artificial language processing: Evidence challenging the critical period hypothesis. *Proceedings of the National Academy of Sciences of the United States of America, 99*(1), 529–534. https://doi.org/10.1073/pnas.012611199

Fusté-Herrmann, B., Silliman, E. R., Bahr, R. H., Fasnacht, K. S., & Federico, J. E. (2006). Mental state verb production in the oral narratives of English- and Spanish-speaking preadolescents: An exploratory study of lexical diversity and depth. *Learning Disabilities Research & Practice, 21*(1), 44–60. https://doi.org/10.1111/j.1540-5826.2006.00206.x

Golestani, N., & Zatorre, R. J. (2004). Learning new sounds of speech: Reallocation of neural substrates. *NeuroImage, 21*(2), 494–506. https://doi.org/10.1016/j.neuroimage.2003.09.071

Green, D. W. (2003). The neural basis of the lexicon and the grammar in L2 acquisition. In R. van Hout, A. Hulk, F. Kuiken, & R. Towell (Eds.), *The interface between syntax and the lexicon in second language acquisition* (vol. 30, pp. 197–208). Amsterdam: John Benjamins Publishing.

Grubb, J. D., Bush, A. M., & Geist, C. R. (1998). Effects of second language study of phonemic discrimination and auditory event-related potentials in adults. *Perceptual & Motor Skills, 87*(2), 447–456. https://doi.org/10.2466/pms.1998.87.2.447

Gunter, T. C., Friederici, A. D., & Hahne, A. (1999). Brain responses during sentence reading: Visual input affects central processes. *Neuroreport: For Rapid Communication of Neuroscience Research, 10*(15), 3175–3178.

Hahne, A. (2001). What's different in second-language processing? Evidence from event-related brain potentials. *Journal of Psycholinguistic Research, 30*(3), 251–266. https://doi.org/10.1023/A:1010490917575

Hahne, A., Eckstein, K., & Friederici, A. D. (2004). Brain signatures of syntactic and semantic processes during children's language development. *Journal of Cognitive Neuroscience, 16*(7), 1302–1318. https://doi.org/10.1162/0898929041920504

Hahne, A., & Friederici, A. D. (1999). Electrophysiological evidence for two steps in syntactic analysis: Early automatic and late controlled processes. *Journal of Cognitive Neuroscience, 11*(2), 194–205. https://doi.org/10.1162/089892999563328

Hahne, A., & Friederici, A. D. (2001). Processing a second language: Late learners' comprehension mechanisms as revealed by event-related brain potentials. *Bilingualism: Language & Cognition, 4*(2), 123–141. https://doi.org/10.1017/S1366728901000232

Hahne, A., & Friederici, A. D. (2002). Differential task effects on semantic and syntactic processes as revealed by ERPs. *Cognitive Brain Research, 13*(3), 339–356. https://doi.org/10.1016/s0926-6410(01)00127-6

Hahne, A., Mueller, J. L., & Clahsen, H. (2006). Morphological processing in a second language: Behavioral and event-related brain potential evidence for storage and decomposition. *Journal of Cognitive Neuroscience, 18*(1), 121–134. https://doi.org/10.1162/089892906775250067

Hernandez, A. E., & Li, P. (2007). Age of acquisition: Its neural and computational mechanisms. *Psychological Bulletin*, *133*(4), 638–650. https://doi.org/10.1037/0033-2909.133.4.638

Hisagi, M., Garrido-Nag, K., Datta, H. I. A., & Shafer, V. L. (2015). ERP indices of vowel processing in Spanish – English bilinguals. *Bilingualism: Language and Cognition*, *18*(2), 271–289. https://doi.org/10.1017/S1366728914000170

Holcomb, P. J., Coffey, S. A., & Neville, H. J. (1992). Visual and auditory sentence processing: A developmental analysis using event-related brain potentials. *Developmental Neuropsychology*, *8*, 203–241. https://doi.org/10.1080/87565649209540525

Jarvis, S., & Pavlenko, A. (2008). *Crosslinguistic influence in langauge and cognition*. New York: Routledge.

Johnson, J. S., & Newport, E. L. (1989). Critical period effects in second language learning: The influence of maturational state on the acquisition of English as a second language. *Cognitive Psychology*, *21*(1), 60–99. https://doi.org/10.1016/0010-0285(89)90003-0

Kaan, E., Harris, A., Gibson, E., & Holcomb, P. (2000). The P600 as an index of syntactic integration difficulty. *Language and Cognitive Processes*, *15*(2), 159–201. https://doi.org/10.1080/016909600386084

Kaan, E., & Swaab, T. Y. (2003). Repair, revision, and complexity in syntactic analysis: An electrophysiological differentiation. *Journal of Cognitive Neuroscience*, *15*(1), 98–110. https://doi.org/10.1162/089892903321107855

Kasparian, K., Vespignani, F., & Steinhauer, K. (2016). First language attrition induces changes in online morphosyntactic processing and re-analysis: An ERP study of number agreement in complex Italian sentences. *Cognitive Science*, *41*, 1760–1803. https://doi.org/10.1111/cogs.12450

Kimppa, L., Shtyrov, Y., Hut, S. C. A., Hedlund, L., Leminen, M., & Leminen, A. (2019). Acquisition of L2 morphology by adult language learners. *Cortex*, *116*, 74–90. https://doi.org/10.1016/j.cortex.2019.01.012

King, J. W., & Kutas, M. (1995). Who did what and when? Using word- and clause-level ERPs to monitor working memory usage in reading. *Journal of Cognitive Neuroscience*, *7*(3), 376–395. https://doi.org/10.1162/jocn.1995.7.3.376

Kluender, R., & Kutas, M. (1993). Bridging the gap: Evidence from ERPs on the processing of unbounded dependencies. *Journal of Cognitive Neuroscience*, *5*(2), 196–214. https://doi.org/10.1162/jocn.1993.5.2.196

Kotz, S. A. (2009). A critical review of ERP and fMRI evidence on L2 syntactic processing. *Brain and Language*, *109*(2–3), 68–74. https://doi.org/10.1016/j.bandl.2008.06.002

Kuhl, P. K., Conboy, B. T., Padden, D., Nelson, T., & Pruitt, J. (2005). Early speech perception and later language development: Implications for the "critical period." *Language Learning and Development*, *1*(3–4), 237–264. https://doi.org/10.1080/15475441.2005.9671948

Kutas, M., & Hillyard, S. A. (1980). Reading senseless sentences: Brain potentials reflect semantic incongruity. *Science*, *207*(4427), 203–205. https://doi.org/10.1126/science.7350657

Lindholm, K. J., Padilla, A. M., & Romero, A. (1979). Comprehension of relational concepts: Use of bilingual children to separate cognitive and linguistic factors. *Hispanic Journal of Behavioral Sciences*, *1*(4), 327–343. https://doi.org/10.1177/073998637900100402

Lindsey, K. A., Manis, F. R., & Bailey, C. E. (2003). Prediction of first-grade reading in Spanish-speaking English-language learners. *Journal of Educational Psychology*, *95*(3), 482–494. https://doi.org/10.1037/0022-0663.95.3.482

López, L. M., & Greenfield, D. B. (2004). The cross-language transfer of phonological skills of hispanic Head Start children. *Bilingual Research Journal*, *28*(1), 1–18. https://doi.org/10.1080/15235882.2004.10162609

Lu, S., Wayland, R., & Kaan, E. (2015). Effects of production training and perception training on lexical tone perception – A behavioral and ERP study. *Brain Research*, *1624*, 28–44. https://doi.org/10.1016/j.brainres.2015.07.014

MacSwan, J., & Pray, L. (2005). Learning English bilingually: Age of onset of exposure and rate of acquisition among English language learners in a bilingual education program. *Bilingual Research Journal*, *29*(3), 653–678. https://doi.org/10.1080/15235882.2005.10162857

Manis, F. R., Lindsey, K. A., & Bailey, C. E. (2004). Development of reading in grades K-2 in Spanish-speaking English-language learners. *Learning Disabilities Research & Practice*, *19*(4), 214–224. https://doi.org/10.1111/j.1540-5826.2004.00107.x

Marchman, V. A., & Bates, E. (1994). Continuity in lexical and morphological development: A test of the critical mass hypothesis. *Journal of Child Language*, *21*(2), 339–366. https://doi.org/10.1017/S0305000900009302

Marchman, V. A., Martínez-Sussmann, C., & Dale, P. S. (2004). The language-specific nature of grammatical development: Evidence from bilingual language learners. *Developmental Science*, *7*(2), 212–224. https://doi.org/10.1111/j.1467-7687.2004.00340.x

Mayberry, R. I., & Kluender, R. (2018). Rethinking the critical period for language: New insights into an old question from American Sign Language. *Bilingualism: Language and Cognition*, *21*. https://doi.org/10.1017/S1366728917000724

McCandliss, B. D., Fiez, J. A., Protopapas, A., Conway, M., & McClelland, J. L. (2002). Success and failure in teaching the [r]-[l] contrast to Japanese adults: Tests of a Hebbian model of plasticity and stabilization in spoken language perception. *Cognitive, Affective, & Behavioral Neuroscience*, *2*(2), 90–108. https://doi.org/10.3758/CABN.2.2.89

McLaughlin, J., Osterhout, L., & Kim, A. (2004). Neural correlates of second-language word learning: Minimal instruction produces rapid change. *Nature Neuroscience*, *7*(7), 703–704. https://doi.org/10.1038/nn1264

Moreno, E. M., & Kutas, M. (2005). Processing semantic anomalies in two languages: An electrophysiological exploration in both languages of Spanish-English bilinguals. *Cognitive Brain Research*, *22*(2), 205–220. https://doi.org/10.1016/j.cogbrainres.2004.08.010

Mueller, J. L., Hahne, A., Fujii, Y., & Friederici, A. D. (2005). Native and nonnative speakers' processing of a miniature version of Japanese as revealed by ERPs. *Journal of Cognitive Neuroscience*, *17*(8), 1229–1244. https://doi.org/10.1162/0898929055002463

Mueller, J. L., Oberecker, R., & Friederici, A. D. (2009). Syntactic learning by mere exposure: An ERP study in adult learners. *BMC Neuroscience*, *10*. https://doi.org/10.1186/1471-2202-10-89

Nation, P., & Waring, R. (1997). Vocabulary size, text coverage, and words lists. In N. Schmitt & M. McCarthy (Eds.), *Vocabulary: Description, acquisition, pedagogy* (pp. 6–19). New York: Cambridge University Press.

Neville, H. J. (1995). Developmental specificity in neurocognitive development in humans. In M. Gazzaniga (Ed.), *The cognitive neurosciences* (pp. 219–231). Cambridge, MA: MIT Press.

Neville, H. J., Coffey, S. A., Lawson, D. S., Fischer, A., Emmorey, K., & Bellugi, U. (1997). Neural systems mediating American Sign Language: Effects of sensory experience and age of acquisition. *Brain & Language*, *57*(3), 285–308. https://doi.org/10.1006/brln.1997.1739

Neville, H. J., Mills, D. L., & Lawson, D. S. (1992). Fractionating language: Different neural subsystems with different sensitive periods. *Cerebral Cortex*, *2*(3), 244–258. https://doi.org/10.1093/cercor/2.3.244

Neville, H. J., Nicol, J. L., Barss, A., Forster, K. I., & Garrett, M. F. (1991). Syntactically based sentence processing classes: Evidence from event-related brain potentials. *Journal of Cognitive Neuroscience*, *3*(2), 151–165. https://doi.org/10.1162/jocn.1991.3.2.151

Newman, A. J., Bavelier, D., Corina, D., Jezzard, P., & Neville, H. J. (2001). A critical period for right hemisphere recruitment in American Sign Language processing. *Nature Neuroscience*, *5*(1), 76–80. https://doi.org/10.1038/nn775

Newman, A. J., Tremblay, A., Nichols, E. S., Neville, H. J., & Ullman, M. T. (2012). The influence of language proficiency on lexical semantic processing in native and late learners of english. *Journal of Cognitive Neuroscience*, *24*(5), 1205–1223. https://doi.org/10.1162/jocn_a_00143

Newport, E. L. (1990). Maturational constraints on language learning. *Cognitive Science*, *14*(1), 11–28. https://doi.org/10.1016/0364-0213(90)90024-Q

Oberecker, R., & Friederici, A. D. (2006). Syntactic event-related potential components in 24-month-olds' sentence comprehension. *Neuroreport: For Rapid Communication of Neuroscience Research*, *17*(10), 1017–1021. https://doi.org/10.1097/01.wnr.0000223397.12694.9a

Oberecker, R., Friedrich, M., & Friederici, A. D. (2005). Neural correlates of syntactic processing in two-year-olds. *Journal of Cognitive Neuroscience*, *17*(10), 1667–1678. https://doi.org/10.1162/089892905774597236

Ojima, S., Nakamura, N., Matsuba-Kurita, H., Hoshino, T., & Hagiwara, H. (2010). Neural correlates of foreign-language learning in childhood: A 3-year longitudinal ERP study. *Journal of Cognitive Neuroscience*, *23*(1), 183–199. https://doi.org/10.1162/jocn.2010.21425

Ojima, S., Nakata, H., & Kakigi, R. (2005). An ERP study of second language learning after childhood: Effects of proficiency. *Journal of Cognitive Neuroscience*, *17*(8), 1212–1228. https://doi.org/10.1162/0898929055002436

Osterhout, L., & Holcomb, P. J. (1992). Event-related brain potentials elicited by syntactic anomaly. *Journal of Memory and Language*, *31*(6), 785–806. https://doi.org/10.1016/0749-596x(92)90039-z

Osterhout, L., & Holcomb, P. J. (1993). Event-related potentials and syntactic anomaly: Evidence of anomaly detection during the perception of continuous speech. *Language and Cognitive Processes*, *8*(4), 413–437. https://doi.org/10.1080/01690969308407584

Osterhout, L., Holcomb, P. J., & Swinney, D. A. (1994). Brain potentials elicited by garden-path sentences: Evidence of the application of verb information during parsing. *Journal of Experimental Psychology: Learning, Memory, and Cognition*, *20*(4), 786–803. https://doi.org/10.1037/0278-7393.20.4.786

Osterhout, L., McLaughlin, J., Pitkanen, I., Frenck-Mestre, C., & Molinaro, N. (2006). Novice Learners, longitudinal designs, and event-related potentials: A means for exploring the neurocognition of second language processing. *Language Learning*, *56*(Suppl. 1), 199–230. https://doi.org/10.1111/j.1467-9922.2006.00361.x

Pakulak, E., & Neville, H. J. (2010). Proficiency differences in syntactic processing in monolingual native speakers indexed by event-related brain potentials. *Journal of Cognitive Neuroscience*, *22*(12), 2728–2744. https://doi.org/10.1162/jocn.2009.21393

Pakulak, E., & Neville, H. J. (2011). Maturational constraints on the recruitment of early processes for syntactic processing. *Journal of Cognitive Neuroscience*, *23*(10), 2752–2765. https://doi.org/10.1162/jocn.2010.21586

Pavlenko, A., & Malt, B. C. (2011). Kitchen Russian: Cross-linguistic differences and first-language object naming by Russian – English bilinguals. *Bilingualism: Language and Cognition, 14*(1), 19–45. https://doi.org/10.1017/S136672891000026X

Peltola, M. S., Kuntola, M., Tamminen, H., Hämäläinen, H., & Aaltonen, O. (2005). Early exposure to non-native language alters preattentive vowel discrimination. *Neuroscience Letters, 388*(3), 121–125. https://doi.org/10.1016/j.neulet.2005.06.037

Peña, E., Bedore, L. M., & Rappazzo, C. (2003). Comparison of Spanish, English, and bilingual children's performance across semantic tasks. *Language, Speech, and Hearing Services in Schools, 34*(1), 5–16. https://doi.org/10.1044/0161-1461(2003/001)

Rinker, T., Alku, P., Brosch, S., & Kiefer, M. (2010). Discrimination of native and non-native vowel contrasts in bilingual Turkish – German and monolingual German children: Insight from the Mismatch Negativity ERP component. *Brain and Language, 113*(2), 90–95. https://doi.org/10.1016/j.bandl.2010.01.007

Rivera-Gaxiola, M., Johnson, M. H., Csibra, G., & Karmiloff-Smith, A. (2000). Electrophysiological correlates of category goodness. *Behavioural Brain Research, 112*(1), 1–11. https://doi.org/10.1016/S0166-4328(00)00218/7

Rivera-Gaxiola, M., Silva-Pereyra, J., & Kuhl, P. K. (2005). Brain potentials to native and non-native speech contrasts in 7- and 11-month-old American infants. *Developmental Science, 8*(2), 162–172. https://doi.org/10.1111/j.1467-7687.2005.00403.x

Rossi, S., Gugler, M. F., Friederici, A. D., & Hahne, A. (2006). The impact of proficiency on syntactic second-language processing of German and Italian: Evidence from event-related potentials. *Journal of Cognitive Neuroscience, 18*(12), 2030–2048. https://doi.org/10.1162/jocn.2006.18.12.2030

Sabisch, B., Hahne, A., Glass, E., von Suchodoletz, W., & Friederici, A. D. (2006). Lexical-semantic processes in children with specific language impairment. *Neuroreport: For Rapid Communication of Neuroscience Research, 17*(14), 1511–1514.

Sabourin, L., & Stowe, L. A. (2008). Second language processing: When are first and second languages processed similarly. *Second Language Research, 24*(3), 397–430. https://doi.org/10.1177/0267658308090186

Sabourin, L., Stowe, L. A., & de Haan, G. J. (2006). Transfer effects in learning a second language grammatical gender system. *Second Language Research, 22*(1), 1–29. https://doi.org/10.1191/0267658306sr259oa

Sheng, L., Bedore, L. M., Peña, E. D., & Fiestas, C. (2013). Semantic development in Spanish – English bilingual children: Effects of age and language experience. *Child Development, 84*(3), 1034–1045. https://doi.org/10.1111/cdev.12015

Snow, C. E., & Hoefnagel-Hohle, M. (1977). Age differences in the pronunciation of foreign sounds. *Language and Speech, 20*(4), 357–365. https://doi.org/10.1177/002383097702000407

Snow, C. E., & Hoefnagel-Hohle, M. (1978). The critical period for language acquisition: Evidence from second language learning. *Child Development, 49*(4), 1114–1128. https://doi.org/10.2307/1128751

Steinhauer, K., & Drury, J. E. (2012). On the early left-anterior negativity (ELAN) in syntax studies. *Brain & Language, 120*, 135–162. https://doi.org/10.1016/j.bandl.2011.07.001

Steinhauer, K., & Kasparian, K. (2020). Brain plasticity in adulthood – ERP evidence for L1-attrition in lexicon and morphosyntax after predominant L2 use. *Language Learning, 70*(S2), 171–193. https://doi.org/10.1111/lang.12391

Steinhauer, K., White, E. J., & Drury, J. E. (2009). Temporal dynamics of late second language acquisition: Evidence from event-related brain potentials. *Second Language Research, 25*(1), 13–41. https://doi.org/10.1177/0267658308098995

Tanner, D., Inoue, K., & Osterhout, L. (2014). Brain-based individual differences in online L2 grammatical comprehension. *Bilingualism: Language and Cognition, 17*(2), 277–293. https://doi.org/10.1017/S1366728913000370

Tokowicz, N., & MacWhinney, B. (2005). Implicit and explicit measures of sensitivity to violations in second language grammar: An event-related potential investigation. *Studies in Second Language Acquisition, 27*(2), 173–204. https://doi.org/10.1017/S0272263105050102

Uchikoshi, Y. (2006). English vocabulary development in bilingual kindergartners: What are the best predictors? *Bilingualism: Language and Cognition, 9*(1), 33–49. https://doi.org/10.1017/S1366728905002361

Ullman, M. T. (2020). The declarative/procedural model: A neurobiologically motivated theory of first and second language 1. In *Theories in second language acquisition* (pp. 128–161). New York, NY: Routledge. https://doi.org/10.1017/S014271640606019X

Viberg, Å. (1998). Crosslinguistic perspectives on lexical acquistion: The case of language-specific semantic differentiation. In K. Haastrup & Å. Viberg (Eds.), *Perspectives on lexical acquisition in a second language* (pp. 175–208). Lund: Lund University Press.

Wartenburger, I., Heekeren, H. R., Abutalebi, J., Cappa, S. F., Villringer, A., & Perani, D. (2003). Early setting of grammatical processing in the bilingual brain. *Neuron, 37*, 159–170. https://doi.org/10.1016/S0896-6273(02)01150-9

Weber-Fox, C., & Neville, H. J. (1996). Maturational constraints on functional specializations for language processing: ERP and behavioral evidence in bilingual speakers. *Journal of Cognitive Neuroscience, 8*(3), 231–256. https://doi.org/10.1162/jocn.1996.8.3.231

Weber-Fox, C., & Neville, H. J. (2001). Sensitive periods differentiate processing of open- and closed-class words: An ERP study of bilinguals. *Journal of Speech, Language, & Hearing Research, 44*(6), 1338–1353. https://doi.org/10.1044/1092-4388(2001/104)

Werker, J. F., & Lalonde, C. E. (1988). Cross-language speech perception: Initial capabilities and developmental change. *Developmental Psychology, 24*(5), 672–683. https://doi.org/10.1037/0012-1649.24.5.672

Werker, J. F., & Tees, R. C. (1984). Cross-language speech perception: Evidence for perceptual reorganization during the first year of life. *Infant Behavior and Development, 7*(1), 49–63. https://doi.org/10.1016/S0163-6383(84)80022-3

Yamada, Y., & Neville, H. J. (2007). An ERP study of syntactic processing in English and nonsense sentences. *Brain Research, 1130*, 167–180. https://doi.org/10.1016/j.brainres.2006.10.052

4

EXPLORING THE EFFECTS OF AGING ON LANGUAGE ABILITIES IN DEAF SIGNERS

David P. Corina, Lucinda O'Grady Farnady,
Todd LaMarr, Svenna Pedersen, Kurt Winsler,
and Laurel A. Lawyer

This chapter provides an account of our efforts to use sentence repetition to assess language capacities in older adult deaf users of American Sign Language (ASL). We discuss how research in deaf signing communities provides a novel means to investigate the effects of chronological aging on human language processing. Four aspects of this work call to mind the contributions of Dr. Helen Neville, who served as a mentor and senior colleague early in my career. First, Helen recognized the unique insights that studies of profoundly deaf individuals can offer in understanding the dynamics of brain plasticity. She was one of the first neuroscientists who boldly related the experience of deafness in humans to burgeoning neuroscientific accounts of brain plasticity in non-human species. Second, Helen was cogent in her investigations of the human capacity for language and the implications this specialization has for brain organization. She marshaled the life experiences of sign-exposed individuals to lay contrast to processes and brain changes that occur as a function of auditory deprivation from those that result from visual language exposure. Third, Helen understood that the particulars of our attempts to characterize behavioral and brain activity at any moment in time were a snapshot of the trajectory of human brain development, which extends through the lifespan. Finally, Helen was a humanist and keenly respectful of working with the Deaf community and its vibrant members.

Language behaviors are subserved by both linguistic and cognitive systems. An active area of research seeks to understand the degree to which age-related language decline represents the degradation of the linguistic system specifically or owes to interactions between cognitive and linguistic factors. In particular, attention, working memory, and executive functions factor significantly in these inquiries (Henderson & Wright, 2016).

DOI: 10.4324/9780429342356-9

To the extent that aging impacts core properties of linguistic systems, we would expect to see commonalities in changes that occur for users of spoken and signed languages. However, differential impacts of aging on spoken and signed language processing may be observed. Such a pattern may be a reflection of differential cognitive processes and resources required as a function of the language modality. Studies of deaf and hearing users of signed language present a unique opportunity to further understand how differences in the time course of language acquisition and sensory experience interact with cognitive aging. Here, we demonstrate how studies of signed languages can serve as a basis to explore the influence of grammatical properties of language form in the context of normative chronological aging (CA).

Studies of spoken language abilities indicate that the core aspects of speech comprehension are generally well preserved across the lifespan, including the automatic access to lexical representations and the online construction of syntactic and semantic representations (Burke & Graham, 2012; Burke & Shafto, 2008; Shafto & Tyler, 2014). However, age-related changes in language use are well documented; for example, older adults appear to use a simplified speech register (Benjamin, 1988; Cooper, 1990; Davis, 1984; Kemper et al., 1989; Kynette & Kemper, 1986; Shewan & Henderson, 1988), and this simplification appears to be progressive with age. Reductions in the complexity of structural properties and information density as a function of aging have been well studied (see Kemper, 2006 for an overview). Studies of language production show that spoken language production declines with aging. Compared to younger speakers, older adults show increased word-finding difficulties, tip-of-the tongue states, and evidence of more speech dysfluencies (e.g., lexical fillers, word repetitions, and lengthy pauses). Mounting evidence points to a problem in phonological retrieval rather than articulatory or motor planning deficits (Burke & Graham, 2012; see Burke & Shafto, 2008 for a review). Whether or not patterns of relative stability in language comprehension with changes in aspects of language use and production holds for users of signed languages is largely unknown. We introduce some prominent issues in the endeavor below.

Studies of the effects of aging on spoken languages take for granted that the instantiation of language knowledge under study arises from the expected interplay between biological and social–cultural constraints that characterize typical language acquisition. However, the characterization of age-related changes in primary language (L1) functions learned under ideal conditions reflects but one possibility. The study of profoundly deaf individuals who have acquired sign language as their primary language presents another eventuality. As 95% of deaf infants are born to parents who are not deaf and do not know a signed language, initial exposure to a signed language may be quite delayed in time, often not occurring until early childhood or beyond. Multiple factors, including etiological differences in the expression of congenital deafness, choices in educational and rehabilitative practices, parental beliefs, and government policies, comport to influence a deaf child's exposure to a signed language. Though a multi-factored construct, the influence of the age of language acquisition (AoA) on linguistic and cognitive competencies and educational achievement in deaf children has received considerable attention; however, the impact of AoA as a function of CA in deaf adults is far less studied.

A second prominent issue concerns the differences in the signaling modality of spoken and signed languages. While it is well established that both spoken and signed languages constitute full-fledged instances of human language with fully expressive grammatical and symbolic capacities, there are differences in cognitive requirements for the production and processing of oral-aural and visual-manual languages. To the extent that CA differentially affects physical and cognitive processes (e.g., motoric constraints, verbal versus visual working memory, auditory versus visual attention), these factors may differentially conspire to influence the use of spoken and signed languages. For example, there is research to suggest that visuospatial working memory is affected more by age than is performance on verbal working memory tasks (Craik & Rose, 2012; Jenkins et al., 2000; Myerson et al., 2003; Park et al., 2002). Differential age-related vulnerabilities of verbal and non-verbal working memory are especially interesting in light of the characterization of signed language as linguistic systems forged within a visual–spatial modality (Bellugi et al., 1989).

Third, grammar-internal properties of signed (and spoken) languages may influence processing in the face of typical aging. Just as with spoken languages, natural sign languages vary in structural and grammatical form. For example, sign languages tend to be largely mono-syllabic languages, are topic-prominent languages, make use of complex predicative constructions (e.g., classifier forms), and permit omission of pronominal makers (i.e., pro-drop) in selected environments. The impact of typological linguistic differences and grammar-internal properties of signed (and spoken) language use in the face of typical aging has received little attention.

In an earlier published study (Corina et al., 2020), we reported test performance from a large cohort of adult deaf signers on an ASL sentence repetition task (ASL-SRT; Supalla et al., 2014). The goal addressed in this initial report was to document how performance on the ASL-SRT varied with chronological age and AoA. In addition, we investigated the potential interaction between these factors. In this chapter, we first briefly recount the methods and main findings from this study. In this context, we discuss how cognitive factors may differentially impact sentence repetition in spoken and signed languages. Next, we extend these initial findings and present additional statistical and descriptive linguistic analyses of error data from the original study. The examination of these data permits some preliminary insights into how the grammatical properties of ASL, specifically grammatical word class, are distinctly susceptible to repetition errors.

Chronological aging and age of acquisition

Three groups of healthy congenitally deaf adult users of ASL ($n = 107$; ages 45–85, see Table 4.1) were recruited and tested individually on an ASL sentence repetition test. The participants included native signers ($n = 33$), who had learned ASL from deaf signing parents, and two groups of non-native signers. Early non-native signers ($n = 40$) were exposed to ASL before the age of 8. Late non-native signers (n = 34) were exposed to ASL after the age of 8, typically in adolescence. Sentence repetition is a complex language task that indexes both linguistic and memory processing. Potter and colleagues (Lombardi & Potter, 1992; Potter & Lombardi, 1990) have demonstrated that verbatim recall of a spoken sentence involves reconstructing the surface representation from a conceptual representation of the sentence using recently activated lexical and syntactic forms accessible in working memory. Therefore, sentence repetition is a task that taxes both linguistic processing and memory functions (Lombardi & Potter, 1992; Potter & Lombardi, 1990).

The ASL-SRT developed by Supalla and colleagues (2014) presents participants with 20 sentences that gradually increase in length, the complexity of morphology, and the number of propositions; Table 4.2 lists word span, syntactic complexity, and content for each item. The test is administered on a laptop computer, where participants view a video of a woman who serves both as an instructor and as a model producing the set of practice and test sentence items. She instructs participants to copy the model's exact signing, stressing the need for a verbatim response. The test is self-paced without a time limit for response: subjects view each sentence only once, but they then have unlimited time to make their response. The responses are video-recorded for subsequent offline scoring. The raters compared each participant's responses to the intended sentence.[1] A response was marked incorrect if it deviated from the model sentence beyond a few agreed-upon alternatives (Hauser et al., 2006). Following Supalla and colleagues (2014), the error types reflect incorrect reproductions and not regional pronunciation or accent differences.

Statistical analysis of sentence reproduction data made use of a logistic mixed-effects regression model predicting whether or not a sentence was accurately

TABLE 4.1 Participant characteristics

ASL experience			
	Native	*Early*	*Late*
Age group	*n*	*n*	*n*
45–54	9 (6 female)	9 (9 female)	8 (5 female)
55–64	10 (6 female)	10 (6 female)	9 (4 female)
65–74	9 (4 female)	9 (4 female)	8 (7 female)
75–85	5 (5 female)	12 (9 female)	9 (5 female)

TABLE 4.2 ASL–SRT items with sentence content and inflections

Item	Word span	Syntactic complexity	Sentence content and inflections	English translation
1	5	Transitive predication	INDEX-first FINISH BUY OLD HOUSE	I bought the old house.
2	5	Adjectival predication	THAT-i TREE TALL	That tree is tall.
3	4	Transitive predication	INDEX-i FINISH FIND KEY	I found the key.
4	6	Adjectival predication	MY LAST VACATION SEVEN YEARS AGO	My last vacation was seven years ago.
5	4	Adjectival predication	THAT MAN NICE SWEET	That man is sweet and nice.
6	4	Transitive predication	INDEX-i NOT LIKE INDEX-j	(She/He) does not like (him/her).
7	4	Adjectival predication	SUNDAY NEWSPAPER TEND CL: thickness-on-surface	Sunday newspapers tend to be thick.
8	4	Adjectival predication	MY DAUGHTER SELF-i AGE-THREE	My daughter, she (herself) is three years old.
9	4	Intransitive action	MY DOG CONTINUE+rep BARK	My dog barked and barked.
10	4	Adjectival predication	WOMAN SELF-i COMPETENT MATH	The woman, she (herself) is competent in math.
11	7	Copular object	WASHINGTON #DC HAVE MANY GOVERNMENT BUILDING, CL: huge-object-alternating-ijk	Washington D.C. has many large government buildings in various locations.
12	4	Adverbial predication	INDEX-first DRIVE FIVE-HOUR, ARRIVE WORN-OUT	I drove for five hours and arrived exhausted.
13	7	Conditional clause with transitive predication, consequence clause with adverbial predication	IF INDEX-i NOT BELIEVE INDEX-self, THAT FINE	If you do not believe me, so be it.
14	4	Conjunction of intransitive action and locative predication	MOTORCYCLE CL: vehicle-slide-off-ground, HIT TREE	The motor cycle skidded off the road and hit a tree.

Item	Word span	Syntactic complexity	Sentence content and inflections	English translation
15	6	Locative predication, transitive predication, locative predication	WOMAN RIDE-horse HORSE, SEE-i FENCE, CL:jump-over-fence-i	A woman rides a horse, sees a fence ahead and jumps over it.
16	6	Locative predication, intransitive action	THREE-OF-US GO-i-rep GRANDMOTHER HOUSE, HELP CLEAN-UP-arc-i	The three of us regularly go to grandmother's house to help clean.
17	6	Locomotion, locative predication, POV predication	INDEX-first LIKE GO BIKE PATH CL: trees-go-by	I like to pedal the bike path and experience the trees flying by.
18	7	Transitive predication, object complement, adjectival predication	#DAVID GO WATCH-i MAN LECTURE, CL: in- back-of-audience FULL	David went to watch the man lecture; the auditorium was packed.
19	9	Transitive predication, transitive predication	SCIENCE TEACHER DISTRIBUTE TEST, INDEX-arc STUDENT HAVE-TO NAME+rep-on-list STAR	The science teacher gave out the tests, and the students were required to name all the stars.
20	7	Locative predication, transitive predication	ONE LITTLE GIRL GO OUT, FLOWER CL: pick-up/ put-in-basket+rep-arc	One little girl went outside, picked flowers and put them in her basket.

Notes: CAP = lexical sign, INDEX = first person pronoun, INDEX-I = indexical sign to a spatial location, -ijk = distinct spatial locations, INDEX-self = reflective pronoun, CL: = classifier predicate, rep = repeated, #D-C, fingerspelled letters, -arc = arced movement of the sign path. From "Effects of age on American Sign Language sentence repetition" by D.P. Corina, et al, 2020, *Psychology and Aging, 35*(4), 529–535 (https://doi.org/10.1037/pag0000461)

Source: Copyright 2020 by the American Psychological Association.

repeated. Predictors were age (continuous), AoA (native, early, or late), and the interaction between these two variables.

The results of the model (see Table 4.3) show that increased age and later ASL acquisition decreased the likelihood of ASL sentence reproduction. Interested readers are encouraged to consult the original paper (Corina et al., 2020), whose findings we summarize in Table 4.3.

The study revealed that ASL sentence repetition was a challenging test for deaf participants. The ability to fully repeat single and multi-clausal ASL sentences decreased as a function of chronological age ($p < 0.001$), with increased age being associated with decreased likelihood to reproduce a sentence (see Figure 4.1). A comparison of our findings with those reported by Supalla and colleagues (2014) is shown in Figure 4.2. As shown, school-age (10–14 years) and young adult native signers (15–30 years) correctly reproduce approximately 14/20 sentences, while 45-year-old native signers reproduce approximately 12/20 sentences and 85-year-old signers produced roughly 4/20 sentences.

Figure 4.1 further illustrates the performance of the three groups as a function of AoA. In the model, the effect of AoA was significant ($p = 0.019$); relative to the native signers, those who acquired ASL early were less likely to successfully reproduce a sentence ($p < 0.003$), as were subjects who learned ASL later ($p < 0.001$). However, there was no difference between the late and early AoA groups ($p = 0.158$). Although the late learners appear to show a shallower decline than do both the native and early signers, the interaction between age and AoA did not reach significance. Rather, the effects of AoA and CA appear independent.

Two important findings that emerge from these data are that typical aging does impact ASL sentence repetition ability in this deaf cohort and that AoA was correlated with repetition ability. We consider the implications of each of these findings in turn.

The decline in sentence repetition as a function of chronological age is broadly consistent with cross-sectional data that indicate linear declines in declarative memory and visual–spatial abilities beginning in the early twenties (Rönnlund & Nilsson, 2008; see also Nyberg et al., 2012). However, there appears to be a sharp

TABLE 4.3 Model 1 Summary – age and AoA on sentence production Fixed effects:

	Estimate	Std. error	z-Value	Pr(> |z|)
(Intercept)	−0.4815	0.4105	−1.173	0.2408
AoA-E	−0.8759	0.2975	−2.945	0.0032 ★★
AoA-L	−1.3120	0.3192	−4.110	<0.0001 ★★★
AGE	−0.5714	0.2231	−2.561	0.0104 ★
AoA-E:AGE	−0.2014	0.2914	−0.691	0.4895
AoA-L:AGE	0.3464	0.2933	1.181	0.2376

Notes: Summary of model 1, a logistic mixed-effects regression model predicting sentence reproduction. Includes parameter effect estimates (in log-odds), standard errors, z-values, and p-values (based on a Wald test).

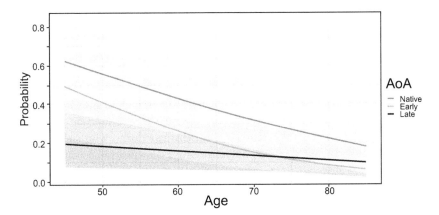

FIGURE 4.1 Model 1 predicted values – sentence repetition likelihood. Probability of correct ASL sentence reproduction as a function of chronological age and AoA. Data from deaf signers exposed to ASL as a native language, in early childhood (<8 years) and late childhood (>8 years). Predicted values from model 1 with a 95% prediction interval.

Source: From "Effects of age on American Sign Language sentence repetition" by D.P. Corina et al., 2020, *Psychology and Aging, 35*(4), 529–535 (https://doi.org/10.1037/pag0000461). Copyright 2020 by the American Psychological Association.

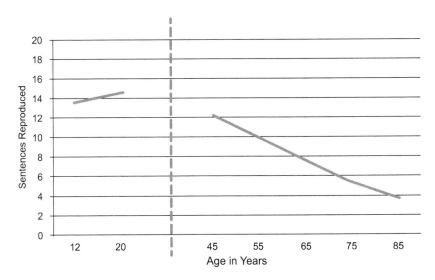

FIGURE 4.2 Comparison of ASL sentence repetition performance in younger and older deaf native signers. Sign language sentence repetition performance in young ASL native signers (*n* = 50) adapted from Supalla et al. (2014; left panel) compared to sentence repetition performance in a cohort of older native adult signers (*n* = 33; right panel).

Source: From "Effects of age on American Sign Language sentence repetition" by D.P. Corina, et al., 2020, *Psychology and Aging, 35*(4), 529–535 (https://doi.org/10.1037/pag0000461). Copyright 2020 by the American Psychological Association

decline in ASL sentence repetition in the older cohort. Verbatim ASL sentence repetition ability falls to approximately 85% of young adult levels by age 45, to 50% by age 65, and to less than 30% by age 80. This level of performance appears to be qualitatively different from the verbatim recall of spoken language sentences, which is reported to be quite good in both young adults and older persons (Lombardi & Potter, 1992; Wingfield et al., 1985; Potter & Lombardi, 1990). For example, Meyers et al. (2000), tested 104 healthy participants who ranged in age from 16 years to 86, and found no influence of age on repetition performance on a 22-item clinical sentence repetition test (Spreen & Strauss, 1998).

The Corina and colleagues (2020) study was not designed to directly evaluate the effects of language (i.e., ASL versus spoken English) and hearing status on verbatim sentence repetition; therefore, we must view comparisons with prior studies of spoken language repetition with caution. Nevertheless, this reported difference between spoken and signed language repetition is noteworthy, and may be a reflection of language-specific processing factors. Prior studies comparing memory functions in deaf signers and hearing users of spoken languages provide some basis for understanding the current data.

Hearing individuals exhibit short-term memory performance advantages for speech-based stimuli compared to analogous sign-based stimuli used in testing deaf individuals (Bellugi et al., 1974; Boutla et al., 2004; Conrad, 1970, 1972; see Hall & Bavelier, 2010, and Wilson & Emmorey, 2006 for reviews). This difference has been obtained in within-subject designs, with native ASL-English hearing bilinguals, suggesting that this difference reflects encoding differences of sign versus speech rather than an outcome of deafness per se (Boutla et al., 2004; Rönnberg et al., 2004). An enduring finding in this literature indicates that the spoken language advantage emerges especially when the memory task requires participants to recall stimulus items in adherence to the temporal order of stimulus presentation. Such findings have led some researchers to posit a differential utilization of working memory components used in the service of sign language understanding. Hirshorn and colleagues (2012) suggest that signers make greater use of visual–spatial and episodic storage mechanisms for linguistic processing compared to hearing individuals who depend more strongly on the phonological loop and its rehearsal mechanisms. The ASL-SRT (Supalla et al., 2014) requires verbatim recall, so deviations from the linear ordering of signs in each target sentence is marked as incorrect. The performance of our participants may reflect the difficulty that signers experience with ordered recall of linguistic material (see also Rudner et al., 2010). It remains an open question whether the age-related declines noted may be an indication of age-related vulnerabilities within working memory or episodic storage mechanisms.

Regarding the effects of AoA, these data add to the now substantial literature which indicates native sign language experience affords significant linguistic and cognitive processing advantages. It is noteworthy that, despite decades of experience using ASL as their primary and preferred means of communication, the ability of early and late learners of ASL to faithfully reproduce ASL sentences remains impacted by their initial AoA. This is particularly striking in the comparison between native and early signers, who show a consistent AoA difference well into life despite the relatively modest differences in the ages at which signing was introduced. However, one must be cognizant of the correlational nature of these data. Furthermore, cross-sectional studies in aging are potentially confounded by cohort effects in which apparent differences, often attributed to cognitive aging, instead reflect historical influences, such as educational opportunity, cultural factors, and SES (Hofer & Sliwinski, 2001; Salthouse & Nesselroade, 2002).

Seminal contributions of Helen Neville and others suggest that there is a critical or sensitive period for language acquisition (Chomsky, 1965; Hahne & Friederici, 2001; Hartshorne et al., 2018; Lennenberg, 1967; Newport et al., 2001; Pakulak & Neville, 2011; Weber-Fox & Neville, 1996). The delayed acquisition of second language has pronounced effects on grammatical processing and its representation in the brain (Weber-Fox & Neville, 1996; see also Rossi et al., 2006). Studies using both direct and indirect measures have reported a loss of grammatical sensitivity as a function of age of sign language acquisition (Cormier et al., 2012; Emmorey et al., 1995; Mayberry & Eichen, 1991).

Finally, there were no indications of higher-order interactions in these data; instead, the effects of AoA and CA appeared to be independent. Primary language delay appears to establish setpoints in the capacities for language processing and these capacities do not catch up merely through years of increased use (see also Mayberry et al., 2002). Moreover, while native language acquisition affords processing advantages in ASL sentence repetition, it does not appear to protect individuals from age-related declines.

Linguistic error analysis

In the assessment of participants' performance reported in Corina and colleagues (2020), the number of correct sentence reproductions served as the dependent variable. Here, we extend the analysis with an examination of omission errors observed during the SRT. Errors of omission were by far the most common error observed, and accounted for approximately 69% of errors. Semantic errors were the next most common, accounting for 17.5% of errors. Morphological and phonological errors accounted for 4.6 and 3.3% of errors, respectively. Transposition and intrusion errors were relatively uncommon, accounting for 3.4 and 1.6% of the errors, respectively. These data show a pattern similar to those reported in Supalla and colleagues (2014), where errors of omission were overwhelmingly more prevalent than morphological, syntactic, lexical, and phonological errors across all signers tested. Errors of omission likely reflect moments of processing overload and capacity limitations.

To further understand these errors, we assessed whether signs that were incorrectly omitted were randomly distributed across word classes, or whether grammatical class influenced the patterns of omissions. In ASL, as with spoken languages, verbs and pronouns carry grammatical and syntactic function, for example, participating in predication and anaphoric co-reference. In contrast, nouns and modifiers carry lexical-semantic meaning, but are devoid of grammatical inflection, as there is no case marking in ASL. Furthermore, it is worth noting that in ASL, verbs and especially pronouns make demands on spatial devices in their usage. Spatially inflecting verbs that signal grammatical roles (e.g., subject and object) require the use of contrastive articulatory space. Pronouns also are directed to locations on the body (i.e., the trunk) and in articulatory space to designate person marking (e.g., first, second, and third). Nouns and modifiers in ASL generally do not have the same requirements for spatial marking. Based upon differences in grammatical and syntactic function, and the difference in the requirements for spatial usage, we chose to examine whether the omissions of verbs and pronouns differed from the omission of nouns and modifiers.

A logistic mixed-effects regression model was used to predict sign omissions during the reproduction of sentences. The fixed effects in this model were the same as in model 1 described earlier, but with the addition of word class (verb + pronoun versus noun + adjective) and its interactions with the other variables. The random effect structure for model 2 was similar to the first model, with random intercepts for subject and item (word), by-item random slopes for the effect of CA and AoA, and by-subject random slopes for word class.

The results from the sign omissions analysis parallels the overall pattern of sentence reproduction, where the rate of omitted signs increases with CA and AoA (see Table 4.4). Age was a significant predictor, with older signers producing more word omissions [odds ratio (OR) = 1.65, $p = 0.025$].

TABLE 4.4 Model 2 summary – age, AoA, and word class on word omission fixed effects

	Estimate	Std. error	z-Value	Pr(> |z|)
(Intercept)	−3.4753	0.3696	−9.402	<0.0001★★★
AoA-E	0.7045	0.3029	2.326	0.0200★
AoA-L	0.9097	0.3178	2.862	0.0042★★
AGE	0.4997	0.2222	2.249	0.0245★
ClassVP	1.0350	0.4958	2.087	0.0368★
AoA-E:AGE	−0.0738	0.2768	−0.267	0.7898
AoA-L:AGE	−0.1818	0.2782	−0.654	0.5133
AoA-E:ClassVP	0.1166	0.2095	0.556	0.5779
AoA-L:ClassVP	0.2110	0.2393	0.882	0.3779
AGE:ClassVP	0.0654	0.1735	0.377	0.7060
AoA-E:AGE:ClassVP	−0.2027	0.1946	−1.041	0.2977
AoA-L:AGE:ClassVP	−0.0378	0.1945	−0.194	0.8459

Notes: Summary of model 2, a logistic mixed-effects regression model predicting word omissions. Includes parameter effect estimates (in log-odds), standard errors, z-values, and p-values (based on a Wald test).

Moreover, we observe an effect of AoA with late exposed signers and early signers omitting more signs than the native AoA group (late AoA, OR = 2.48, p = 0.004; early AoA, OR = 2.02, p = 0.02). Word class also showed an overall effect, with verb and pronoun signs being omitted more often than the nouns and modifiers (OR = 2.82, p = 0.037). However, there were no interactions between any of the variables. Figure 4.3 illustrates the probability of omitting noun and modifiers (left panel) and verbs and pronouns (right panel) in the cohort of adult deaf signers.

In the following, we consider selected examples to illustrate error tendencies observed during sentence repetition. Consider the target sentence I DRIVE+ FIVE-HOURS ARRIVE EXHAUSTED ("I drove for 5 hours and arrived exhausted"). This is a multi-clausal sentence and we often observed the omission of the second verb ARRIVE. Interestingly, while only 5/33 (15%) native signers omitted this lexical verb, 9/40 (22.5%) early signers and 12/34 (35.3%) late signers failed to include this lexical verb in their sentence repetition attempts. A common strategy was to treat this sentence as two separate sentences, essentially (I) DRIVE+ FIVE-HOURS, (I) EXHAUSTED ("I drove 5 hours. I'm exhausted"). This strategy may reflect a difference in the initial parse of the target sentence or reflect a memory recall strategy. Serial position effects may also have contributed to this omission of the second verb (Small et al., 2000).

In another example, we observe an 83-year-old late learner incorrectly reproducing this sentence as "FIVE-YEARS SAFE." Note how this repetition attempt fails to preserve the meaning of the original sentence and omits both pronouns and verbs. The substitution of the sign SAFE for the sign DRIVE may be motivated by the formational surface properties of these signs. Both of these signs are two-handed signs that are articulated in a neutral space in front of the signer, with

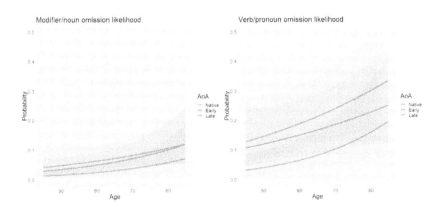

FIGURE 4.3 Probability of word omissions as a function of age and AoA. Left panel, omission of nouns and modifiers; right panel, omissions of verbs and pronouns. Predicted values from model 2, with a 95% prediction interval.

identical closed-fist handshapes, but with different movements. Processing inefficiencies in resolving surface-level details may have led to a misunderstanding of the intended sentence by this late learner or affected the accurate reconstruction of the surface form during the repetition of the sentence.

In contrast, consider the repetition of the 85-year-old native signer who produced I DRIVE++ #FIVE HOURS ARRIVE EXHAUSTED. Here, the participant fingerspells #F-I-V-E and signs HOUR, rather than producing the intended numeral-incorporated form of FIVE-HOURS, but correctly includes the first-person pronoun, and the verbs DRIVE and ARRIVE. In contrast to the late learner, despite the minor error (i.e., the fingerspelled #F-I-V-E HOURS, rather than verbatim morphologically complex FIVE-HOURS), the native signer preserves the overall gist of the sentence. This pattern of behavior accords with previous studies of sentence repetition where late learners' renditions resulted in misinterpretation of intended semantic content, perhaps driven by a bottom-up failure to appreciate important differences in the surface form of the signs or making use of this information during the reconstructive recall process. In contrast, for native signers, processing efficiencies afford greater repetition accuracy guided by the successful semantic-conceptual encoding of the message. This efficiency may permit greater top-down control of message reconstitution during the verbatim repetition.

Errors involving pronouns were very common and both omissions and substitutions of pronoun forms were observed. Consider the target sentence INDEX-j NOT LIKE INDEX-i ("He does not like her"). This mono-clausal sentence consists of four separate signs. In the native signers, we find only 4/33 (12.1%) omissions of the subject pronoun. However, 9/40 of the early signers, approximately 23%, failed to mention the initial subject pronoun, while three participants failed to repeat the object pronoun. For late signers, we find 12/34 (35.3%) incorrect repetitions with six omissions and six substitutions. In the substitutions, we observe the replacement of the third-person pronoun either with first- or second-person pronouns. We also note one instance of a spatial reversal of the subject and object pronouns.

Consider again the target sentence I DRIVE+ FIVE-HOURS ARRIVE EXHAUSTED with the initial first-person pronoun. Here, we observe the omission of the first-person subject pronoun "I". While only 4/33 (12.2%) native signers omitted this pronoun, early and late signers show more frequent omissions: 7/40 (17.5%) and 12/34 (35.3%), respectively. In this sentence, it was not unusual to see the incorrect substitution of the personal possessive pronoun MY for the first-person subject pronoun in the early and late learners. This type of pronoun substitution was not observed in the native signers.

Studies of spoken languages have shown that the omission of pronouns may be amplified in cases where processing difficulties interact with language-specific grammatical properties that license pro-drop. For example, Bencini and colleagues (2011) reported that, relative to age-matched controls, omissions of pronouns were common in patients with mild to moderate Alzheimer's disease (AD) in SRT in Italian, a pro-drop language. In addition, these Italian patients were shown to omit pronouns far more frequently than a comparable group of English speakers with AD, suggesting that language-specific grammatical properties interact with processing difficulties. ASL is a pro-drop language, but there are specific restrictions on when pronouns can be omitted (Lillo-Martin, 1991). One wonders whether, in cases of late L1 acquisition, such grammatical rules are less well instantiated, leading to more idiosyncratic omission and substitution of pronouns, even in cases where it is not licensed.

The second type of pronoun omission error suggests a different mechanism: diachronic change in ASL. Two sentences make use of a reflexive pronoun. MY DAUGHTER *HERSELF* THREE-YEARS-OLD and WOMAN *HERSELF* +right SKILLED MATH. Across these two sentences, and collapsing across AoA, we observe that a younger cohort of signers (45–64 years) omitted HERSELF 14/55 (25%) times, while over two-thirds of the older respondents (65–85 years) omitted these forms 33/52 times (63.5%).

ASL has been generally assumed to have reflexive pronouns (often glossed as *SELF*), but more recent work has suggested that these forms have a more common emphatic role than purely reflexive function (Koulidobrova, 2009; Wilkinson, 2013). This form of emphasis marking is common in ASL but, in Wilkinson's (2013) analysis, is more likely to occur in monologues including video blogs (i.e., vlogs) and formal and informal presentations that take place with little or no interaction with the discourse participants in their immediate physical environment. Wilkinson (2013) raises the question of whether there is a diachronic change in the use of SELF in ASL, prompted perhaps in part by the proliferation of vlogs popular with younger signers. In the present data, we see a marked reduction in the repetition of the form SELF in our oldest cohorts which may be a reflection of the diachronic change in the use of sign SELF in the Deaf community.

Finally, in addition to the pronoun and verb errors, chronological age affected the details of sentential semantics. Consider the sentence SUNDAY NEWSPAPER TEND CLC:C (Sunday newspapers tend to be thick). A striking pattern was seen with the sign TEND. Collapsing across AoA, in the younger signers (ages 45–64 years) this sign was omitted only 1/55 (1.8%) times, while in the older cohorts (65–85 years) this sign was omitted 15/52 (29%) times, with 11 instances in the oldest group. The omission of the verb "TEND" in this case results in only a subtle meaning change, equivalent to "Sunday's newspapers are thick." A similar simplification is seen in the sentence MY DOG CONTINUE +REP BARK (My dog continued to bark). Here we see the omission of the adverb CON-TINUE in 3/55 (5%) signers in the two younger age groups (ages 45–64 years), but we see 15/52 (29%) omissions in the older age groups (65–85 years). Here again, a subtle semantic distinction is lost in this rendition of the sentence, but it remains grammatical. These omissions, which preserve the semantic meaning of the intended sentence, appear similar to reports of spoken language repetition errors in which older participants retain the gist of sentences despite subtle changes in surface form (Wingfield et al., 1985).

Discussion of omission errors

The analysis of omission errors as a function of word class showed that verbs and pronouns were more likely to be omitted than nouns and modifiers, but this effect did not interact with the effects of CA or AoA. A priori, it was not clear whether the grammatical properties of verbs and pronouns in comparison to nouns and modifiers might serve to increase the saliency of these items and protect them from omission. It is clear from our data that the reverse is true: the relatively greater load on grammatical and syntactic processing may make these signs vulnerable to omission. Limitations in visual–spatial working memory may also contribute to the increased processing load of these forms.

It is curious (and perplexing) to note that, in an early developmental study of ASL, Anderson and Reilly (2002) reported that children acquiring ASL show a higher proportion of verbs to nouns than children learning English. A recent analysis of native signing parents' input to their deaf infants shows a far greater proportion of verbs to nouns (Fieldsteel et al., 2020). Given the prominence of verb forms in early ASL signing, it is surprising to find that verb (and pronoun) forms are most likely to be omitted during sentence repetition in older deaf adults. Further work is required to understand this counterintuitive finding and whether it reflects a pattern that is unique to signed languages or is common to languages whose acquisition profiles weight the early expression of verbs over nouns, such as Italian (Camaioni & Longobardi, 2001) and Mandarin (Tardif et al., 1997).

Errors of omission likely reflect moments of processing overload and capacity limitations. The vulnerability of verbs and pronouns relative to nouns and modifiers may reflect differential processing requirements. In spoken language sentence repetition, the syntactic structure serves to integrate and bind forms in working memory for efficient recall (Lombardi & Potter, 1992; Potter & Lombardi, 1990). If delayed exposure to a signed language results in less well-ensconced grammatical knowledge, this may lead to deficiencies in syntactic scaffolding necessary for ASL sentence encoding and recall.

Rönnberg and colleagues (2008) provide a general model to understand language processing capacity limitations. Under optimal conditions, spoken and signed language understanding requires the rapid integration of multiple levels of linguistic structure (phonology, semantics, syntax, and prosody), which are rapidly and automatically bound together at the cognitive level to form a stream of phonological information. As long as optimum conditions prevail, the rapid automatic multimodal binding of phonological information mediates rapid and implicit unlocking of the lexicon by matching input with stored phonological representations in long-term memory (Rönnberg et al., 2010). Under suboptimal conditions, the probability that information will fail to match stored representations increases. In this view, a mismatch may occur because of slow lexical access or less precise phonological representations in long-term memory (Andersson, 2002). When a mismatch occurs, the system will signal a need for explicit processing and storage capacity. This capacity is needed to infer meaning, prospectively as well as retrospectively, on the basis of incomplete information, and the capacity to infer meaning is crucial for compensatory purposes (Rönnberg et al., 2008). In the present data, the simplification of sentence structures, the omission of grammatically rich sign forms, and the presence of formational errors are all suggestive of capacity limitations.

Our data suggest that delayed primary language acquisition may interfere with the rapid automatic encoding of language. The relative poorer performance of early exposed and later exposed signers suggests a compounding of these effects over and above the effects of normal aging.

Lifespan theories of cognitive development (LTCD) provide a framework for interpreting the effects of AoA and CA. The LTCD model proposed by Baltes and colleagues (1998) holds that cognitive development reflects the operation of two intertwined components, one biological and the other cultural (Baltes et al., 1998; Lindenberger & Baltes, 1997). Children's language acquisition is often regarded as a quintessential example of the interplay between these two components, as the ontological unfolding of the biologically governed linguistic capacities is dependent upon culturally specific exposure to one's mother tongue. For many deaf individuals, this expected relationship is disrupted, resulting in the delayed acquisition of an accessible L1 (i.e., a signed language). It is an open question whether such disruptions, with time, can be overcome, or whether the imbalance engenders persistent lifelong effects. The present data strongly suggest the latter – language ability, rather than exhibiting a functional resilience (which over decades of consistent use may normalize), instead is subject to stage-like constraints which establish enduring setpoints in linguistic capacities. It is worthwhile to note that the observation of sensitive periods in the development of grammar was a major theme in the work of Helen Neville. Helen and her colleagues provided some of the finest examples of how neural indices of language are impacted by AoA (Pakulak & Neville, 2011; Weber-Fox & Neville, 1996).

In infancy and early childhood, age-related biological changes often yield domain-specific and predisposed processing capabilities (Wellman & Gelman, 1992), whereas age-related biological changes after maturity affect broad processing capabilities (e.g., information processing rate, working memory, and inhibition) that may cut across perceptual, cognitive, and action domains. We speculate that the age-related declines observed across the deaf signing cohorts may be a reflection of changes to domain-general cognitive processes. The question raised, but not answered by the current study, is whether changes (for example in working memory) could lead to differential impacts that vary as a function of a language's modality of expression. Future research aimed at directly comparing rates of sentence repetition ability decline in native ASL-English hearing bilinguals could provide important evidence for this possible state of affairs. The documentation of the vulnerabilities and resilience of modality-specific language systems in the face of aging may allow us to better understand the role of human language in LTCD.

Conclusion

This chapter reports some of the first efforts to explore the effects of aging on language abilities in deaf signers. The study of this population provides a unique opportunity to assess the impact of age-related changes on primary language ability in cases where (L1) was acquired under delayed or protracted development. This research calls attention to the need to understand how cognitive and linguistic factors contribute to age-related maintenance and declines in language processing. Our data suggest that early imbalances in the temporal coordination between biological and cultural factors driving language acquisition have persistent and long-lasting effects across the lifespan. This work is a fitting tribute to Helen Neville, whose research legacy and mentorship propelled a new generation of cognitive neuroscientists to carefully consider the interplay between biological and cultural factors in our explorations of the human mind.

Note

1 The responses were rated by two native signers (L.F. and S.P.).

References

Anderson, D., & Reilly, J. (2002). The MacArthur communicative development inventory: Normative data for American Sign Language. *The Journal of Deaf Studies and Deaf Education*, 7(2), 83–106. https://doi.org/10.1093/deafed/7.2.83

Andersson, U. (2002). Deterioration of the phonological processing skills in adults with an acquired severe hearing loss. *European Journal of Cognitive Psychology*, 14(3), 335–352. https://doi.org/10.1080/09541440143000096

Baltes, P. B., Lindenberger, U., & Staudinger. U. M. (1998). Life-span theory in developmental psychology. In R. M. Lerner (Ed.), *Handbook of child psychology: Vol. 1. Theoretical models of human development* (5th ed., pp. 1029–143). New York: Wiley.

Bellugi, U., Klima, E., & Siple, P. (1974). Remembering in signs. *Cognition*, 3(2), 93–125.

Bellugi, U., Poizner, H., & Klima, E. S. (1989). Language, modality and the brain. *Trends in Neurosciences*, 12(10), 380–388. https://doi.org/10.1016/0166–2236(89)90076–3

Bencini, G. M. L., Pozzan, L., Biundo, R., McGeown, W. J., Valian, V. V., Venneri, A., & Semenza, C. (2011). Language-specific effects in Alzheimer's disease: Subject omission in Italian and English. *Journal of Neurolinguistics*, 24(1), 25–40. https://doi.org/10.1016/j.jneuroling.2010.07.004.

Boutla, M., Supalla, T., Newport, L., & Bavelier, D. (2004). Short-term memory span: Insights from sign language. *Nature Neuroscience*, 7, 997–1002.

Benjamin, B. J. (1988). Changes in speech production and linguistic behavior with aging. In B. Shadden (Ed.), *Communication behavior and aging* (pp. 163–181). Baltimore, MD: Williams & Wilkins.

Burke, D. M., & Graham, E. R. (2012). The neural basis for aging effects on language. In M. Faust (Ed.), *The handbook of the neuropsychology of language* (pp. 778–800). Oxford, UK: Blackwell Publishing.

Burke, D. M., & Shafto, M. A. (2008). Language and aging. In F. I. M. Craik & T. A. Salthouse (Eds.), *The handbook of aging and cognition* (pp. 373–443). Mahwah, NJ: Lawrence Erlbaum Associates.

Camaioni, L., & Longobardi, E. (2001). Noun versus verb emphasis in Italian mother-to-child speech. *Journal of Child Language, 28*(3), 773–785. https://doi.org/10.1017/S0305000901004846

Chomsky, N. (1965). *Aspects of the theory of syntax*. Cambridge, MA: The MIT Press.

Conrad, R. (1970). Short-term memory processes in the deaf. *British Journal of Psychology, 61*(2), 179–195.

Conrad, R. (1972). Short-term memory in the deaf: A test for speech coding. *British Journal of Psychology, 63*(2), 173–180.

Cooper, P. V. (1990). Discourse production and normal aging: Performance on oral picture description tasks. *Journal of Gerontology: Psychological Sciences, 45*, P210–P214.

Corina, D. P., Farnady, L., LaMarr, T., Pedersen, S., Lawyer, L., Winsler, K., Hickok, G., & Bellugi, U. (2020). Effects of age on American Sign Language sentence repetition. *Psychology and Aging, 35*(4), 529–535. https://doi.org/10.1037/pag0000461

Cormier, K., Schembri, A., Vinson, D., & Orfanidou, E. (2012). First language acquisition differs from second language acquisition in prelingually deaf signers: Evidence from sensitivity to grammaticality judgment in British Sign Language. *Cognition, 124*, 50–65.

Craik, F. I., & Rose, N. S. (2012). Memory encoding and aging: A neurocognitive perspective. *Neuroscience & Biobehavioral Reviews, 36*(7), 1729–1739.

Davis, G. A. (1984). Effects of aging on normal language. In A. Holland (Ed.), *Language disorders in adults* (pp. 79–111). San Diego, CA: College-Hill Press.

Emmorey, K., Bellugi, U., Friederici, A., & Horn, P. (1995). Effects of age of acquisition on grammatical sensitivity: Evidence from on-line and off-line tasks. *Applied Psycholinguistics, 16*(1), 1–23. https://doi.org/10.1017/S0142716400006391

Fieldsteel Z., Bottoms A., & Lieberman, A. M. (2020). Nouns and verbs in parent input in American Sign Language during interaction among deaf dyads. *Language Learning and Development, 16*(4), 351–363. https://doi.org/10.1080/15475441.2020.1784737

Hahne, A., & Friederici, A. (2001). Processing a second language: Late learners' comprehension mechanisms as revealed by event-related brain potentials. *Bilingualism: Language and Cognition, 4*(2), 123–141. https://doi.org/10.1017/S1366728901000232

Hall, M. L., & Bavelier, D. (2010). Working memory, deafness, and sign language. In M. Marschark & P. E. Spencer (Eds.), *The Oxford handbook of deaf studies, language, and education* (vol. 2, pp. 458–472). Oxford: Oxford University Press.

Hartshorne, J. K., Tenenbaum, J. B., & Pinker, S. (2018). A critical period for second language acquisition: Evidence from 2/3 million English speakers. *Cognition, 17*, 263–277. https://doi.org/10.1016/j.cognition.2018.04.007

Hauser, P., Paludneviciene, R., Supalla, T., & Bavelier, D. (2006). *American Sign Language – Sentence reproduction test: Development & implications*. Retrieved from http://scholarworks.rit.edu/other/596

Henderson, A., & Wright, H. H. (2016). Cognition, language, and aging: An introduction. In H. H. Wright (Ed.), *Cognition, language and aging* (pp. 1–12). Amsterdam, The Netherlands: John Benjamins B. V., https://doi.org/10.1075/z.200.01hen.

Hirshorn, E. A., Fernandez, N. M., & Bavelier, D. (2012). Routes to short-term memory indexing: Lessons from deaf native users of American Sign Language. *Cognitive Neuropsychology, 29*(1–2), 85 – 103. https://doi.org/10.1080/02643294.2012.704354

Hofer, S. M., & Sliwinski, M. J. (2001). Understanding ageing. An evaluation of research designs for assessing the interdependence of ageing-related changes. *Gerontology, 47,* 341–352 (2001). https://doi.org/10.1159/000052825

Jenkins, L., Myerson, J., Joerding, J. A., & Hale, S. (2000). Converging evidence that visuospatial cognition is more age-sensitive than verbal cognition. *Psychology and Aging, 15*(1), 157–175. https://doi.org/I0.1037/0882-7974.15.1.157

Kemper, S. 2006. Language in adulthood. In E. Bialystok & F. I. Craik (Eds.), *Lifespan cognition: Mechanisms of change* (pp. 223–238). New York: Oxford University Press.

Kemper, S., Kynette, D., Rash, S., Sprott, R., & O'Brien, K. (1989). Life-span changes to adults' language: Effects of memory and genre. *Applied Psycholinguistics, 10,* 49–66.

Koulidobrova, E. (2009). SELF: Intensifier and "long-distance" effects in ASL. In *Proceedings of the European summer school in logic, language and information.* Retrieved from http://tinyurl.com/3qnhclf.

Kynette, D., & Kemper, S. (1986). Aging and the loss of grammatical forms: A cross-sectional study of language performance. *Language and Communication, 6,* 43–49.

Lennenberg, E. H. (1967). *Biological foundations of language.* New York: Wiley.

Lillo-Martin, D. C. (1991). Universal grammar and American Sign Language. In: *Universal grammar and American Sign Language. Studies in theoretical psycholinguistics* (vol. 13). Dordrecht: Springer. https://doi.org/10.1007/978-94-011-3468-2_1

Lindenberger, U., & Baltes, P. B. (1997). Intellectual functioning in old and very old age: Cross-sectional results from the Berlin Aging Study. *Psychology and Aging, 12*(3), 410–432. https://doi.org/10.1037/0882-7974.12.3.410

Lombardi, L., & Potter, M. C. (1992). The regeneration of syntax in short term memory. *Journal of Memory and Language, 31,* 713–733. https://doi.org/10.1016/0749-596X(92)90036-W

Mayberry, R., & Eichen, E. (1991). The long-lasting advantage of learning sign language in childhood: Another look at the critical period for language acquisition. *Journal of Memory and Language, 30,* 486–512. https://doi.org/10.1016/0749-596X(91)90018-F

Mayberry, R. I., Lock, E., & Kazmi, H. (2002). Linguistic ability and early language exposure. *Nature, 417,* 38. https://doi.org/10.1038/417038a

Meyers, J. E., Volkert, K., & Diep, A. (2000). Sentence repetition test: Updated norms and clinical utility. *Applied Neuropsychology, 7,* 154–159.

Myerson, J., Emery, L., White, D. A., & Hale, S. (2003). Effects of age, domain, and processing demands on memory span: Evidence for differential decline. *Aging, Neuropsychology, and Cognition, 10*(1), 20–27. https://doi.org/10.1076/anec.10.1.20.13454

Newport, E. L., Bavelier, D., & Neville, H. J. (2001). Critical thinking about critical periods: Perspectives on a critical period for language acquisition. In E. Dupoux (Ed.), *Language, brain, and cognitive development: Essays in honor of Jacques Mehler* (pp. 481–502). Cambridge, MA: The MIT Press.

Nyberg, L., Lövdén, M., Riklund, K., Lindenberger, U., & Bäckman, L. (2012). Memory aging and brain maintenance. *Trends in Cognitive Sciences, 16*(5), 292–305. https://doi.org/10.1016/j.tics.2012.04.005

Pakulak, E., & Neville, H. J. (2011). Maturational constraints on the recruitment of early processes for syntactic processing. *Journal of Cognitive Neuroscience, 23*(10), 2752–2765. http://doi.org/10.1162/jocn.2010.21586

Park, D. C., Lautenschlager, G., Hedden, T., Davidson, N. S., Smith, A. D., & Smith, P. K. (2002). Models of visuospatial and verbal memory across the adult life span. *Psychology and Aging, 17*(2), 299–320. http://dx.doi.org/10.1037/0882-7974.17.2.299

Potter, M. C., & Lombardi, L. (1990). Regeneration in the short-term recall of sentences. *Journal of Memory and Language, 29*, 633–654. https://doi.org/10.1016/0749-596X(90)90042-X

Rönnberg, J., Rudner, M., Foo, C., & Lunner, T. (2008). Cognition counts: A working memory system for ease of language understanding (ELU). *International Journal of Audiology, 47*(suppl. 2), S99–S105. https://doi.org/10.1080/14992020802301167

Rönnberg, J., Rudner, M., & Ingvar, M. (2004). Neural correlates of working memory for sign language. *Cognitive Brain Research, 20*, 165–182. https://doi.org/10.1016/j.cogbrainres.2004.03.002

Rönnberg, J., Rudner, M., Lunner, T., & Zekveld, A. (2010). When cognition kicks in: Working memory and speech understanding in noise. *Noise and Health, 12*(49), 263–269, https://doi.org/10.4103/1463-1741.70505.

Rönnlund, M., & Nilsson, L. G. (2008). The magnitude, generality and determinants of Flynn effects on declarative memory and visuospatial ability: Time-sequential analyses of data from a Swedish cohort study. *Intelligence, 36*(3), 192–209. https://doi.org/10.1016/j.intell.2007.05.002

Rossi, S., Gugler, M. F., Friederici, A. D., & Hahne, A (2006). The impact of proficiency on syntactic second-language processing of German and Italian: Evidence from event-related potentials. *Journal of Cognitive Neuroscience, 18*(12), 2030–2048. https://doi.org/10.1162/jocn.2006.18.12.2030

Rudner, M., Davidsson, L., & Rönnberg, J. (2010). Effects of age on the temporal organization of working memory in deaf signers. *Aging, Neuropsychology, and Cognition, 17*(3), 360–383. https://doi.org/10.1080/13825580903311832

Salthouse, T. A., & Nesselroade, J. R. (2002). An examination of the Hofer and Sliwinski evaluation. *Gerontology, 48*, 18–21.

Shafto, M. A., & Tyler, L. K. (2014). Language in the aging brain: The network dynamics of cognitive decline and preservation. *Science, 346*(6209), 583–587. https://doi.org/10.1126/science.1254404

Shewan, C. M., & Henderson, V. L. (1988). Analysis of spontaneous language in the older normal population. *Journal of Communication Disorders, 21*, 139–154.

Small, J. A., Kemper, S., & Lyons, K. (2000). Sentence repetition and processing resources in Alzheimer's disease. *Brain and Language, 75*(2), 232–258. https://doi.org/10.1006/brln.2000.2355.

Spreen, O., & Strauss, E. (1998). *A compendium of neuropsychological tests: Administration, norms, and commentary* (2nd ed.). Oxford: Oxford University Press.

Supalla, T., Hauser, P. C., & Bavelier, D. (2014). Reproducing American Sign Language sentences: Cognitive scaffolding in working memory. *Frontiers in Psychology, 5*, 859. http://doi.org/10.3389/fpsyg.2014.00859

Tardif, T., Shatz, M., & Naigles, L. (1997). Caregiver speech and children's use of nouns versus verbs: A comparison of English, Italian, and Mandarin. *Journal of Child Language, 24*(3), 535–565. https://doi.org/10.1017/S030500099700319X

Weber-Fox, C., & Neville, H. J. (1996). Maturational constraints on functional specializations for language processing: ERP and behavioral evidence in bilingual speakers. *Journal of Cognitive Neuroscience, 8,* 231–256.

Wellman, H. M., & Gelman, S. A. (1992). Cognitive development: Foundational theories of core domains. *Annual Review of Psychology, 43,* 337–375.

Wilkinson, E. (2013). A functional description of SELF in American Sign Language. *Sign Language Studies, 13*(4), 462–490.

Wilson, M., & Emmorey, K. (2006). No difference in short-term memory span between sign and speech. *Psychological Science, 17*(12), 1093–1094. https://doi.org/10.1111/j.1467-9280.2006.01835.x

Wingfield, A., Poon, L. W., Lombardi, L., & Lowe, D. (1985). Speed of processing in normal aging: Effects of speech rate, linguistic structure, and processing time. *Journal of Gerontology, 40*(5), 579–585. https://doi.org/10.1093/geronj/40.5.579

5

CHANGES IN OCCIPITO-TEMPORAL CORTEX WITH LITERACY

Electrophysiological evidence

Giordana Grossi and Elizabeth Sacchi

The idea that the brain changes with experience has been widely accepted only fairly recently, after neurophysiological evidence for brain plasticity in non-human animals started accumulating in the 1960s and 1970s (e.g., Bennett et al., 1964; Bliss & Lømo, 1973; Hubel & Wiesel, 1964). Helen Neville was one of the first researchers to investigate how experience shapes the development of the human brain. After charting the neural changes that accompany language acquisition and the differentiation of systems subserving the semantic and grammatical aspects of language processing, her research showed that these systems are differentially affected by experiences such as sensory deprivation or learning a second language (Neville & Mills, 1997). Indeed, one of Neville's major contributions illustrates that the effects of experience are heterogeneous and do not affect all cognitive and neural systems identically (Stevens & Neville, 2013). Importantly, her work also established that some of these changes are associated with language skills, not chronological age (e.g., Mills et al., 1997; Pakulak & Neville, 2010). Therefore, Helen Neville contributed to the view of the human brain as a dynamic system, whose development is not simply the product of context-blind maturational changes but reflects the individual's specific experiences.

The purpose of this paper, informed and inspired by the research framework and approach developed by Helen Neville, is to discuss some of the literature pertaining to the development of the neural systems involved in reading and the factors that shape, or are associated with, their recruitment. This review is not intended to be comprehensive and will focus on the posterior N1, a negative event-related potential (ERP) elicited over occipito-temporal sites by visual stimuli.

DOI: 10.4324/9780429342356-10

The left ventral occipito-temporal region and the posterior N1

The left ventral occipito-temporal region[1] is known to be involved in the early visual processing of objects of expertise. Of particular importance in this review, the region is critical to the early stages of reading when developing readers gain familiarity with the language in its written form. Evidence comes from brain-lesioned patients with deficits in letter and word identification (e.g., Miozzo & Caramazza, 1998; Patterson & Kay, 1982) and from neuroimaging studies, which have shown a link between activation in this region and skilled reading (Bolger et al., 2005; for a discussion, see Price, 2012). Activation of this area has also been found to be invariant to the color, font type, font size, and case in which letters are presented (for a review, see McCandliss et al., 2003) and regardless of the writing system (Bolger et al., 2005). Consequently, this area has been called the visual word form area (Cohen et al., 2000; McCandliss et al., 2003). Activation in this region reflects expertise with a specific language, as it is greater in magnitude for readers than non-readers of that language (Baker et al., 2007; Szwed et al., 2014). Although the precise computational properties and specificity of this area have been a matter of debate (Binder et al., 2006; Cohen & Dehaene, 2004; Glezer et al., 2009; Hirshorn et al., 2016; Price & Devlin, 2003, 2011; Price & Friston, 2005; Reich et al., 2011; Vogel et al., 2014), evidence suggests that this region is part of a circuit involved in – but not exclusively dedicated to – various aspects of written word recognition; more specifically, the aspects of orthographic processing and the grapheme–phoneme (GP) mapping. Indeed, this region has been found to be activated in tasks not involving reading (e.g., naming color patches and picture naming; for a summary, see Price & Friston, 2005). Because of this pattern, here we refer to this area as left ventral occipito-temporal cortex (vOT).

Due to their exquisite temporal resolution, ERPs have provided complementary information regarding the temporal characteristics of word recognition processes. The posterior N1 ERP, observed between 130 and 200 ms and often referred to as the N170, is part of a family of posterior components hypothesized to reflect mechanisms involved in the identification of visual stimuli (e.g., Rossion et al., 2003). Indeed, it is modulated by properties of non-text-based visual stimuli such as faces and objects (Bentin et al., 1996; Rossion et al., 2003), but the N1 elicited by faces and visual objects usually differs from that elicited by letter strings in terms of timing (the N1 to words has been found to peak as early as 150 ms versus 170 ms for faces) and scalp distribution (e.g., the N1 to faces is typically right-lateralized whereas the response to words is left-lateralized). Importantly, the N1 is modulated by expertise with a visual category, with larger amplitude N1 responses when experts view images in their domain of expertise (Tanaka & Curran, 2001).

In studies with written, text-based stimuli, the N1 is the earliest component modulated by orthographic (e.g., Bentin et al., 1999; Compton et al., 1991;

Grossi & Coch, 2005; McCandliss et al., 1997) and lexical variables (Hauk & Pulvermüller, 2004; Sereno et al., 1998). Furthermore, the N1 has been found to be larger over the left than the right posterior sites in a variety of studies and tasks employing alphabetic stimuli (e.g., Emmorey et al., 2017; Grossi et al., 2010; Yum et al., 2011). Differences in N1 amplitude between words and consonant strings and between words and non-alphabetic symbols are also usually observed over the left posterior sites (Cohen et al., 2000; Maurer et al., 2005; Emmorey et al., 2017). Similar results have been found in magnetoencephalography (MEG) studies (e.g., Helenius et al., 1999; Solomyak & Marantz, 2009; Tarkiainen et al., 1999).

Intracranial recordings, dipole localization studies, and MEG studies have identified the left ventral occipito-temporal regions as the generator region for the N1 (Allison et al., 1994; Rossion et al., 2003; Tarkiainen et al., 1999). In addition, some authors have made a tentative link between the N1 and the vOT (Brem et al., 2006, 2009; Proverbio et al., 2005). For instance, Brem et al. (2006) have shown a correlation between N1 amplitude and vOT activation in a joint functional magnetic resonance imaging (fMRI)/ERP study.

Developmental changes in literacy instruction

While reading is effortless for most adults, learning to read requires prolonged training, typically starting at the beginning of the school years, with exposure to visual symbols and their sounds. In alphabetic languages, learning to read requires developing an expertise in identifying a set of visual symbols (e.g., Roman or Cyrillic alphabets) and the combinatorial rules followed to form words (orthography). In addition, letters or letter combinations must be translated to sounds, through GP conversion rules, and then ultimately to meanings. Therefore, in fluent readers, written words are processed through multiple levels of analysis and representations to support whole-word comprehension (e.g., Rayner & Pollatsek, 1989).

As with other ERP deflections, the N1 decreases in latency and amplitude during development (Grossi et al., 2001; Holcomb et al., 1992). Studies focusing on changes in N1 amplitude associated with literacy training have documented two major changes: the development of tuning to print (typically operationalized as a difference in amplitude between print and non-print stimuli, such as non-alphanumeric symbols or false fonts) and a shift in scalp distribution from bilateral to left-lateralized, as detailed later.

In alphabetic languages, the N1 tuning to print develops during the early school years. Absent in children not yet exposed to literacy instruction (Maurer et al., 2005), tuning for print was present in the same children, bilaterally, after 1.5 years of literacy training (Maurer et al., 2006). In contrast, adult participants exhibited a left-lateralized tuning effect and N1. A bilateral N1 tuning to print was also observed in other studies with children between 6.5 and 11 years of age (Coch & Meade, 2016; Eberhard-Moscicka et al., 2015; Hasko et al., 2013).

Importantly, the emergence of the tuning effect was not due to sheer exposure but reflected a new form of expertise, as it positively correlated with measures of reading proficiency and was smaller or absent in younger non-reading children and less proficient readers (e.g., Eberhard-Moscicka et al., 2015; Maurer et al., 2006).

Further research suggested that the N1 tuning to print can be established with just a few hours of instruction. In a study combining ERPs and fMRI, Brem et al. (2010) found a bilateral tuning effect for both the N1 amplitude and activation in the vOT (fMRI data) after 3–4 hours of training on single-letter GP correspondences in 6-year-old children not yet exposed to literacy instruction (no differences were found after a non-linguistic control training in a different group of participants).[2]

The N1 asymmetry for words seems to emerge later and requires a prolonged period of instruction, at least in studies with alphabetic languages. For example, the N1 was slightly right-lateralized in second graders but left-lateralized in fifth graders (Maurer et al., 2011). Spironelli and Angrilli (2009) found a later and right-lateralized N1 to words in 10-year-old children. This prolonged pattern of development seems to apply to the lateralization of the tuning effect as well, which shows evidence of being established as early as 10 years of age. In a cross-sectional study including 10-year-old children, adolescents, and adults, the difference in N1 amplitude between words and false fonts was present in all groups, as expected. Furthermore, the effect was larger over the left than right posterior sites in all groups (Brem et al., 2009). Overall, these findings suggest that the initial bilateral tuning of the N1 to print and the later change in lateralization reflect non-identical processes.

Development of N1 lateralization: theories and evidence

What drives the change in N1 lateralization that follows the initial tuning for print is still a matter of debate; differences in tasks, stimuli, languages, behavioral and neural measures, and participants' characteristics all prevent us from reaching an unequivocal answer. Two main hypotheses have been proposed: phonological mapping, and visual expertise with a language's orthography. The phonological mapping hypothesis (McCandliss & Noble, 2003) suggests an association between lateralization and the ability to map graphemes into phonemes. For example, Sacchi and Laszlo (2016) found that, while the overall pattern of N1 responses to words was left-lateralized in fifth and sixth graders, such lateralization was predicted by phonological awareness, but not by vocabulary. In an intervention study, Italian children with developmental dyslexia showed a change from a bilateral to a left-lateralized N1 after six months of phonological training (Spironelli et al., 2010). While this study did not employ a control group of dyslexic children undergoing a different type of training, correlational analyses revealed a relationship between increases in reading speed and N1 lateralization. This relationship was found only in a phonological task, not in orthographic or semantic tasks. In a study with adults learning an artificial script with a hidden (i.e., characterized by non-evident GP correspondences revealed only upon instruction) orthography, Yoncheva et al. (2010) showed that the lateralization of the N1 depended on the type of reading strategy training: while participants assigned to a whole-word reading strategy showed a strong right hemisphere lateralization, participants assigned to training based on GP decoding showed a slightly more left-lateralized N1. Therefore, some evidence suggests that the left-lateralization of the N1 in studies with alphabetic languages is tied to phonological decoding at the level of individual graphemes (small grain size; Ziegler & Goswami, 2005).

An alternative interpretation is that the N1 lateralization reflects a sensitivity, or tuning, to the orthography of a language, that is, to regularities in its letter combinations and word forms (McCandliss et al., 1997). As such, the lateralization would reflect a form of visual expertise, not necessarily associated with grapheme-to-phoneme decoding mechanisms (Maurer et al., 2008). This hypothesis is supported by work on logographic languages. While in alphabetic languages graphemes map onto phonemes, the mapping system is different in other languages. In syllabaries, such as the Japanese Kana, characters are mapped onto syllables. In logographic languages, like Chinese and the Japanese Kanji, single characters map to both sound and meaning units. These characters correspond to syllables, which are also morphemes, and often words (morpho-syllabic system; Perfetti et al., 2010). Therefore, the association between a character and a sound mostly occurs at a coarser grain size than in alphabetic languages and can vary[3] (Ziegler & Goswami, 2005).

Because of differences in mapping, some authors have suggested that neural correlates of reading would be different for alphabetic and logographic languages, for example in terms of the lateralization pattern (e.g., Maurer & McCandliss, 2007). Neuroimaging studies have provided support for this hypothesis: two meta-analyses have reported that processing of Chinese or logographic stimuli activates the posterior occipito-temporal regions, including the fusiform gyrus, bilaterally (i.e., inferior occipital and posterior fusiform gyri; Bolger et al., 2005; Tan et al., 2005). While the left vOT is recruited consistently regardless of the language, the recruitment of posterior regions in the right hemisphere has been hypothesized as being due to the visual–spatial processing demands of Chinese characters (e.g., spatial arrangement of radicals) or reliance on a coarser (e.g., syllabic) mapping between visual constituents and sounds (Bolger et al., 2005; Hirshorn et al., 2016).

Electrophysiological studies have provided a mixed picture, complicated by the fact that participants in these studies were often bilingual. We consider here studies concerning the participants' first language (L1). A bilateral N1 to Chinese or Kanji stimuli has been observed in several studies, sometimes accompanied by a left-lateralized or bilateral tuning for the print effect (Liu & Perfetti, 2003; Niermeyer et al., 2018; Xue et al., 2008; Wang & Maurer, 2017; Wong et al., 2005;

Zhang et al., 2011; Zhao et al., 2012). However, other studies have observed a left-lateralized N1 for these stimuli, but a bilateral N1 for readers unfamiliar with these scripts (Cao et al., 2011; Ji et al., 2016; Lin et al., 2011; Maurer et al., 2008[4]; Yum et al., 2011). Interestingly, the same left-lateralization pattern for Chinese characters was found in children aged 7.3–11.5 years learning to read (Cao et al., 2011) and even in 5- and 6-year-old preschool children learning to read (Li et al., 2013). In the latter case, the degree of leftward asymmetry of the N1 was positively correlated with the child's vocabulary score. According to Cao and colleagues (2011), these findings reveal the same developmental pattern in terms of recruitment of left posterior regions, although it would happen earlier in Chinese children, in line with their earlier literacy education. Therefore, the N1 left-lateralization would reflect reading expertise per se, regardless of the visual characteristics of the script.

In summary, the N1 elicited by logographic stimuli has been found to be less consistently left-lateralized than the N1 elicited by alphabetic stimuli, in line with findings from neuroimaging studies. However, a left-lateralized N1 has been observed for logographic stimuli in some studies. The reasons behind the discrepancy between findings in ERP studies remain to be clarified.

Bilingualism

Bilingualism raises interesting issues regarding the development of brain organization. In late bilinguals, who learn a second language during or after puberty, neural tuning is already present for L1. The second language (L2) might share some orthographic characteristics with the first language (e.g., alphabet, letter combinations) or might be substantially different (e.g., different alphabet, different mapping system). How are different orthographies integrated and implemented at the neural level? Does the already-established tuning for L1 in occipito-temporal regions somehow shape the organization for L2? This seems to be the case in a complex way that depends on both the nature of the L2 script and the first language (Nelson et al., 2009). For example, Chinese (L1)–English (L2) bilinguals showed a bilateral N1 for both languages, suggesting a reliance of L2 on the L1 organization (Liu & Perfetti, 2003). In contrast, in native Korean speakers, Kim and Kim (2006) found a left-lateralized N1 for Korean (L1) and English (L2) – both alphabetic languages – but a bilateral N1 for Chinese (L2) characters; similar results were found by Kim et al. (2004). A similar pattern was found in neuroimaging studies with bilinguals (Nelson et al., 2009) and studies of native English speakers learning Chinese characters (Liu et al., 2007). These findings suggest that the bilateral circuit activated by logographic L1s can assimilate an alphabetic L2, whereas a logographic language as L2 needs additional circuits to be processed if the L1 is alphabetic and associated with a left-lateralized N1 (Perfetti et al., 2010).

However, Yum et al. (2014) found that native English speakers learning Chinese words over a period of ten weeks showed larger N1 amplitudes with training over the left (but not the right) posterior sites in fast learners (who reached high accuracy levels in the translation task earlier). This increase was observed after four sessions and was stable afterward. On the contrary, slow learners showed a right-lateralized N1 during the first sessions, and then a decrease in lateralization at the end of training. According to the authors, the N1 asymmetry in fast learners would index the extraction of structural representations (parts and their combinations, similar to what occurs for processing alphabetic languages) in Chinese words for efficient identification. In contrast, slow learners would focus on holistic representations (the word as a whole) to identify each word. If true, the N1 lateralization would be observed when participants would process the stimulus focusing on small units (smaller grain size), regardless of the nature of the script (as also proposed by Yoncheva et al., 2010).

Relationship between N1 lateralization and bilingualism

A different set of studies also suggest an association between the N1 left-lateralization and bilingualism. In a study with early and late English–Welsh bilinguals performing a semantic categorization task with English and Welsh stimuli (presented in separate blocks), the N1 was left-lateralized in both groups. In addition, the N1 asymmetry to Welsh (L2) words correlated with years of experience with Welsh in late bilinguals: the longer the experience with Welsh, the more left-lateralized the N1 (Grossi et al., 2010). As this relationship was not observed before, we attempted to replicate these results with a new group of bilinguals and a control group. In the section that follows, we present novel findings from this study (previously presented at a conference; Grossi et al., 2013).

We tested English L1 students of Spanish who were taking classes at either the intermediate ($n = 20$) or advanced ($n = 19$) level at SUNY New Paltz; we also tested a group of participants who had no familiarity with Spanish or some, but very limited, exposure to Spanish during their school years ($n = 19$).[5] Excluding foreign language classes, English was the only language of instruction for all participants from elementary school to college, with the exception of one participant who spent one semester in college in a Spanish-speaking country. No participants were fluent in other languages besides English and Spanish. All participants performed two lexical decision tasks, one with Spanish stimuli and one with English stimuli,[6] with the order of language counterbalanced across participants. After the task, they were asked to translate the Spanish word stimuli into English.[7]

Behavioral measures revealed that, as expected, sensitivity in discriminating words from pseudowords, measured with d', was overall higher for English than Spanish targets (Table 5.1). In addition, sensitivity for English targets was similar for the three groups, while sensitivity for Spanish differed among groups: it was higher for advanced, followed by the intermediate, and then control participants. As also expected, translation accuracy differed among groups: it was higher in advanced learners, followed by intermediate learners, and control participants (Table 5.2).

TABLE 5.1 Participants' accuracy (defined as d') in the two lexical decision tasks (standard deviations are shown in parentheses)

d'	Advanced	Intermediate	Control
English	3.47	3.14	3.10
	(0.34)	(0.65)	(0.54)
Spanish	1.98	1.16	0.66
	(0.48)	(0.38)	(0.39)

Notes:

Language [$F_{(1,55)}$ = 630.77, p < 0.0001, η^2_p = 0.92): higher sensitivity for English than Spanish stimuli.

Language × Group interaction [$F_{(2,55)}$ = 12.51, p < 0.0001, η^2_p = 0.31]: sensitivity for English targets was similar for the three groups, although there was a trend for significance [$F_{(2,55)}$ = 2.97, p = 0.06). Tukey's honest significant difference (HSD) post hoc comparisons showed that there was a trend for sensitivity to be higher in advanced than control participants (p = 0.078, corrected). Sensitivity for Spanish differed among groups [$F_{(2,55)}$ = 49.96, p < 0.0001, η^2_p = 0.65]: it was higher for advanced, followed by intermediate, and then control participants (for all comparisons, p < 0.005, corrected).

TABLE 5.2 Participants' translation accuracy (Spanish into English; values refer to percentages; standard deviations are shown in parentheses)

	Advanced	Intermediate	Control
Translation accuracy	66.55	38.95	15.50
	(14.48)	(12.31)	(10.88)

Notes:

Group [$F_{(2,55)}$ = 79.28, p < 0.0001, η^2_p = 0.74]: accuracy was higher in advanced learners, followed by intermediate learners, and control participants (all ps < 0.0001, corrected)

The N1 was quantified in terms of mean amplitude with respect to the baseline in the 120–220 ms time window over parieto-occipital sites. The degree of N1 lateralization differed depending on the group: for both languages, the N1 was bilateral in controls and left-lateralized in both intermediate and advanced learners of Spanish (Table 5.3 and Figure 5.1). Importantly, correlational analyses across all groups showed that the N1 asymmetry for Spanish stimuli was correlated with translation accuracy: the higher the accuracy, the more left-lateralized the N1 (Table 5.4 and Figure 5.2). A similar, although weaker, correlation was found between N1 asymmetry and number of semesters of Spanish. As in Grossi and colleagues (2010), the N1 asymmetry for Spanish highly correlated with the N1 asymmetry for English. Interestingly, translation accuracy was significantly related to N1 asymmetry for L1 as well: the higher the translation accuracy, the more left-lateralized the N1 for English stimuli (see Table 5.4 for detailed correlation results).

TABLE 5.3 Analysis of variance results pertaining to the N1 lateralization

		F	df	P	η^2_p
Hemisphere		22.09	1,55	<0.0001	0.29
Hemisphere × Group		5.58	2,55	0.006	0.17
Hemisphere analyses	Advanced	11.87	1,19	0.003	0.38
by group	Intermediate	19.51	1,18	<0.0001	0.52
	Control	0.02	1,18	0.88, n.s.	0.001
Hemisphere analyses	Hemisphere	18.00	1,55	<0.0001	0.25
for English	Hemisphere × Group	4.92	2,55	0.01	0.15
Hemisphere analyses	Hemisphere	24.74	1,55	<0.0001	0.31
for Spanish	Hemisphere × Group	5.91	2,55	0.005	0.18

TABLE 5.4 Correlations pertaining to the N1 lateralization

	r	p	r^2
N1 asymmetry for Spanish and translation accuracy	−0.37	0.004	0.14
N1 asymmetry for Spanish and number of semesters of Spanish	−0.29	<0.03	0.08
N1 asymmetry for Spanish and N1 asymmetry for English	0.93	<0.0001	0.87
N1 asymmetry for English and translation accuracy	−0.33	0.012	0.11

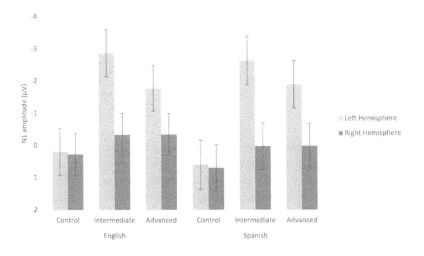

FIGURE 5.1 N1 mean amplitudes (120–220 ms) to Spanish and English stimuli over the two hemispheres in the three groups. Mean amplitudes reflect averages across the three parieto-occipital sites for each hemisphere. Negative is plotted up. Error bars represent 95% confidence intervals.

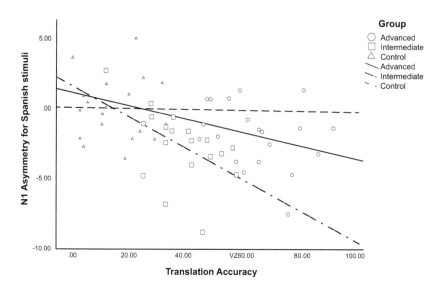

FIGURE 5.2   The correlation between translation accuracy and N1 left-lateralization (left–right) for Spanish stimuli in learners of Spanish and control participants. N1 lateralization is expressed in microvolts as the difference between N1 amplitude on left sites and N1 amplitude on right sites. More negative values indicate a more left-lateralized N1.

Therefore, increased proficiency in a second language was associated with a more left-lateralized N1 for both the first and the second language. This finding replicated Grossi and colleagues (2010) while employing a different task, as well as previous work by McCandliss and colleagues (1997). The nature of this relationship remains to be clarified. In both Grossi and colleagues (2010) and the present study, L1 was English – characterized by a shallow orthography – and L2 was a more transparent language (Welsh and Spanish). One possibility is that learning an L2 that relies on clear GP conversion rules had shaped the participants' attentional focus toward smaller units and increased the likeness of adopting a decoding strategy more often, even when they read English words – although this hypothesis might not apply to familiar words. Alternatively, the increased N1 lateralization might reflect the increased expertise with a new orthography. Regardless, these findings show that the lateralization of the posterior N1 to linguistic stimuli is associated with reading expertise, at least for alphabetic languages; they also suggest that learning a second language is associated with changes in systems dedicated to the native language as well, as also shown by neuroimaging studies (e.g., Nosarti et al., 2010; Zou et al., 2012).

Interestingly, the N1 lateralization was absent in the control group, even for words in their L1. A bilateral pattern in adults has been observed in some studies with alphabetic languages, such as Coch and Meade (2016). It is tempting to speculate that the context of the experiment, such as having to make decisions on words of an unknown language, might have shaped the participants' strategies in performing the task. However, these findings are the exception relative to the general trend in the literature. Future research will need to address the causes of this variability. In the meantime, these results suggest that the bilingualism status, or experience with reading in other languages, may be an important variable to consider in research on reading and N1 lateralization.

Conclusions and new developments

Helen Neville's pioneering work provided some of the earliest evidence showing how experience shapes the development of the human brain. We discussed evidence showing how a very specific type of experience, exposure to a written language, during childhood changes the pattern of electrophysiological responses (i.e., posterior N1) over the occipito-temporal regions of the scalp in terms of tuning for print and lateralization. Increased left-lateralization of the N1 has been described in adults as well: in correlational studies with late bilinguals (correlating with L2 proficiency; Grossi et al., 2010, and the novel findings presented here), in controlled experiments on L2 vocabulary learning or learning of artificial scripts (McCandliss et al., 1997; Yoncheva et al., 2010; Yum et al., 2014), and even in individuals who learn to read during adulthood (Pegado et al., 2014). This dynamic pattern shows that the neural systems indexed by the posterior N1 retain a remarkable degree of plasticity during adulthood and that this plasticity is tied to reading expertise. Some questions still await an answer, concerning what specifically drives the N1 lateralization, in late bilinguals as well, and why a more bilateral pattern is sometimes observed in studies with logographic languages.

Recent studies are exploring how far-reaching the role of experience is by investigating the relationship between reading and the processing of other visual stimuli. As reading is a recent development in human history, it has been proposed that its neural representation piggybacks on the recruitment of regions that have evolved for other purposes, setting up a competition for neural space (Dehaene et al., 2005). This hypothesis has generated a number of predictions pertaining to shifts in functional specialization of posterior regions with literacy. Some studies support these predictions. For example, activation in the left vOT to faces was reduced with increasing experience in letter knowledge both in 4- to 5-year-old children and in illiterate adults learning to read (Braga et al., 2017; see Dehaene et al., 2015, for a summary). In addition, the degree of lateralization for faces has been found to correlate with standardized reading scores in children and adolescents (Dundas et al., 2013); electrophysiologically, correlations have been found between the N1 to words and the N1 to faces, in terms of amplitude (Dundas et al., 2014) and lateralization (Li et al., 2013; for a recent discussion, see Behrmann & Plaut, 2020).

In summary, literacy is associated with neurophysiological changes that include the tuning of the ventral occipito-temporal regions to print and a shift in their degree of functional specialization and lateralization. These changes, which not only engage the posterior left regions across languages but also reflect the individual's specific experiences with literacy training (e.g., type of writing system, reading strategy, and exposure to a written second language), are linked to alterations in the processing of other visual stimuli. These findings demonstrate the importance of considering cortical organization at any point in time as reflecting an ongoing and highly interactive developmental process, embedded in a specific cultural context and characterized by specific cognitive demands.

Acknowledgments

We would like to thank Emily Heimbender for her help with data collection and analysis and Courtney Stevens for her comments on a previous version of the manuscript.

Notes

1 In alphabetic languages, the "reading network" has been associated with three main regions: occipito-temporal, temporoparietal, and frontal. This network has been updated to include other regions consistently activated in studies of logographic languages, such as superior parietal regions and middle frontal regions. Readers interested in a more general overview of the cognitive neuroscience of reading and reading development can consult, among others, Perfetti et al. (2010), Ben-Shachar et al. (2011), Wandell et al. (2012), Dehaene et al. (2015).

2 Written words in the study were German words; therefore, the children in the study might have had already developed a degree of familiarity with the orthographic structure of the language.

3 Alphabetic and logographic languages do not differ simply in terms of script and mapping. For example, while alphabetic languages are arranged in strings of letters (whose combination forms the phonological representation of words), Chinese characters are formed by component radicals arranged in squares; different arrangements of the same radicals within the square are associated with different characters. Due to this method of combining constituent elements, processing of Chinese characters has been associated with holistic or configurational processing, similar to the processing methods employed during face recognition (Perfetti et al., 2010). In addition, compared to alphabetic languages, logographic languages like Chinese are learned differently. Chinese children rely less on phonology and more on orthographic information, as phonology does not guarantee lexical access due to the conspicuous presence of homophones. Indeed, while phonological awareness is a strong predictor of learning to read, reading skills in Chinese children are strongly associated with character copying skills (Perfetti et al., 2010).

4 It is important to note that the N1 lateralization for Kanji in native Japanese speakers in Maurer et al. (2008) was only a marginal effect ($p < 0.1$).

5 Of the 19 control participants, seven never took Spanish classes; nine took introductory classes in middle schools, two took introductory classes in high school, and one took one introductory class in college. As it is extremely rare for American students not to have exposure to Spanish in school (the students who did not were from foreign English-speaking countries such as Australia and Great Britain), we decided to form a heterogeneous control group of students with no or minimal proficiency in Spanish for correlational analysis purposes.

6 The stimuli included 74 Spanish and 74 English words. Spanish words were selected from the LEXESP database (Sebastián-Gallés et al., 2000) and in collaboration with the Spanish instructors at SUNY New Paltz; English words were selected from the CELEX database (Baayen et al., 1995). Written frequency and orthographic measures were calculated based on the same databases and the programs N-Watch (English; Davis, 2005) and Busca Palabras (Spanish; Davis & Perea, 2005). Pseudowords were created by changing one or two letters from the word stimulus lists. Words and pseudowords within each language differed in terms of written frequency (both p's < 0.0001); Spanish and English word lists were matched in terms of lexical frequency (words), length, within-language and cross-language bigram frequency, and within-language and cross-language neighborhood density (all p's > 0.13).

7 The electroencephalogram (EEG) was recorded from 29 tin electrodes mounted in an elastic cap (Electro-Cap) according to an extended International 10–20 System. In addition, tin electrodes were placed beneath one eye to monitor blinking and vertical eye movements and at the outer canthus of each eye to monitor horizontal eye movements (bipolar eye channel). Except for the bipolar eye channel, online recordings were referenced to the right mastoid and re-referenced to averaged mastoids in the final data averaging. Impedances were kept below 3 kΩ for scalp electrodes, 2 kΩ for the mastoids, and 10 kΩ for the eye channels. The EEG was amplified by a set of 32 SA Instrumentation isolated amplifiers with a bandpass of 0.01–100 Hz and digitized online at a sampling rate of 250 Hz. A 60 Hz filter was applied to the data offline. ERPs to stimuli were averaged over an epoch of 1000 ms using a 200 ms pre-stimulus baseline. Trials characterized by eye movements, muscular activity, and electrical noise were rejected by an automatized routine and were not included in the analyses.

References

Allison, T., McCarthy, G., Nobre, A., Puce, A., & Belger, A. (1994). Human extrastriate visual cortex and the perception of faces, words, numbers, and colors. *Cerebral Cortex*, *4*(5), 544–554.

Baayen, R. H., Piepenbrock, R., & Gulikers, L. (1995). *The CELEX lexical database (Release 2)*. Philadelphia, PA: Linguistic Data Consortium.

Baker, C., Liu, J., Wald, L., Kwong, K., Benner, T., & Kanwisher, N. (2007). Visual word processing and experiential origins of functional selectivity in human extrastriate cortex. *Proceedings of the National Academy of Sciences*, *104*(21), 9087–9092.

Behrmann, M., & Plaut, D. C. (2020). Hemispheric organization for visual object recognition: A theoretical account and empirical evidence. *Perception*, *49*(4), 373–404. https://doi.org/10.1177/0301006619899049

Bennett, E. L., Diamond, M. C., Krech, D., & Rosenzweig, M. R. (1964). Chemical and anatomical plasticity of the brain. *Science*, *146*(3644), 610–619.

Ben-Shachar, M., Dougherty, R. F., Deutsch, G. K., & Wandell, B. A. (2011). The development of cortical sensitivity to visual word forms. *Journal of Cognitive Neuroscience*, *23*(9), 2387–2399. https://doi.org/10.1162/jocn.2011.21615.

Bentin, S., Allison, T., Puce, A., Perez, E., & McCarthy, G., (1996). Electrophysiological studies of face perception in humans. *Journal of Cognitive Neuroscience*, *8*, 551–565.

Bentin, S., Muochetant-Rostaing, Y., Giard, M. H., Echallier, J. F., & Pernier, J. (1999). ERP manifestations of processing printed words at different psycholinguistic levels: Time course and scalp distribution. *Journal of Cognitive Neuroscience*, *11*, 235–260.

Binder, J. R., Medler, D. A., Westbury, C. F., Liebenthal, E., & Buchanan, L. (2006). Tuning of the human left fusiform gyrus to sublexical orthographic structure. *NeuroImage*, *33*, 739–748.

Bliss, T., & Lømo, T. (1973). Long-lasting potentiation of synaptic transmission in the dentate area of the anaesthetized rabbit following stimulation of the perforant path. *Journal of Physiology, 232,* 331–356.

Bolger, D. J., Perfetti, C. A., & Schneider, W. (2005). Cross-cultural effects on the brain revisited: Universal structures plus writing system variation. *Human Brain Mapping, 25,* 92–104.

Braga, L., Amemiya, E., Tauil, A., Suguieda, D., Lacerda, C., Klein, E., Dehaene-Lambertz, G., & Dehaene, S. (2017). Tracking adult literacy acquisition with functional MRI: A single-case study. *Mind, Brain, and Education, 11*(3), 121–132.

Brem, S., Bach, S., Kucian, K., Guttorm, T. K., Martin, E., Lyytinen, H., Brandeis, D., & Richardson, U. (2010). Brain sensitivity to print emerges when children learn letter-speech sound correspondences. *Proceedings of the National Academy of Sciences, 107*(17), 7939–7944.

Brem, S., Bucher, K., Halder, P., Summers, P., Dietrich, T., Martin, E., & Brandeis, D. (2006). Evidence for developmental changes in the visual word processing network beyond adolescence. *NeuroImage, 19,* 822–837.

Brem, S., Halder, P., Bucher, K., Summers, P., Martin, E., & Brandeis, D. (2009). Tuning of the visual word processing system: Distinct developmental ERP and fMRI effects. *Human Brain Mapping, 30,* 1833–1844.

Cao, X., Li, S., Zhao, J., Lin, S., & Weng, X. (2011). Left-lateralized early neurophysiological response for Chinese characters in young primary school children. *Neuroscience Letters, 492,* 165–169.

Coch, D., & Meade, G. (2016). N1 and P2 to words and wordlike stimuli in late elementary school children and adults. *Psychophysiology, 53*(2), 115–128. https://doi.org/10.1111/psyp.12567.

Cohen, L., & Dehaene, S. (2004). Specialization within the ventral system: The case for the visual word form area. *NeuroImage, 22,* 466–476.

Cohen, L., Dehaene, S., Naccache, L., Lehéricy, S., Dehaene-Lambertz, G., Hénaff, M.-A., & Michel, F. (2000). The visual word form area: Spatial and temporal characterization of an initial stage of reading in normal subjects and posterior split-brain patients. *Brain, 123,* 291–307.

Compton, P. E., Grossbacher, P., Posner, M. I., & Tucker, D. M. (1991). A cognitive-anatomical approach to attention in lexical access. *Journal of Cognitive Neuroscience, 3*(4), 304–312.

Davis, C. J. (2005). N-Watch: A program for deriving neighborhood size and other psycholinguistic statistics. *Behavior Research Methods, 37,* 65–70.

Davis, C. J., & Perea, M. (2005). BuscaPalabras: A program for deriving orthographic and phonological neighborhood statistics and other psycholinguistc indices in Spanish. *Behavior Research Methods, 37,* 665–671.

Dehaene, S., Cohen, L., Morais, J., & Kolinsky, R. (2015). Illiterate to literate: Behavioral and cerebral changes induced by reading acquisition. *Nature Reviews Neuroscience, 16,* 234–244.

Dehaene, S., Cohen, L., Sigman, M., & Vinckier, F. (2005). The neural code for written words: A proposal. *Trends in Cognitive Science, 9*(7), 335–341.

Dundas, E. M., Plaut, D. C., & Behrmann, M. (2013). The joint development of hemispheric lateralization for words and faces. *Journal of Experimental Psychology: General, 142*(2), 348–358.

Dundas, E. M., Plaut, D. C., & Behrmann, M. (2014). An ERP investigation of the co-development of hemispheric lateralization of face and word recognition. *Neuropsychologia, 61,* 315–323.

Eberhard-Moscicka, A. K., Jost, L. B., Raith, M., & Maurer, U. (2015). Neurocognitive mechanisms of learning to read: Print tuning in beginning readers related to word-reading fluency and semantics but not phonology. *Developmental Science*, *18*(1), 106–118.

Emmorey, K., Midgley, K. J., Kohen, C., Sehyr, Z., & Holcomb, P. J. (2017). The N170 ERP component differs in laterality, distribution, and association with continuous reading measures for deaf and hearing readers. *Neuropsychologia*, *106*, 298–309.

Glezer, L. S., Jiang, X., & Riesenhuber, M. (2009). Evidence for highly selective neuronal tuning to whole words in the "Visual Word Form Area." *Neuron*, *62*(2), 199–204. https://doi.org/10.1016/j.neuron.2009.03.017.

Grossi, G., & Coch, D. (2005). Automatic word form processing in masked priming: An ERP study. *Psychophysiology*, *42*(3), 343–355.

Grossi, G., Coch, D., Coffey-Corina, S., Holcomb, P. J., & Neville, H. J. (2001). Phonological processing in a rhyming task: A developmental ERP study. *Journal of Cognitive Neuroscience*, *13*(5), 610–625.

Grossi, G., Sacchi, E., Heimbender, E., Earl, N., & Acerra, M. (2013, March 20–23). Posterior N1 asymmetry in late learners of Spanish [Conference presentation]. In *11th International Symposium of Psycholinguistics*, Tenerife, Canary Islands.

Grossi, G., Savill, N., Thomas, E., & Thierry, G. (2010). Posterior N1 asymmetry to English and Welsh words in early and late English-Welsh bilinguals. *Biological Psychology*, *85*, 124–133.

Hasko, S., Groth, K., Bruder, J., Barling, J., & Schulte-Körne, G. (2013). The time course of reading processes in children with and without dyslexia: An ERP study. *Frontiers in Human Neuroscience*, 7, 570. https://doi.org/10.3389/fnhum.2013.00570.

Hauk, O., & Pulvermüller, F. (2004). Effects of word length and frequency on the human event-related potential. *Clinical Neurophysiology*, *115*, 1090–1103.

Helenius, P., Tarkiainen, A., Cornelissen, P., Hansen, P. C., & Salmelin, R. (1999). Dissociation of normal feature analysis and deficient processing of letter-strings in dyslexic adults. *Cerebral Cortex*, *9*(5), 476–483.

Hirshorn, E. A., Wrencher, A., Durisko, C., Moore, M. W., & Fiez, J. A. (2016). Fusiform gyrus laterality in writing systems with different mapping principles: An artificial orthography training study. *Journal of Cognitive Neuroscience*, *28*(6), 882–894. https://doi.org/10.1162/jocn_a_00940.

Holcomb, P. J., Coffey, S. A., & Neville, H. J. (1992). Visual and auditory sentence processing: A developmental analysis using event-related brain potentials. *Developmental Neuropsychology*, *8*(2–3), 203–241.

Hubel, D., & Wiesel, T. (1964). Effects of monocular deprivation in kittens. *Naunyn-Schmiedebergs Archiv für Experimentelle Pathologie und Pharmakologie*, *248*, 492–497.

Ji, L., Cao, X., & Xu, B. (2016). Sex differences of hemispheric lateralization for faces and Chinese characters in early perceptual processing. *Neuroscience Letters*, *635*, 77–82.

Kim, K. H., & Kim, J. H. (2006). Comparison of spatiotemporal cortical activation pattern during visual perception of Korean, English, Chinese words: An event-related potential study. *Neuroscience Letters*, *394*, 227–232.

Kim, K. H., Yoon, H. W., & Park, H. W. (2004). Spatiotemporal brain activation pattern during word/picture perception by native Koreans. *NeuroReport*, *15*(7), 1099–1103.

Li, S., Lee, K., Zhao, J., Yang, Z., He, S., & Weng, X. (2013). Neural competition as a developmental process: Early hemispheric specialization for word processing delays specialization for face processing. *Neuropsychologia*, *51*, 950–959.

Lin, S. E., Chen, H. C., Zhao, J., Li, S., He, S., & Weng, X. C. (2011). Left-lateralized N170 response to unpronounceable pseudo but not false Chinese characters – The key role of orthography. *Neuroscience, 190*, 200–206.

Liu, Y., Dunlap, S., Fiez, J., & Perfetti, C. A (2007). Evidence for neural accommodation to a writing system following learning. *Human Brain Mapping, 28*, 1223–1234.

Liu, Y., & Perfetti, C. A. (2003). The time course of brain activity in reading English and Chinese: An ERP study of Chinese bilinguals. *Human Brain Mapping, 18*(3), 167–175.

Maurer, U., Brandeis, D., & McCandliss, B. D. (2005). Fast, visual specialization for reading in English revealed by the topography of the N170 ERP response. *Behavioral and Brain Functions, 1*(13), 1–12.

Maurer, U., Brem, S., Bucher, K., & McCandliss, B. D. (2005). Emerging neurophysiological specialization for letter strings. *Journal of Cognitive Neuroscience, 17*(10), 1532–1552.

Maurer, U., Brem, S., Kranz, F., Bucher, K., Benz, R., Halder, P., Steinhausen, H.-C., & Brandeis, D. (2006). Coarse neural tuning for print peaks when children learn to read. *NeuroImage, 33*, 749–758.

Maurer, U., & McCandliss, B. D. (2007). The development of visual expertise for words: The contribution of electrophysiology. In E. L. Grigorenko & A. J. Naples (Eds.), *Single-word reading: Biological and behavioral perspectives*. Mahwah, NJ: Lawrence Erlbaum Associates.

Maurer, U., Schulz, E., Brem, S., van der Mark, S., Bucher, K., Martin, E., & Brandeis, M. (2011). The development of print tuning in children with dyslexia: Evidence from longitudinal ERP data supported by fMRI. *NeuroImage, 57*, 714–722.

Maurer, U., Zevin, J. D., & McCandliss, B. D. (2008). Left-lateralized N170 effects of visual expertise in reading: Evidence from Japanese syllabic and logographic scripts. *Journal of Cognitive Neuroscience, 20*(10), 1878–1891.

McCandliss, B. D., Cohen, L., & Dehaene, S. (2003). The visual word form area: Expertise for reading in the fusiform gyrus. *Trends in Cognitive Sciences, 7*(7), 293–299.

McCandliss, B. D., & Noble, K. G. (2003). The development of reading impairment: A cognitive neuroscience model. *Mental Retardation and Developmental Disability Research Reviews, 9*(3), 196–204.

McCandliss, B. D., Posner, M. I., & Givón, T. (1997). Brain plasticity in learning visual words. *Cognitive Psychology, 33*, 88–110.

Mills, D. L., Coffey-Corina, S. A., & Neville, H. J. (1997). Language comprehension and cerebral specialization from 13 to 20 months. *Developmental Neuropsychology, 13*(3), 397–445.

Miozzo, M., & Caramazza, A. (1998). Varieties of alexia: The case of failure to access graphemic representations. *Cognitive Neuropsychology, 15*, 203–238.

Nelson, J. R., Liu, Y., Fiez, J., & Perfetti, C. A. (2009). Assimilation and accommodation patterns in ventral occipitotemporal cortex in learning a second writing system. *Human Brain Mapping, 30*, 810–820.

Neville, H. J., & Mills, D. (1997). Epigenesis of language. *Mental Retardation and Developmental Disabilities Research Reviews, 3*(4), 282–292.

Niermeyer, M. A., Miller, E., Tamaoki, Y., Wiggins, E., & Stevens, C. (2018). Single and compound logographic Kanji words elicit distinct early neurophysiological responses: ERP evidence from fluent and naïve Kanji readers. *Journal of Neurolinguistics, 47*, 91–104.

Nosarti, C., Mechelli, A., Green, D. W., & Price, C. J. (2010). The impact of second language learning on semantic and nonsemantic first language reading. *Cerebral Cortex, 20*, 315–327.

Pakulak, E., & Neville, H. J. (2010). Proficiency differences in syntactic processing of monolingual native speakers indexed by event-related potentials. *Journal of Cognitive Neuroscience*, *22*(12), 2728–2744.

Patterson, K., & Kay, J. (1982). Letter-by-letter reading: Psychological descriptions of a neurological syndrome. *The Quarterly Journal of Experimental Psychology Section A: Human Experimental Psychology*, *34*(3), 411–441.

Pegado, F., Comerlato, E., Ventura, F., Jobert, A., Nakamura, K., Buiatti, M., Ventura, P., Dehaene-Lambertz, G., Kolinsky, R., Morais, J., Braga, L. W., Cohen, L., & Dehaene, S. (2014). Timing the impact of literacy on visual processing. *Proceedings of the National Academy of Science*, *111*(49), E5233–E5242.

Perfetti, C. A., Nelson, J., Liu, Y., Fiez, J., & Tan, L. H. (2010). The neural bases of reading: Universals and writing system variations. In P. Cornelissen, M. Kringelbach, & P. Hansen (Eds.), *The neural basis of reading* (pp. 147–172). Oxford: Oxford University Press.

Price, C. J. (2012). A review and synthesis of the first 20 years of PET and fMRI studies of heard speech, spoken language and reading. *NeuroImage*, *62*, 816–847.

Price, C. J., & Devlin, J. T. (2003). The myth of the visual word form area. *NeuroImage*, *19*, 473–481.

Price, C. J., & Devlin, J. T. (2011). The Interactive Account of ventral occipitotemporal contributions to reading. *Trends in Cognitive Sciences*, *15*(6), 246–253.

Price, C. J., & Friston, K. J. (2005). Functional ontologies for cognition: The systematic definition of structure and function. *Cognitive Neuropsychology*, *22*(3–4), 262–275.

Proverbio, A. M., Del Zotto, M., & Zani, A. (2005). Greek language processing in naive and skilled readers: Functional properties of the VWFA investigated with ERPs. *Cognitive Neuropsychology*, *23*(3), 355–375.

Rayner, K., & Pollatsek, A. (1989). *The psychology of reading*. Englewood Cliffs, NJ: Prentice-Hall.

Reich, L., Szwed, M., Cohen, L., & Amedi, A. (2011). A ventral visual stream reading center independent of visual experience. *Current Biology*, *21*, 363–368. https://doi.org/10.1016/j.cub.2011.01.040.

Rossion, B., Joyce, C. A., Cottrell, G. W., & Tarr, M. J. (2003). Early lateralization and orientation tuning for face, word, and object processing in the visual cortex. *NeuroImage*, *20*, 1609–1624.

Sacchi, E., & Laszlo, S. (2016). An event-related potential study on the relationship between N170 lateralization and phonological awareness in developing readers. *Neuropsychologia*, *91*, 415–425.

Sebastián-Gallés, N., Martí, M. A., Cuetos, F., & Carreiras, M. (2000). *LEXESP: Léxico informatizado del Español*. Barcelona, Spain: Edicions de la Universitat de Barcelona.

Sereno, S. C., Rayner, K., & Posner, M. I. (1998). Establishing a time-line of word recognition: Evidence from eye movements and event-related potentials. *NeuroReport*, *9*(10), 2195–2200.

Solomyak, O., & Marantz, A. (2009). Lexical access in early stages of visual word processing: A single-trial correlational MEG study of heteronym recognition. *Brain & Language*, *108*, 191–196.

Spironelli, C., & Angrilli, A. (2009). Developmental aspects of automatic word processing: Language lateralization of early ERP components in children, young adults and middle-aged subjects. *Biological Psychology*, *80*, 35–45.

Spironelli, C., Penolazzi, B., Vio, C., & Angrilli, A. (2010). Cortical reorganization in dyslexic children after phonological training: Evidence from early evoked potentials. *Brain*, *133*, 3385–3395.

Stevens, C., & Neville, H. J. (2013). Specificity of experiential effects in neurocognitive development. In M. Gazzaniga (Ed.), *The cognitive neurosciences*. Cambridge, MA: The MIT Press.

Szwed, M., Qiao, E., Jobert, A., Dehaene, S., & Cohen, L. (2014). Effects of literacy in early visual and occipitotemporal areas of Chinese and French readers. *Journal of Cognitive Neuroscience*, *26*(3), 459–475.

Tan, L. H., Laird, A. R., Li, K., & Fox, P. T. (2005). Neuroanatomical correlates of phonological processing of Chinese characters and alphabetic words: A meta-analysis. *Human Brain Mapping*, *25*, 83–91.

Tanaka, J. W., & Curran, T. (2001). A neural basis for expert object recognition. *Psychological Science*, *12*(1), 43–47.

Tarkiainen, A., Helenius, P., Hansen, P. C., Cornelissen, P. L., & Salmelin, R. (1999). Dynamics of letter string perception in the human occipitotemporal cortex. *Brain*, *122*, 2119–2131.

Vogel, A. C., Petersen, S. E., & Schlaggar, B. L. (2014). The VWFA: It's not just for words anymore. *Frontiers in Human Neuroscience*, *8*, 88. https://doi.org/10.3389/fnhum.2014.00088.

Wandell, B. A., Rauschecker, A. M., & Yeatman, J. D. (2012). Learning to see words. *Annual Review of Psychology*, *63*, 31–53. https://doi.org/10.1146/annurev-psych-120710-100434.

Wang, F., & Maurer, U. (2017). Top-down modulation of early print-tuned neural activity in reading. *Neuropsychologia*, *102*, 29–38.

Wong, A. C.-N., Gautheir, I., Woroch, B., DeBuse, C., & Curran, T. (2005). An early electrophysiological response associated with expertise in letter perception. *Cognitive, Affective, & Behavioral Neuroscience*, *5*(3), 306–318.

Xue, G., Jiang, T., Chen, C., & Dong, Q. (2008). Language experience shapes early electrophysiological responses to visual stimuli: The effects of writing system, stimulus length, and presentation duration. *NeuroImage*, *39*, 2025–2037.

Yoncheva, Y. N., Blau, V. C., Maurer, U., & McCandliss, B. D. (2010). Attentional focus during learning impacts N170 ERP responses to an artificial script. *Developmental Neuropsychology*, *35*(4), 423–445.

Yum, Y., Grainger, J., Midgley, K. J., & Holcomb, P. J. (2014). An ERP study on initial second language vocabulary learning. *Psychophysiology*, *51*, 364–373.

Yum, Y., Holcomb, P. J., & Grainger, J. (2011). Words and pictures: An electrophysiological investigation of domain specific processing in native Chinese and English speakers. *Neuropsychologia*, *49*, 1910–1922.

Zhang, M., Jiang, T., Mei, L., Yang, H., Chen, C., Xue, G., & Dong, Q. (2011). It's a word: Early electrophysiological response to the character likeness of pictographs. *Psychophysiology*, *48*, 950–959.

Zhao, J., Li, S., Lin, S.-E., Cao, X.-H., He, S., & Weng, X.-C. (2012). Selectivity of N170 in the left hemisphere as an electrophysiological marker for expertise in reading Chinese. *Neuroscience Bulletin*, *28*(5), 577–584.

Ziegler, J. C., & Goswami, U. (2005). Reading acquisition, developmental dyslexia, and skilled reading across languages: A psycholinguistic grain size theory. *Psychological Bulletin*, *131*(1), 3–29.

Zou, L., Abutalebi, J., Zinszer, B., Yan, X., Shu, H., Peng, D., & Ding, G. (2012). Second language experience modulates functional brain network for the native language production in bimodal bilinguals. *NeuroImage*, *62*, 1367–1375.

6

READING IN DEAF INDIVIDUALS

Examining the role of visual word form area

Elizabeth A. Hirshorn, Matthew W.G. Dye,
Peter C. Hauser, Ted Supalla, and Daphné Bavelier

The goal of reading is arguably to comprehend text. However, reading comprehension ultimately relies on successful word identification. Thus, the cognitive and neural underpinnings of successful word identification have been the focus of a large portion of the literature on reading. Typically, word identification occurs when the phonological and semantic representations of a word are accessed in response to seeing a visual word form. Across the board, speech-based phonological awareness, or the metalinguistic knowledge that spoken language is made of sound units, such as phonemes, that can be combined to make new sounds, is one of the main predictors of present and future reading skills in alphabetic writing systems (Mann, 1993; McCardle et al., 2001). Furthermore, deficits in speech-based phonological awareness are thought to be a cause of reading problems (Snowling, 1981; Wagner & Torgesen, 1987). It also makes intuitive sense that phonological awareness would be related to reading skills because, no matter how a written system is organized, reading involves decoding a visual representation of a spoken language. Thus, single-word reading, with an emphasis on phonological decoding, continues to be an important area of investigation.

Reading and deafness

One general assumption of reading research and models is that people know and speak the language that they are going to learn to read, including being familiar with the sounds and grammar of the written language. However, in the case of profoundly deaf individuals, many aspects of the learning problem that are often taken for granted are not applicable. Depending on the specific background of a profoundly deaf individual, one or both of those assumptions could be false. For example, a subset of profoundly deaf individuals, deaf native signers, have

DOI: 10.4324/9780429342356-11

little-to-no experience speaking or reading lips (i.e., don't use spoken language), whereas oral deaf largely rely on spoken language for receptive (lipreading) and productive language (speaking). These differences in language background are likely to impact the cognitive challenges posed by learning to read and the kind of information that will be useful to solve such challenges. The current chapter examines what it means to be a skilled deaf reader and what neural markers are linked with successful reading as language backgrounds vary.

Despite clear differences between deaf and hearing readers, or even within the deaf population, much of the literature on deafness and reading – and the focus on deaf education – has been based on a hearing model of reading, with a focus on speech-based phonological awareness (Hanson & Fowler, 1987; Harris & Beech, 1998; Perfetti & Sandak, 2000). Some have challenged the approach of studying reading in deaf individuals from a "hearing framework." Rather, these authors have argued for a more careful examination of the reading processes within primarily homogenous sub-populations of deaf individuals, such as native signers of American Sign Language (ASL) or orally trained deaf. In doing so, they have uncovered evidence that deaf native signing individuals do not necessarily use speech-based phonological information when reading words or comprehending text (Bélanger et al., 2012a, 2013). Notably, some deaf native signers can achieve high reading comprehension levels with little access to the phonology of English (Bélanger et al., 2012a; Chamberlain & Mayberry, 2000; Hirshorn et al., 2015; Koo et al., 2008). The study of deaf native signers, therefore, affords a unique perspective on word identification and its neural substrates.

Neural correlates of word reading

A left ventral occipito-temporal area, often termed the visual word form area (VWFA), has received significant attention as a neural correlate of literacy (Dehaene et al., 2002; McCandliss & Noble, 2003; van der Mark et al., 2009). As perceptual expertise for words increases and literacy improves during development, the VWFA starts to respond selectively to a written text compared to visual control stimuli (Binder et al., 2006; Vinckier et al., 2007). Interestingly, this selectivity can be induced by training later in life, as shown in late-literates taught to read in adulthood (Dehaene et al., 2010). It is important to highlight that the VWFA is defined functionally, rather than anatomically, and there is considerable variability in how it is defined in the literature. Factors that vary include characteristics of the words, how they are presented, the control stimulus, the task used for word and/or control stimulus, using group versus individual statistics, and the statistical methods used (univariate versus multivariate; Carlos et al., 2019). These all have consequences in precisely which voxels are examined. While acknowledging that the VWFA is part of a larger network and is not exclusively specialized for words or even visual stimuli (Devlin et al., 2006; Price & Devlin, 2003; Striem-Amit et al., 2012), the data discussed here focuses on the consistent link between activity in that occipito-temporal cortex region and overall reading skill in the extant literature.

Although the role of the VWFA in skilled reading cannot be denied, there is debate as to the sources of its functional selectivity. The recruitment of the VWFA during reading may be driven by the systematic mapping of orthography to spoken language phonology (Blomert, 2011; Dietz et al., 2005; Yoncheva et al., 2010) that most readers are trained to perform. The recruitment of the VWFA during reading may also reflect surface visual familiarity with print (Dehaene et al., 2002, 2004; Gaillard et al., 2006). Whether driven by orthographic-to-phonological decoding or print-to-meaning, selectivity in the VWFA has become a marker for skilled reading. It is well documented that less-skilled readers with poor word identification tend to have underactivation or less selectivity for words in the VWFA (Monzalvo et al., 2012; Richlan et al., 2009; Shaywitz et al., 2004; van der Mark et al., 2009, 2011). Because less-skilled readers are likely to have deficits in phonological processing, it is difficult to disentangle the two competing hypotheses in hearing individuals.

Neural correlates of reading in deaf readers

The present work follows the pioneering work of Helen Neville in investigating the impact of altered language experience on reading processes, answering not only basic questions about the plasticity of the brain structures mediating reading but also pushing our understanding of the fundamental principles of brain organization. Examining deaf readers offers a unique opportunity to understand the relative contribution of orthographic familiarity and spoken phonological skill in the underlying patterns of VWFA selectivity. To our knowledge, only eight published studies have reported on the neural correlates of reading [using functional MRI (fMRI)] at the word level in deaf individuals (Aparicio et al., 2007; Corina et al., 2013; Emmorey et al., 2013, 2015, 2016; Glezer et al., 2018; Wang e al., 2014; Waters et al., 2007). The studies varied in task (e.g., semantic, phonological, low-level vision, adaptation), written language (e.g., English, French), linguistic background of deaf populations (e.g., deaf native signers or more heterogeneous deaf population), and whether they compared to hearing controls or deaf individuals with different reading skill. Additionally, there was variability in whether the VWFA location was defined functionally (e.g., words versus false font, words versus fixation, etc.) or anatomically (see Table 6.1).

Overall, these studies found VWFA activation and location to be largely similar in deaf and hearing individuals. In hearing readers, the location, especially in the left hemisphere, is at least partially attributed to connections with the speech-based language system that tends to be left-lateralized (Canário et al., 2020; Gerrits et al., 2019). Evidence comes from the VWFA being modulated by auditory speech processing (Yoncheva et al., 2010), phonological processing (Zhao et al., 2017), and irregular VWFA activity in less-skilled

TABLE 6.1 Summary of fMRI studies of deaf readers and VWFA

First author	Year	Deaf linguistic background	Hearing control group	Written language	Experimental task	Control task/stimulus	VWFA definition
Waters	2007	Deaf native British Sign Language (BSL) signers	x	English	Semantic categorization	Visual target detection	Anatomical based on prior research
Aparicio	2007	Mixed language background (signing, oral, cued speech)	x	French	Visual lexical decision; rhyming judgment	"Identical Strings" Judgment	Anatomical based on prior research
Corina	2013	Deaf ASL signers (17/21 native signers)		English	Word visual detection	Falsefont: visual decision	Words versus falsefont
Wang	2014	Deaf signers (3/15 native signers)	x	Chinese	Passive viewing	Phase-scrambled Chinese characters	Chinese characters versus phase-scrambled characters
Emmorey	2013	Deaf ASL Signers (12/14 native signers)	x	English	Semantic judgment; phonological task	Falsefont: visual decision	Experimental task versus falsefont task
Emmorey	2015	Deaf ASL Signers (21/28 native signers)	x	English	Semantic Categorization	Falsefont: Visual Decision	Experimental task versus falsefont task
Emmorey	2016	Deaf ASL Signers (21/28 native signers)		English	Semantic decision; phonological decision	Falsefont: visual decision	Experimental task versus falsefont task
Glezer	2018	Deaf ASL signers	x	English	Adaptation paradigm: word matching, word rhyming, word meaning	Different control stimuli	Word matching/word meaning/word rhyming versus fixation

readers with phonological deficits (Van der Mark et al., 2009). However, there were no neural differences based on reading skills in a phonological task among deaf native signers (Emmorey et al., 2016). Furthermore, Glezer and colleagues (2018) reported that skilled deaf readers showed adaptation in the VWFA that was sensitive to orthographic similarity but showed no adaptation for homophones, with identical phonology, suggesting that the VWFA is not coding for phonological representations in this group. Rather, Emmorey and colleagues (2016) found that activation in several regions, including one just anterior to the VWFA, was modulated by reading skills in a semantic task among deaf native signers. The VWFA in deaf readers may therefore be more responsive to the whole-word orthographic structure of the written word rather than the phonological structure. This aligns with the behavioral findings that phonological skill plays a less central role in reading in deaf readers (Bélanger et al., 2012; Hirshorn et al., 2015).

The study presented in this chapter addresses these hypotheses, by both explicitly examining the role of speech-based phonological skill in VWFA (and more broadly occipito-temporal regions), and by taking advantage of diversity in language experience and levels of hearing loss across different sub-populations of deaf readers. Lastly, its design mirrors that of the original studies identifying the VWFA (Cohen et al., 2002) in order to establish a baseline for comparison.

Current study

The current study focuses on academically successful deaf readers and evaluates the contribution of speech-based phonological knowledge to VWFA selectivity. To this end, three groups with similar levels of reading comprehension and graded levels of speech-based knowledge were compared: deaf native signers, hearing individuals, and oral deaf individuals who acquired knowledge of spoken English through experience speaking and lipreading, and thus exhibited greater speech-based phonological knowledge than deaf signers (Cardin et al., 2013; Hirshorn et al., 2014; Koo et al., 2008). All deaf participants experienced severe-to-profound deafness before the age of two and had early access to a natural language – a factor known to impact reading skills (Chamberlain & Mayberry, 2000). By comparing groups with different experiences, this work leverages naturally occurring variability to ask how fundamental speech-based phonological processing may be in VWFA selectivity. At the same time, it also provides invaluable information about the neural processes that may mediate literacy achievement in the presence of altered speech-based phonological processing. As illustrated by Helen Neville's commitment to education, this approach opens doors to translational work such as ways to better assist poor readers, whether because of deafness or dyslexia – a goal we should all strive toward.

To the extent that the VWFA selectivity (alphabetic stimuli versus visual control/checkerboards) is a result of mapping orthographic patterns to meanings, we would expect all three populations to exhibit the same level of VWFA selectivity, owing to their similar reading level. However, if VWFA selectivity critically depends on phonological processes, deaf native signers were expected to exhibit less VWFA selectivity than hearing controls, owing to their (expected) lower phonological skills. We further predicted that VWFA selectivity in oral deaf people would fall in between that of hearing and of deaf native signers because their phonological skills were expected to be weaker than hearing individuals, but stronger than deaf native signers (Emmorey et al., 2016). Importantly, speech-based phonological knowledge was assessed by tasks specifically developed for deaf participants that distinguished between shallow phonological knowledge that can be inferred from orthographic regularities, and deep phonological knowledge that requires mastering inconsistent grapheme-to-phoneme mapping (Hirshorn et al., 2015).

Method

Participants

The study included 17 profoundly deaf native signers of ASL [M_{age} = 22 (18–32); 11 female; $M_{unaided\ PTA\ loss\ in\ better\ ear}$ = 91 dB (70–105)], 11 oral profoundly deaf people [M_{age} = 22 (18–24); 3 female; $M_{unaided\ PTA\ loss\ in\ better\ ear}$ = 83 dB, (63–98)], and 18 hearing controls [M_{age} = 24 (18–33); 10 female] recruited from the local community in Rochester, NY. All deaf participants were attending the Rochester Institute of Technology. Inclusion criteria for all deaf participants were: unaided hearing loss of 75 dB or greater in the better ear,[1] and the onset of deafness before 2 years of age.[2] Specific inclusion criteria for deaf native signers included: being born to deaf parents, being exposed to ASL from infancy, and having little oral English skill (see English Fluency). In contrast, specific inclusion criteria for oral deaf subjects included: being born to hearing parents, being educated in mainstream schools that adopted oral-aural approaches that promoted spoken language ability, minimal or absent ASL skills with no exposure to ASL until their college years (see ASL Fluency), using oral communication as the primary mode of communication, and relying on lipreading to comprehend spoken English. Four deaf native signers reported using hearing aids for environmental sounds and all oral deaf participants reported using hearing aids for both environmental sounds and aiding speech perception. No participants wore cochlear implants. Hearing participants were recruited to have no more than a high school diploma in an effort to have a larger range of reading skills. All participants were right-handed. All participants were treated in accordance with the University of Rochester's Research Subjects Review Board guidelines and were paid for their participation in the study.

Behavioral assessments materials and procedures

Non-verbal IQ

The TONI-3 (Brown et al., 1997) was used as a test of non-verbal intelligence.

Native language fluency

The Speaking Grammar Sub-test of the Test of Adolescent Language (TOAL-3; Hammill et al., 1994) was used as a test of English Fluency. The American Sign Language Sentence Recall Test (ASL-SRT) was modeled after the TOAL-3 and was used as a test of ASL Fluency (Hauser et al., 2008).

Reading comprehension

The Peabody Individual Achievement Test (PIAT-R; Markwardt, 1998) was used as our measure of English reading comprehension, as it is well-suited to assess reading skills in deaf populations (Allen & Morere, 2012).

Speech-based phonological tasks

To measure knowledge of speech-based phonology in profoundly deaf partici-pants required developing "deaf-friendly" phonological skill tasks that do not require overt verbal responses (McQuarrie & Parrila, 2009). Picture-based pho-nological tasks (Hirshorn, 2011; Hirshorn et al., 2015) assessed knowledge of the orthographic-to-phonological regularities of English (*shallow phonological condition*) and knowledge of phonology when spelling-to-sound correspondences are challeng-ing due to, for example, small featural differences (/ch/ in **ch**ef versus **ch**air – *deep phonological condition*). For instance, in an "odd one out" paradigm focusing on word onsets, participants saw three pictures and had to decide which one had a different initial sound. A triad of pictures in the shallow phonological condition was "bed, doll, and door," where the task could be answered based on spelling alone. A triad of pictures in the deep phonological condition was "chef, cheese, chicken," where the spelling does not aid in finding the correct response (Hirshorn et al., 2015).

fMRI VWFA experiment

Data collection

See Hirshorn and colleagues (2014).

fMRI task stimuli

The stimuli were modeled after those of Cohen and colleagues (2002) using an equal number of words, consonant letter strings, and checker stimuli. Words (nouns) were chosen to be in a defined frequency range (mean CELEX frequency= 489; range: 200–900), highly concrete, familiar, and imageable based upon the MRC database measures (www.psych.rl.ac.uk/MRC_Psych_Db.html). Frequency was chosen to be neither very low nor very high, to avoid potential frequency effects observed in the literature (Kronbichler et al., 2004). Words were 4–6 letters and 1 or 2 syllables long. Twenty-five percent of all stimuli were animal names. Consonant letter strings were created to follow the same global form as the words (e.g., milk changed to nctf). Checkerboards consisted of an array of 12 × 4 horizontally elongated black and white squares chosen to approximate the spatial extent of the alphabetic stimuli.

fMRI task design

Participants viewed stimuli one at a time and were instructed to press a response button whenever the stimuli correspond to an animal name, to encourage full word identification. Animal trials were not analyzed. Each stimulus was presented for 500 ms. Stimuli were presented in an event-related design in four runs (7 min each) with a jittered presentation order and variable interstimulus interval (ranging from 0 to 20) determined by optseq2 (http://surfer.nmr.mgh.harvard.edu/optseq/).

fMRI processing and analysis

Data were collected on a Siemens Trio 3T scanner. Data were processed and analyzed using AFNI. Preprocessing steps included slice time and movement correction, and spatial smoothing. Statistics were performed using AFNi's 3dDeconvolve and 3dANOVA2. Structural and functional normalization to standard space was completed using @auto_tlrc and adwarp functions. See Hirshorn et al., 2014 for further details.

Defining region of interests (ROIs)

Left and right VWFA were defined in a combined analysis examining the contrast between alphabetic (words and consonants) and fixation baseline, as in other works (Mechelli et al., 2003; Reinke et al., 2008). This was done to eliminate possible biases based on control tasks in how the area was defined since we were interested in the selectivity itself. Note that this ROI definition was chosen after checking that there was no significant shift in the location of the fusiform activation in each of the deaf groups as compared to the hearing one, justifying the use of a common area. The analysis was therefore performed with all subjects from all groups (using AFNI's 3dANOVA2). The significance threshold was raised until circumscribed areas within the fusiform gyrus (not contiguous with the rest of the occipital cortex) were distinguishable ($t = 8.39$ for left and $t = 7.09$ for right). The defined ROIs had peak voxel and boundaries that fell within where the literature typically places the VWFA (left peak: −37, −51, −14; right peak: 39, −54, −17). After resampling to be in the same functional space (using AFNI's 3dresample), each ROI contained 34 and 35 voxels (2176 and 2240 mm^3), respectively, for left and right VWFA.

Previous work highlights the idea that there is a functional gradient within the occipito-temporal cortex with posterior regions more likely to be tuned to basic visual features and anterior regions (such as the VWFA) to orthographic regularities as stimuli become more "word-like" (Binder et al., 2006; Vinckier et al., 2007). Accordingly, we identified a posterior "checker" area that was similarly responsive to checkerboards in all groups as a posterior boundary for investigation, with three additional equally spaced ROIs moving forward (Vinckier et al., 2007). A similar method was employed with the left and right VWFA to define peak checker activation, relative to fixation, within the inferior temporal cortex in all groups. A combined analysis for all subjects (checker versus fixation) revealed a peak area outside of the visual cortex in the left fusiform gyrus at −23, −69, and −13. A 6 mm radius spherical ROI was created at the peak and moved by 9 mm steps anterior and 8 mm lateral toward and past the VWFA along the fusiform gyrus. A total of four ROIs were created (Figure 6.3a). Checker activation across groups was examined in peak checker activation (checkered circle; −23, −69, and −13), in an ROI in between the peak checker activation and peak VWFA (−31, −60, and −13), in the peak VWFA (star; −39, −51, and −14) and in a more anterior portion of the VWFA (−47, −42, and −14). The slope of the decline in checker activation from the four equally spaced ROIs (posterior checker ROI to the anterior VWFA ROI) was calculated from the linear regression for each subject by plotting the checker activation beta coefficients versus the ROI locations (1–4; Figure 6.3b) (Hirshorn et al., 2015).

Statistical analyses for group comparison

Individual subjects' mean beta coefficients were extracted using AFNI's 3dmaskave from each of the four ROIs separately for words, consonant strings, and checkerboards, each relative to the baseline periods in between word presentations, and used for offline statistical analyses.

Results

Behavioral

Although we attempted to match the deaf groups for unaided dB loss, the deaf native signers, $M_{DeafNativeSigners}$ = 91.78 dB (SD ±9.12), had a greater hearing loss as a group than oral deaf, $M_{OralDeaf}$ = 82.64 dB (±10.73), $t(26)$ = 2.42, d = 0.92, p = 0.023, although all participants did meet the standard criterion for

TABLE 6.2 Group comparisons in behavioral tasks

Test	Group	Mean	SD	F/t	p
Non-verbal IQ	Deaf native signers	99	10	1.15	0.33
	Oral deaf	99	11		
	Hearing	93	14		
English fluency	Deaf native signers	NA	NA	7.37	<0.001
	Oral deaf	0.34	0.14		
	Hearing	0.65	0.1		
ASL fluency	Deaf native signers	0.68	0.12	13.71	<0.001
	Oral deaf	0.02	0.04		
	Hearing	NA	NA		
Reading Comprehension	Deaf native signers	6.71	3.35	0.73	0.49
	Oral deaf	7.44	2.55		
	Hearing	8.91	2.85		
Shallow Phonological Task	Deaf native signers	0.82	0.15	5.15	<0.001
	Oral deaf	0.89	0.12		
	Hearing	0.95	0.08		
Deep Phonological Task	Deaf native signers	0.39	0.11	64.8	<0.001
	Oral deaf	0.78	0.13		
	Hearing	0.88	0.13		

Notes: Deaf native signers were on the floor in the English fluency task and hearing individuals were on the floor for the ASL fluency task and were therefore not included in those respective analyses

TABLE 6.3 Group performance on speech-based phonological tasks [mean accuracy (SD)]

	Hearing	Oral deaf	Deaf native signers
Shallow	0.95 (0.08)	0.89 (0.12)	0.82 (0.15)
Deep	0.88 (0.13)	0.78 (0.13)	0.39 (0.11)
Difference (*p*-value)	0.08	0.05	<0.001

"profoundly" deaf. We therefore controlled for hearing loss in the group behavioral analyses reported in Table 6.2.

Of note, in the phonological tasks, an additional two-way analysis of variance (ANOVA) with condition and groups revealed a significant main effect of the condition such that the deep phonological condition was harder than the shallow condition, $F(1,43) = 163.63$, MSE $= 0.006$, $p < 0.001$, and a main effect of group, $F(2,43) = 33.91$, MSE $= 0.026$, $p < 0.001$ (see Table 6.2), as well as a significant interaction between group and condition, $F(2,43) = 54.23$, MSE $= 0.026$, $p < 0.001$. As Table 6.3 shows, this effect was driven by a greater decline in performance from the shallow to the deep phonological condition in deaf native signers, followed by oral deaf, and then hearing individuals. This pattern confirms the greater sensitivity of the deep phonological condition to speech-based phonological knowledge.

fMRI

Participants from all three groups performed equally well and near ceiling on the semantic judgment task, $F(2,43)$ = 0.02, MSE = 0.004, p = 0.99; $M_{Hearing}$ = 0.96 ($\pm$0.08); $M_{OralDeaf}$ = 0.97 ($\pm$0.05); $M_{DeafNativeSigners}$ = 0.96 ($\pm$0.04).

In order to explore group differences, a 2 × 3 (Stimulus Type: alphabetic versus checkerboard; Group: hearing versus oral deaf versus deaf native signers) ANOVA was conducted in the left VWFA[3] (Figure 6.1a). There was a main effect of stimulus, $F(1,43)$ = 8.27, η^2 = .16, p = 0.006, such that alphabetic stimuli had higher levels of activation than checkerboard (Figure 6.1b). There was also a main effect of group, $F(2,43)$ = 3.67, η^2 = 0.15, p = 0.034. Post hoc comparisons using the Tukey honest significant difference (HSD) test indicated that deaf native signers had significantly greater activation levels (M = 0.48, SD = 0.27) overall compared to hearing individuals (M = 0.28, SD = 0.26; p = 0.036), and oral deaf (M = 0.26, SD = 0.34) were not significantly different from hearing (p = 0.94) or deaf native signers (p = 0.15). There was a marginally significant interaction [$F(2,43)$ = 2.88, η^2 = 0.12, p = 0.067], suggesting that the size of the stimulus effect (alphabetic versus checkerboard) was marginally modulated by the group.

To follow up on the source of the marginal interaction in the left VWFA, the hallmark selectivity in the VWFA for alphabetic stimuli (words and consonants) compared to control checkerboard stimuli was replicated in hearing participants, [$t(17)$ = 2.95, d = 1.43, p < 0.005], but it was surprisingly absent in deaf native signers, [$t(16)$ = 0.05, d = 0.025, p = 0.48], despite comparable levels of reading comprehension (PIAT; Figure 6.1c). The hearing and deaf native signers' VWFA selectivity were significantly different [$t(33)$ = 2.24, d = 0.81, p = 0.032]. There was no significant selectivity in oral deaf [$t(10)$ = 1.01, d = 0.25, p = 0.34] but they did not differ from either hearing, $t(27)$ = 1.19, d = 0.46, p = 0.24, or

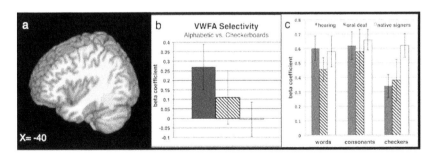

FIGURE 6.1 Recruitment of the VWFA as a function of population and condition. (a) A left VWFA was defined across groups (2176 mm³; peak: −37, −51, and −14). (b) Selectivity in the left VWFA, across all groups (alphabetic stimuli versus checkerboards). (c) Left VWFA activation patterns for word, consonant, and checker stimuli, using fixation as the baseline, in each of the three populations studied. Error bars represent ±1 SEM.

deaf native signers, $t(26) = 0.83$, $d = 0.32$, $p = 0.42$, suggesting an intermediate pattern.

As an additional follow-up in the left VWFA, two exploratory one-way ANO-VAs were run. A one-way ANOVA examining just alphabetic stimuli found no effect of group, $F(2,43) = 0.74$, $p = 0.48$. This result replicates previous research showing no group differences in VWFA activation between deaf native signers and hearing individuals when comparing words versus a fixation baseline (Wang et al., 2014; Waters et al., 2007). However, a one-way ANOVA examining checkerboard stimuli did find a significant effect of group, $F(2,43) = 3.10$, $p = 0.05$. Post hoc comparisons using the Tukey HSD test indicated that the mean hearing activation for checker (M = 0.39, SD = 0.41) was less than that of deaf native signers (M = 0.75, SD = 0.40; $p = 0.05$). The oral deaf did not differ from either group (M = 0.47, SD = 0.51; $p = 0.88$ and $p = 0.24$ versus hearing and deaf native signers, respectively).

This differential recruitment for checkerboards explains the differences in VWFA selectivity across groups shown in Figure 6.1c, where checkerboards were used as the comparison condition. Furthermore, we confirmed this pattern of greater visual control activation in deaf native signers compared to hearing individuals in a second experiment that included a subset of the same participants, in which false fonts were used as the visual control (Hirshorn et al., 2014). Deaf native signers had significantly greater false font activation compared to fixation than hearing controls, $t(30) = 2.60$, $d = 0.92$, $p = 0.014$, whereas there were no group differences during the main reading task, sentence processing, $t(30) = 1.39$, $d = 0.49$, $p = 0.17$.

We next assessed whether there were group differences in the word selectivity within a functional gradient in the occipito-temporal cortex (Binder et al., 2006; Vinckier et al., 2007). Moving from the checker peak anteriorly along the occipito-temporal cortex, we replicated the increase in the magnitude of the activation difference between words and checkers in hearing individuals (Vinckier et al., 2007), but observed a less pronounced decline in the oral deaf, and little-to-no decline in deaf native signers (Figure 6.2). In order to quantitatively assess this pattern, we conducted a 2 × 3 (stimulus type: word versus checkerboard; group: hearing versus oral deaf versus deaf native signers) ANOVA using the posterior to anterior slope of activation as the dependent variable. There was a main effect of stimulus type, $F(1,43) = 36.27$, $\eta^2 = 0.46$, $p < 0.001$, such that checkerboard stimuli had a larger negative slope from posterior to anterior ROIs than word stimuli. There was no main effect of group, $F(2,43) = 0.82$, $\eta^2 = 0.037$, $p = 0.45$. There was a significant interaction, $F(2,43) = 3.99$, $\eta^2 = 0.16$, $p = 0.026$, suggesting that difference in slopes for word versus checkerboard stimuli was modulated by the group.

One question remained: what might be driving the group differences in activation along the occipito-temporal cortex? First, a forward stepwise regression was performed including all subjects, with the slope of the change in checkerboard versus fixation differences along the occipital ROI gradient as the dependent measure, and predictors of reading comprehension, the shallow and deep phonological measures, and non-verbal IQ, first removing any variance due to unaided

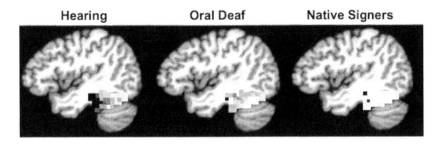

FIGURE 6.2 Checker activation relative to words mapped along the left ventral occipito-temporal cortex in each group. The relative activation of checkerboards compared to words (checkerboard activation/word activation) was different across groups (words = checkerboard, white; words > checkerboards, black).

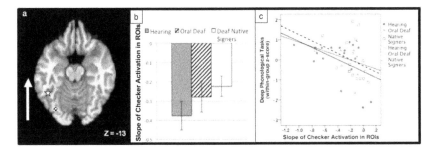

FIGURE 6.3 Analysis of checker activation along a posterior–anterior axis in the inferior temporal gyrus. (a) The four locations at which checker activation was measured (from the posterior checker peak ROI to anterior locations including the left VWFA peak indicated by a star; see Methods section for ROI definition) to compute the slope of the checker activation decline. (b) The mean slopes for checker activation from the checker peak to the most anterior ROI for each group. Error bars represent ±1 SEM. (c) Performance on the deep phonological condition (zero-meaned within each population) versus the slope of the decline in checker activation along posterior to anterior ROIs for all three groups.

hearing losses (dB loss, pure tone average). Unaided hearing loss accounted for a marginally significant amount of variance [$R^2 = 0.07$, $F(1,44) = 3.54$, $p = 0.07$]. However, the remaining variance in the decrease of the checker slope along the occipito-temporal cortex was best predicted by deep phonological skills, [$R^2_{change} = 0.17$, $F_{change}(2,43) = 9.36$, $p = 0.004$], such that better performance on the deep phonological condition resulted in a larger decrease in checker activation from the posterior to the anterior occipito-temporal cortex (Figure 6.3c). No other predictors reached significance and the equivalent analysis with the slope of alphabetic versus fixation differences along the occipital ROI gradient did not yield any significant predictors.

Lastly, we also examined the predictors of the slope of checkerboard activation along the occipital ROI gradient separately within each group. A significant negative correlation between deep phonological knowledge and the slope of checker activation was observed in hearing subjects [$r(16) = -0.49$, $p = 0.04$; Figure 6.3c] such that the greater the phonological knowledge, the steeper the decline in activation to checker in the occipito-temporal cortex. The relationship between the slope of checkerboard activation along the occipito-temporal cortex and phonological knowledge was also negative in oral deaf individuals and deaf native signers, possibly pointing to a similar functional link; these relationships were, however, not statistically significant [oral deaf $r(9) = -0.20$, $p = 0.55$; deaf native signers $r(15) = -0.39$, $p = 0.12$].

Discussion

This work provides new insights into those aspects of literacy that refine VWFA selectivity, by examining skilled readers with varying levels of speech-based phonological knowledge: deaf native signers, oral deaf, and hearing individuals. The current study provides a striking example of individuals with low speech-based phonological knowledge – deaf native signers – who show an atypical VWFA neural profile with a lack of selectivity for words due to a lack of activation reduction for visual control stimuli, despite being matched with hearing controls on reading comprehension. The second contribution of this work is to highlight the relationship between speech-based phonological knowledge and the reduction of responses to visual control stimuli along a posterior to anterior gradient in the occipito-temporal cortex.

Phonologically decoding and extracting meaning from print are two processes that are tightly intertwined in hearing readers and thus are difficult to distinguish (Shankweiler, 1989; Snowling, 1998). Here, we provide an example of a lack of VWFA selectivity in deaf native signers, in whom speech-based phonological knowledge was dissociated from meaning extraction. Indeed, despite low skill levels on speech-based phonological tests, deaf native signers had similar reading comprehension scores to hearing individuals. While we replicated the existing literature concerning hearing readers, the novel finding is the lack of VWFA selectivity for alphabetic stimuli compared to checkerboards in deaf native signers. This result diverges significantly from the widely held beliefs that VWFA selectivity is necessary for skilled reading, or vice versa, based on the reports of atypical VWFA activation in dyslexic readers (Shaywitz et al., 2002; van der Mark et al., 2009) and that damage to the VWFA typically leads to acquired alexia (Gaillard et al., 2006; Kleinschmidt & Cohen, 2006). A note of caution is warranted as VWFA selectivity in deaf native signers does not always differ from that of hearing, as we documented here. Because the current study differed in multiple ways from past studies (see Table 6.1; e.g., checkerboard versus false font visual controls), the source for such discrepancy remains unclear. Although the locations of the VWFA ROIs across studies were similar, a recent finding suggests that there are structural and functionally distinct regions sensitive to lexical/semantic distinction (e.g., real word > pseudoword) more anteriorly and perceptual distinction more posteriorly (e.g., real words versus checkerboards) (Vinckier et al., 2007). It remains possible that the different studies were sampling functionally distinct regions.

The second main contribution comes from identifying the visual control stimuli as the source of the group differences in VWFA selectivity. The lack of VWFA selectivity in deaf native signers was not due to low VWFA recruitment by alphabetic stimuli, but rather strong recruitment of the same patch of cortex by visual control stimuli. Deaf native signers showed a little-to-no reduction in checkerboard activation along the occipito-temporal cortex, whereas hearing subjects exhibited the steepest reduction, with oral deaf falling in-between. Interestingly for future work, the level of response reduction across all three groups correlated best with a measure of deep phonological knowledge, suggesting a potential role for phonological knowledge in shaping VWFA selectivity, at least more anteriorly.

As speech-based phonological knowledge and hearing levels are tightly coupled, one could argue the present results were driven by auditory deprivation, per se, rather than phonological knowledge. We acknowledge that the oral deaf group cannot unambiguously settle this issue, as their hearing loss was significantly less severe than that of deaf signers and they more consistently used hearing aids. This was the case despite taking special care to include in this study only a very select sub-population of oral deaf individuals. Although the results in oral deaf cannot unambiguously distinguish the contribution of phonological knowledge from that of hearing level, several other results support the role of phonological knowledge. Past research suggests that the acquisition of speech-based knowledge in deaf individuals is significantly affected by exposure and usage of an oral language, independent of hearing loss levels (Harris & Beech, 1998; Koo et al., 2008). Accordingly, speech-based phonological knowledge explained a share of the variance in response to visual control stimuli across the occipito-temporal cortex, above and beyond hearing loss levels. Additionally, a strong VWFA response to visual control stimuli was seen only in deaf native signers, whose speech-based phonological skills are typically weakly coupled to reading comprehension (Bélanger et al., 2012a; Hirshorn et al., 2015; Koo et al., 2008). Finally – and most telling – within the hearing population, deep phonological knowledge was the best predictor of decreased visual control activation along the occipito-temporal cortex, showing explanatory power without any potential confounding from auditory deprivation.

Auditory deprivation has been linked to enhanced para-foveal attention during the processing of visual scenes as well as during reading (Bavelier et al., 2006; Bélanger et al., 2012b, 2013; Dye et al., 2009). This raises the possibility that group differences in attention may be at the source of the effects described here.

However, such enhanced attention would be expected to apply to stimuli presented in the para-fovea, not to the center of the visual field as in the present study (Neville & Lawson, 1987; Proksch & Bavelier, 2002).

The present study highlights for the first time not only a case where VWFA activation for visual control stimuli was as high as for print in literate individuals (Dong et al., 2020; Lerma-Usabiaga et al., 2018) but also a key role for speech-based phonological knowledge in shaping the VWFA selectivity, specifically through suppression of activation by non-word-like visual stimuli. Previous studies document how functional selectivity in visual cortical regions, not only for objects such as words but also faces or places, arises during development through both strengthening of the preferred stimulus category *and* decreased sensitivity to non-preferred stimuli (Cantlon et al., 2011). Yet, it remains largely unknown whether these two processes, enhancement and suppression, are the result of different and separable functional constraints. The present work points to a unique role for phonological knowledge in the suppression of activation for non-word visual stimuli in the VWFA. The importance of suppressing non-preferred stimuli in the genesis of VWFA specificity finds support in the report of less activity in response to visual control stimuli compared to words in the VWFA of late-literates, who had recently learned to map print to their spoken language, as compared to illiterate individuals (Dehaene et al., 2010). Dehaene and colleagues further hypothesized that the acquisition of literacy pushes other visual categories (such as checkerboards, faces, or places) away from a reproducible swatch of cortex lateral to the fusiform face area, allowing for the emergence of an area more sensitive to alphabetic stimuli, such as the VWFA.

The present results are in line with this hypothesis and suggest that enhancement for the preferred category alone, in this case alphabetic print, does not necessarily push away non-preferred categories. Rather, enhancement and suppression may be functionally distinct, each being guided by different processing demands. In the case of the VWFA, visual reading experience and reading for meaning may result in enhanced responses to alphabetic-like stimuli, whereas learning to map phonological units to orthographic ones may push away non-preferred categories along the occipito-temporal cortex. This proposal is in line with greater sensitivity along the inferior temporal cortex for more and more complex local analyses of orthographic statistical dependencies (Binder et al., 2006; Dong et al., 2020; Lerma-Usabiaga et al., 2018; Vinckier et al., 2007). Lastly, the proposed link between phonological skills and VWFA selectivity is in line with the importance of letter-to-sound correspondence skills in driving VWFA activation during development (Brem et al., 2010).

The overall pattern of results reported here complements that observed in blind individuals reading Braille, who clearly transform tactile information into a phonological code. As Braille reading has been linked with inner speech (Gizewski et al., 2004), this suggests that VWFA functional selectivity is guided, at least in part, by mapping sensation – not only visual but also tactile or auditory – to speech-based information. Accordingly, blind individuals exhibit robust VWFA selectivity when comparing Braille reading to touching elevated dots that are not part of the Braille alphabet (Reich et al., 2011). Recent work has highlighted that blind individuals show VWFA selectivity for auditory "soundscapes," which are the result of a visual-to-auditory sensory substitution algorithm (Striem-Amit et al., 2012) that represented letters as compared to other object categories. This work illustrates an important role for the VWFA in linking letter shapes (independent of the modality) to their associated phonological content.

In summary, robust levels of reading comprehension can be achieved despite a lack of VWFA selectivity. Although this finding contrasts with the more accepted view that VWFA selectivity is necessary for skilled reading, it is in line with more recent refinement in the field. Both strengthening of the preferred stimulus category *and* decreased sensitivity to non-preferred stimuli shape functional specialization. The case of deaf native signers illustrates the importance of separately considering how neural networks along the occipito-temporal cortex may get recruited for alphabetic stimuli and how these same networks may become less sensitive to other forms of visual stimulation, and thus increase their selectivity through speech-based phonological knowledge. The case of deaf native signers also highlights an alternative route to skilled reading, holding promises not only for deaf readers but also hearing individuals who have specific deficits in phonological processing.

Acknowledgments

The authors would further like to thank sign language interpreters Patty Clark, Betsy Hicks McDonald, and Angela Hauser and the members of the Deaf Studies Lab at the National Technical Institute of Rochester for their help in making this research possible.

Notes

1 One deaf native signer had an unaided hearing loss of 70 dB and one oral deaf had an unaided hearing loss of 63 dB.
2 Two oral deaf became deaf at the age of 4 years.
3 Group differences in selectivity were specific to the left hemisphere in both the current and previous studies and were not observed in the right homolog of the VWFA. In the right VWFA, there was a main effect of group, $F(2,43)=3.51$, $h^2 = 0.14$, $p = 0.039$, such that overall levels of activation were higher in deaf native signers than the other groups, but there was no main effect of stimulus, $F(1,43) = 0.13$, $h^2 = 0.003$, $p = 0.72$. Furthermore, there was no significant interaction, $F(2,43) = 0.71$, $h^2 = 0.032$, $p = 0.50$, suggesting that there were no differences in selectivity in the three groups.

References

Allen, T., & Morere, D. A. (2012). Underlying neurocognitive and achievement factors and their relationship to student background characteristics. In T. Allen & D. A. Morere (Eds.), *Assessing literacy in deaf individuals* (pp. 231–261). New York: Springer.

Aparicio, M., Gounot, D., Demont, E., & Metz-Lutz, M. N. (2007). Phonological processing in relation to reading: An fMRI study in deaf readers. *Neuroimage, 35*(3), 1303–1316.

Bavelier, D., Dye, M., & Hauser, P. (2006). Do deaf individuals see better? *Trends in Cognitive Science, 10*(11), 512–518.

Bélanger, N. N., Baum, S. R., & Mayberry, R. I. (2012a). Reading difficulties in adult deaf readers of French: Phonological codes, not guilty! *Scientific Studies of Reading, 16*(3), 263–285.

Bélanger, N. N., Mayberry, R. I., & Rayner, K. (2013). Orthographic and phonological preview benefits: Parafoveal processing in skilled and less-skilled deaf readers. *Quarterly Journal of Experimental Psychology, 66*(11), 2237–2252.

Bélanger, N. N., Slattery, T. J., Mayberry, R. I., & Rayner, K. (2012b). Skilled deaf readers have an enhanced perceptual span in reading. *Psychological Science, 23*(7), 816–823.

Binder, J. R., Medler, D. A., Westbury, C. F., Liebenthal, E., & Buchanan, L. (2006). Tuning of the human left fusiform gyrus to sublexical orthographic structure. *Neuroimage, 33*(2), 739–748.

Blomert, L. (2011). The neural signature of orthographic – phonological binding in successful and failing reading development. *Neuroimage, 57*(3), 695–703.

Brem, S., Bach, S., Kucian, K., Kujala, J. V., Guttorm, T. K., Martin, E., Lyytinen, H., Brandeis, D., & Richardson, U. (2010). Brain sensitivity to print emerges when children learn letter-speech sound correspondences. *Proceedings of the National Academy of Sciences, 107*(17), 7939–7944.

Brown, L., Sherbenou, R. J., & Johnsen, S. K. (1997). *Manual for the test of nonverbal intelligence* (3rd ed.). Austin, TX: Pro-ED.

Canário, N., Jorge, L., & Castelo-Branco, M. (2020). Distinct mechanisms drive hemispheric lateralization of object recognition in the visual word form and fusiform face areas. *Brain and Language, 210,* 104860.

Cantlon, J. F., Pinel, P., Dehaene, S., & Pelphrey, K. A. (2011). Cortical representations of symbols, objects, and faces are pruned back during early childhood. *Cerebral Cortex, 21*(1), 191.

Cardin, V., Orfanidou, E., Rönnberg, J., Capek, C. M., Rudner, M., & Woll, B. (2013). Dissociating cognitive and sensory neural plasticity in human superior temporal cortex. *Nature Communications, 4,* 1473.

Carlos, B. J., Hirshorn, E. A., Durisko, C., Fiez, J. A., & Coutanche, M. N. (2019). Word inversion sensitivity as a marker of visual word form area lateralization: An application of a novel multivariate measure of laterality. *Neuroimage, 191,* 493–502.

Chamberlain, C., & Mayberry, R. I. (2000). Theorizing about the relation between American Sign Language and reading. In C. Chamberlain, J. P. Morford, & R. I. Mayberry (Eds.), *Language acquisition by eye* (pp. 221–259). Mahwah, NJ: Lawrence Erlbaum Associates.

Cohen, L., Lehèricy, S., Chochon, F., Lemer, C., Rivaud, S., & Dehaene, S. (2002). Language specific tuning of visual cortex? Functional properties of the Visual Word Form Area. *Brain, 125*(5), 1054.

Corina, D. P., Lawyer, L. A., Hauser, P., & Hirshorn, E. (2013). Lexical processing in deaf readers: An fMRI investigation of reading proficiency. *PloS One, 8*(1), 1–10.

Dehaene, S., Jobert, A., Naccache, L., Ciuciu, P., Poline, J.-B., Le Bihan, D., & Cohen, L. (2004). Letter binding and invariant recognition of masked words behavioral and neuroimaging evidence. *Psychological Science, 15*(5), 307–313.

Dehaene, S., Le Clec'H, G., Poline, J., Le Bihan, D., & Cohen, L. (2002). The visual word form area: A prelexical representation of visual words in the fusiform gyrus. *Neuroreport*, *13*(3), 321–325.

Dehaene, S., Pegado, F., Braga, L. W., & Ventura, P. (2010). How learning to read changes the cortical networks for vision and language. *Science*, *330*(6009), 1359.

Devlin, J. T., Jamison, H. L., Gonnerman, L. M., & Matthews, P. M. (2006). The role of the posterior fusiform gyrus in reading. *Journal of Cognitive Neuroscience*, *18*(6), 911–922.

Dietz, N. A. E., Jones, K. M., Gareau, L., Zeffiro, T. A., & Eden, G. F. (2005). Phonological decoding involves left posterior fusiform gyrus. *Human Brain Mapping*, *26*(2), 81–93.

Dong, J., Lu, C., Chen, C., Li, H., Liu, X., & Mei, L. (2020). Functional dissociations of the left anterior and posterior occipitotemporal cortex for semantic and non-semantic phonological access. *Neuroscience*, *430*, 94–104.

Dye, M. W. G., Hauser, P. C., & Bavelier, D. (2009). Is visual attention in deaf individuals enhances or deficient? The case of the useful field of view. *PloS One*, *4*(5).

Emmorey, K., McCullough, S., & Weisberg, J. (2015). Neural correlates of fingerspelling, text, and sign processing in deaf American Sign Language – English bilinguals. *Language, Cognition and Neuroscience*, *30*(6), 749–767.

Emmorey, K., McCullough, S., & Weisberg, J. (2016). The neural underpinnings of reading skill in deaf adults. *Brain and Language*, *160*, 11–20.

Emmorey, K., Weisberg, J., McCullough, S., & Petrich, J. A. F. (2013). Mapping the reading circuitry for skilled deaf readers: An fMRI study of semantic and phonological processing. *Brain and Language*, *126*, 169–180.

Gaillard, R., Naccache, L., Pinel, P., Clémenceau, S., Volle, E., Hasboun, D., Dupont, S., Baulac, M., Dehaene, S., Adam, C., & Cohen, L. (2006). Direct intracranial, FMRI, and lesion evidence for the causal role of left inferotemporal cortex in reading. *Neuron*, *50*(2), 191–204.

Gerrits, R., Van der Haegen, L., Brysbaert, M., & Vingerhoets, G. (2019). Laterality for recognizing written words and faces in the fusiform gyrus covaries with language dominance. *Cortex, 117*, 196–204.

Gizewski, E. R., Timmann, D., & Forsting, M. (2004). Specific cerebellar activation during Braille reading in blind subjects. *Human Brain Mapping*, *22*(3), 229–235.

Glezer, L. S., Weisberg, J., Farnady, C. O. G., McCullough, S., Midgley, K. J., Holcomb, P. J., & Emmorey, K. (2018). Orthographic and phonological selectivity across the reading system in deaf skilled readers. *Neuropsychologia*, *117*, 500–512.

Hammill, D., Brown, V., Larsen, S., & Wiederholt, J. L. (1994). *Test of adolescent and adult language* (3rd ed.). Austin, TX: PRO-ED, Inc.

Hanson, V. L., & Fowler, C. A. (1987). Phonological coding in word reading: Evidence from hearing and deaf readers. *Memory & Cognition*, *15*(3), 199–207.

Harris, M., & Beech, J. R. (1998). Implicit phonological awareness and early reading development in prelingually deaf children. *Journal of Deaf Studies and Deaf Education*, *3*(3), 205–216.

Hauser, P. C., Paludnevičiene, R., Supalla, T., & Bavelier, D. (2008). American Sign Language-Sentence Reproduction Test: Development and implications. In R. M. D. Quadros (Ed.), *Sign language: Spinning and unraveling the past, present and future* (pp. 160–172). Petropolis: Editora Arara Azul.

Hirshorn, E. A. (2011). *Exploring alternate routes to literacy in profoundly deaf Individuals.* (PhD), University of Rochester, Rochester, NY.

Hirshorn, E. A., Dye, M. W. G., Hauser, P. C., Supalla, T. R., & Bavelier, D. (2014). Neural networks mediating sentence reading in the deaf. *Frontiers Human Neuroscience, 8,* 1.

Hirshorn, E. A., Dye, M. W. G., Hauser, P. C., Supalla, T. R., & Bavelier, D. (2015). The contribution of phonological knowledge, memory, and language background to reading comprehension in deaf populations. *Frontiers in Psychology, 6.*

Kleinschmidt, A., & Cohen, L. (2006). The neural bases of prosopagnosia and pure alexia: Recent insights from functional neuroimaging. *Current Opinion in Neurology, 19*(4), 386–391.

Koo, D., Crain, K., LaSasso, C., & Eden, G. F. (2008). Phonological awareness and short term memory in hearing and deaf individuals of different communication backgrounds. *Annals of the New York Academy of Science, 1145*(1), 83–99.

Kronbichler, M., Hutzler, F., Wimmer, H., Mair, A., Staffen, W., & Ladurner, G. (2004). The visual word form area and the frequency with which words are encountered: Evidence from a parametric fMRI study. *Neuroimage, 21*(3), 946–953.

Lerma-Usabiaga, G., Carreiras, M., & Paz-Alonso, P. M. (2018). Converging evidence for functional and structural segregation within the left ventral occipitotemporal cortex in reading. *Proceedings of the National Academy of Sciences, 115*(42), E9981–E9990.

Mann, V. A. (1993). Phoneme awareness and future reading ability. *Journal of Learning Disabilities, 26*(4), 259–269.

Markwardt, F. C., Jr. (1998). *Peabody individual achievement test-revised.* Circle Pines, MN: American Guidance Service.

McCandliss, B. D., & Noble, K. G. (2003). The development of reading impairment: A cognitive neuroscience model. *Mental Retardation and Developmental Disabilities Research Reviews, 9*(3), 196–205.

McCardle, P., Scarborough, H. S., & Catts, H. W. (2001). Predicting, explaining, and preventing children's reading difficulties. *Learning Disabilities Research & Practice, 16*(4), 230–239.

McQuarrie, L., & Parrila, R. (2009). Phonological representations in deaf children: Rethinking the functional equivalence hypothesis. *Journal of Deaf Studies and Deaf Education, 14*(2), 137.

Mechelli, A., Gorno-Tempini, M. L., & Price, C. J. (2003). Neuroimaging studies of word and pseudoword reading: Consistencies, inconsistencies, and limitations. *Journal of Cognitive Neuroscience, 15*(2), 260–271.

Monzalvo, K., Fluss, J., Billard, C., Dehaene, S., & Dehaene-Lambertz, G. (2012). Cortical networks for vision and language in dyslexic and normal children of variable socioeconomic status. *Neuroimage, 61*(1), 258–274.

Neville, H. J., & Lawson, D. S. (1987). Attention to central and peripheral visual space in a movement detection task: An event related potential and behavioral study. II. Congenitally deaf adults. *Brain Research, 405,* 268–283.

Perfetti, C. A., & Sandak, R. (2000). Reading optimally builds on spoken language: Implications for deaf readers. *Journal of Deaf Studies and Deaf Education, 5*(1), 32.

Price, C. J., & Devlin, J. T. (2003). The myth of the visual word form area. *Neuroimage, 19*(3), 473–481.

Proksch, J., & Bavelier, D. (2002). Changes in the spatial distribution of visual attention after early deafness. *Journal of Cognitive Neuroscience, 14*(5), 687–701.

Reich, L., Szwed, M., Cohen, L., & Amedi, A. (2011). A ventral visual stream reading center independent of visual experience. *Current Biology, 21*(5), 363–368.

Reinke, K., Fernandes, M., Schwindt, G., O'Craven, K., & Grady, C. L. (2008). Functional specificity of the visual word form area: General activation for words and symbols but specific network activation for words. *Brain and Language, 104*(2), 180–189.

Richlan, F., Kronbichler, M., & Wimmer, H. (2009). Functional abnormalities in the dyslexic brain: A quantitative meta-analysis of neuroimaging studies. *Human Brain Mapping*, *30*(10), 3299–3308.

Shankweiler, D. (1989). How problems of comprehension are related to difficulties in decoding. In *Phonology and reading disability: Solving the reading puzzle* (pp. 35–67), Ann Arbor, MI: University of Michigan Press.

Shaywitz, B. A., Shaywitz, S. E., Blachman, B. A., Pugh, K. R., Fulbright, R. K., Skudlarski, P., Mencl, W. E., Constable, R. T., Holahan, J. M., Marchione, K. E., Fletcher, J. M., Lyon, G. R., & Gore, J. C. (2004). Development of left occipitotemporal systems for skilled reading in children after a phonologically-based intervention. *Biological Psychiatry*, *55*(9), 926–933.

Shaywitz, B. A., Shaywitz, S. E., Pugh, K. R., Mencl, W. E., Fulbright, R. K., Skudlarski, P., Constable, R. T., Marchione, K. E., Fletcher, J. M., Lyon, G. R., & Gore, J. C. (2002). Disruption of posterior brain systems for reading in children with developmental dyslexia. *Biological Psychiatry*, *52*(2), 101–110.

Snowling, M. J. (1981). Phonemic deficits in developmental dyslexia. *Psychological Research*, *43*(2), 219–234.

Snowling, M. J. (1998). Dyslexia as a phonological deficit: Evidence and implications. *Child and Adolescent Mental Health*, *3*(1), 4–11.

Striem-Amit, E., Cohen, L., Dehaene, S., & Amedi, A. (2012). Reading with sounds: Sensory substitution selectively activates the Visual Word Form Area in the Blind. *Neuron*, *76*(3), 640–652.

Van der Mark, S., Bucher, K., Maurer, U., Schulz, E., Brem, S., Buckelmüller, J., Kronbichler, M., Loenneker, T., Klaver, P., Martin, E., & Brandeis, D. (2009). Children with dyslexia lack multiple specializations along the visual word-form (VWF) system. *Neuroimage*, *47*(4), 1940–1949.

Van der Mark, S., Klaver, P., Bucher, K., Maurer, U., Schulz, E., Brem, S., Martin, E., & Brandeis, D. (2011). The left occipitotemporal system in reading: Disruption of focal fMRI connectivity to left inferior frontal and inferior parietal language areas in children with dyslexia. *Neuroimage*, *54*(3), 2426–2436.

Vinckier, F., Dehaene, S., Jobert, A., Dubus, J. P., Sigman, M., & Cohen, L. (2007). Hierarchical coding of letter strings in the ventral stream: Dissecting the inner organization of the visual word-form system. *Neuron*, *55*(1), 143–156.

Wagner, R. K., & Torgesen, J. K. (1987). The nature of phonological processing and its causal role in the acquisition of reading skills. *Psychological Bulletin*, *101*(2), 192–212.

Wang, X., Caramazza, A., Peelen, M. V., Han, Z., & Bi, Y. (2014). Reading without speech sounds: VWFA and its connectivity in the congenitally deaf. *Cerebral Cortex*, 1–11.

Waters, D., Campbell, R., Capek, C. M., Woll, B., David, A. S., McGuire, P. K., Brammer, M. J., & MacSweeney, M. (2007). Fingerspelling, signed language, text and picture processing in deaf native signers: The role of the mid-fusiform gyrus. *Neuroimage*, *35*(3), 1287–1302.

Yoncheva, Y. N., Zevin, J. D., Maurer, U., & McCandliss, B. D. (2010). Auditory selective attention to speech modulates activity in the visual word form area. *Cerebral Cortex*, *20*(3), 622–632.

Zhao, L., Chen, C., Shao, L., Wang, Y., Xiao, X., Chen, C., Yang, J., Zevin, J., & Xue, G. (2017). Orthographic and phonological representations in the fusiform cortex. *Cerebral Cortex*, *27*(11), 5197–5210.

Interlude 4

ONE LESS SENSE ISN'T NONSENSE

Marta Kutas

When a sense is absent congenitally,
senses that remain intact sometimes react quite expansively
not only making do but doing better, in audition and vision,
especially peripherally.

Sensory brain areas accommodate, compensate, or even go beyond.
Old areas in new combinations through new synapses probe and bond,
brain space co-opted rather than left fallow,
processing different but decidedly not shallow.
Neurons switching allegiances to different functions
without compunctions.

At least in the young, this possibility is not so far-flung, as attested by
sharper than usual tuning of early spatial selective attention,
and the concomitant consequences on improved detection
Experience an unparalleled source of "damage" protection.

DOI: 10.4324/9780429342356-12

7

DEAFNESS AND SIGNED LANGUAGE

Implications of Helen Neville's neuroplasticity research for children receiving cochlear implants

Aaron J. Newman and Mairéad MacSweeney

The lived sensory and linguistic experiences of deaf people are fascinating from the perspective of cognitive neuroscience and neuroplasticity. Early on in her career, Helen Neville began studying the neurophysiological impact of deafness and sign language on reading, then visual perception and attention. Deafness and the use of sign language presented unique opportunities to study neuroplasticity in humans to understand how a unimodal lack of sensory experience and/or the use of a visual language affects brain development. Helen's research brought her and her students into contact with Deaf culture. For many students – including one of the authors of this chapter (A.J.N.) – this was for the first time. For other junior researchers from around the world – including a co-author of this chapter (M.Mac.S) and many other contributors to this book – Helen's pioneering research into the neural basis of sign language processing was an attractive opportunity to visit and learn from her and her lab. Helen's lab provided a rich, vibrant, and fun scientific environment within which researchers were able to develop their ideas in this new and emerging field, in which Helen was at the forefront. We thank Helen for this great opportunity and for her generosity in bringing us, and many others, with her on this journey.

In this chapter, we revisit Helen's pioneering research in neuroplasticity and describe how it inspired our own work and stimulated the field. Helen's work in this area literally established the fields of cognitive neuroscientific research in two areas of relevance in this chapter. One concerns the effects of deafness on visual attention, demonstrating the selective enhancement of particular visual attentional functions and relating them to differences in behavior. The other concerns how sign language is processed in the brain; specifically, Helen's research demonstrated a high degree of similarity in neural signatures of linguistic processing in spoken and signed language, and the impacts that delayed sign language acquisition

DOI: 10.4324/9780429342356-13

has on people born deaf who learned sign language only after childhood. We review this research and then show how Helen's work can help understand and resolve a controversy of great relevance to deaf people and their families – whether deaf children who receive cochlear implants (CIs) to restore hearing should be exposed to sign language.

Deaf children's experience is highly variable

Deafness is one of the three most common congenital disorders, affecting 2–3 out of every 1000 children born in the United States (Vohr, 2003), with higher rates in some other parts of the world, such as Asia Pacific, South Asia, and Sub-Saharan Africa (Global Burden of Disease Study 2013 Collaborators, 2015). The focus of Helen's research was on those who were born severely or profoundly deaf; that is, individuals unable to hear sounds quieter than 80 dB (typical conversation usually occurs at around 50–60 dB). Hearing aids and CIs can offer some amplication of the speech signal. However, the usefulness of these technologies varies greatly between individuals. As well, access to such technologies is far from universal even today (depending on country, medical system/insurance, socioeconomic, and other factors), and was even more limited from the 1970s, when CIs were first developed, through the period when Helen conducted the majority of her research. Beyond this, many deaf individuals and families, especially those who identify with Deaf culture (in which deafness is not viewed as a medical condition to be treated), have simply not seen the need to use assistive hearing technology or even see it as a threat to their cultural identity.

As such, the population of deaf people collectively provides a range of experiences across which different individuals born with a unimodal sensory deficit are provided with auditory input at a range of ages across the lifespan or, in many cases, not at all. Helen Neville recognized that this provided a unique opportunity to study development, neuroplasticity, and the existence of critical or sensitive periods in development. These questions were central to Helen's pursuits in science, and indeed she pursued her Ph.D. under the supervision of Eric Lenneberg at Cornell University because of his pioneering work on critical periods in language development.

Many deaf people use sign languages, such as American Sign Language (ASL) in North America or British Sign Language (BSL) in the UK. These natural sign languages have evolved spontaneously among communities of users, typically including both deaf people and hearing family members and friends. Sign languages are classified as natural human languages because they follow the same patterns of organization as spoken languages; they simply employ the visual-manual, rather than aural-oral, modality. As originally demonstrated by Stokoe and colleagues (Stokoe et al., 1976) for ASL, natural sign languages involve all of the same levels of structure and patterning as do spoken languages. For example, signs correspond to words and are combined together to form phrases and sentences according to grammatical rules; signs themselves are composed of meaningless features comparable to the sounds of spoken language (phonemes), but based on the handshape, orientation, location, and movement of the hands.

While natural sign languages have evolved within communities of deaf users, only an estimated 4–5% of deaf children are born to deaf parents who know a sign language; the vast majority of deaf children are born to hearing parents with no knowledge of sign language (Mitchell & Karchmer, 2004). As a result, only a small minority of deaf children receive natural language input from their parents from birth, as hearing children normally do. Although some parents of deaf babies may start to learn sign language, beginning learners of a language cannot provide the rich, natural input of a fluent language user. Deaf children may also be exposed to any number of signing systems, including auxiliary sign languages and manually coded languages, that have been developed in educational settings (Scott & Henner, 2020). In contrast to natural sign languages (which evolved in communities of users and follow the universal organizational principles of human languages), signing systems are created by hearing people to help provide access to spoken languages and do not follow the universal principles of organization characteristic of natural human languages.

Due to the above factors, most people who are born deaf (or become deaf early in life) receive no, or impoverished, language input until they either receive a CI or are exposed to a community of fluent signers. While in the present day a CI may be implanted before one year of age, this still represents a significant delay in speech input, considering that children typically begin producing phonemes of their native language (canonical babbling) by 7 months and their first words between 9 and 12 months (Kuhl, 2004). Since CIs were first introduced in the late 1970s, the typical age of implantation for children has steadily decreased. As a result, in earlier generations, CIs were implanted later in childhood or even in adulthood, or not at all, and children might not be exposed to sign language until school or even until reaching adulthood. Thus, there is great heterogeneity in the language experience of deaf children. This provides a unique opportunity to investigate and better understand critical or sensitive periods for language acquisition, and the impacts of delayed natural language input on development.

Neuroplasticity in deafness

Helen's first published work with deaf participants was in 1982–1983, with papers reporting the results of event-related potential (ERP) studies done in collaboration with Marta Kutas (see interludes in this volume) and Albert Schmidt (Neville et al., 1982a, 1982b, 1983, 1984). Electroencephalography (EEG) was effectively the only non-invasive neuroimaging technique available at the time, and Helen and her colleagues were pioneers in applying the ERP technique (EEG time-locked to stimulus events of interest) to questions of neuroplasticity. At this time (and up until the mid-1990s), Helen worked at the Salk Institute and was significantly influenced by the pioneering work on sign language process-ing done there by Ursula Bellugi, Howard Poizner, Edward Klima (e.g., Poizner et al., 1987; Klima & Bellugi, 1979) and their students. Helen's initial studies focused on visual stimuli, including words, and showed larger early sensory ERPs in congenitally deaf than hearing people, as well as reduced left-lateralization of an ERP component associated with reading. While the language experience of the deaf participants was not reported, these studies provided perhaps the first neurophysiological evidence of altered neural responses associated with lifelong deafness, suggesting neuroplastic reorganization of visual and linguistic functions.

This early work was followed by a series of publications by Neville and Lawson (Neville, 1990; Neville & Lawson, 1987a, 1987b, 1987c) which provided even clearer and more convincing evidence of neuroplastic reorganization in deaf people, and systematically distinguished the influences of deafness and sign language experi-ence on visual attention. This was done by including three groups of participants: hearing people, congenitally deaf native signers (i.e., who had learned ASL from their parents), and CODAs – a term that is derived from the acronym for "children of Deaf adults", but in common usage also refers to adult hearing children of deaf adults, who had learned ASL as their native language. In these studies, participants had to attend to visual stimuli (squares) located either directly in the center of their field of view, or in the periphery (18° off-center), while maintaining fixation on the center of the screen. Occasionally, a square in the attended location would appear to move slightly in one of eight possible directions, and participants had to press a button when they detected this. ERPs were recorded during the task, as well as accuracy in detecting the direction of motion, and reaction time (RT).

Relative to hearing non-signers, deaf signers showed faster RTs to moving stimuli in the visual periphery, but not in the center of the field of view (Nev-ille & Lawson, 1987b). Deaf and hearing participants showed similar accuracy in detecting the direction of motion when the targets were located centrally or in the left visual field, but deaf participants showed significantly greater accu-racy than hearing participants in the right visual field. Indeed, deaf participants showed a right hemifield advantage in accuracy, whereas hearing non-signers showed a left hemifield advantage. Since visual input to the cortex crosses from the input eye to the opposite hemisphere, this pattern of results suggests greater sensitivity to moving stimuli in the left cerebral hemisphere of deaf signers, in contrast to greater sensitivity in the right hemisphere for hearing non-signers.

This inference was supported by the ERP results, which focused on the visual N1 component. This component is elicited by visual stimuli, is larger contralat-eral to the visual field in which a stimulus is presented, and is larger in amplitude for attended than unattended stimuli (Hillyard & Anllo-Vento, 1998). N1 ampli-tudes to peripheral visual stimuli were larger overall in deaf signers than hearing non-signers and showed a larger enhancement for attended versus unattended locations (Neville & Lawson, 1987b). As well, deaf participants showed particu-lar N1 enhancement over left hemisphere temporal and parietal electrode sites.

In a paper synthesizing these findings, Neville (1990) interpreted these results in terms of two effects. One was *compensatory hypertrophy*, the overdevelopment of the visual system in the absence of auditory input, reflected in the overall larger N1 amplitudes at occipital electrodes. The other was *functional reallocation*, the "takeover" of brain regions typically used for auditory speech processing, by visual functions, as reflected by the larger N1 amplitudes over left temporal and parietal electrodes. An alternative interpretation of this latter finding was that lifelong experience with a visual-manual language enhanced responses to non-linguistic visual motion, due to the fact that language (including sign language) is processed primarily by the left hemisphere.

The third group of participants in the study – CODAs – helped clarify these interpretations (Neville & Lawson, 1987c). Hearing signers showed slower RTs to peripheral stimuli than deaf participants, similar to hearing non-signers. Correspondingly, they showed smaller N1 amplitudes than deaf people over occipital regions, again similar to hearing non-signers. Together these findings supported the interpretation of the deaf group's responses in terms of compensatory hypertrophy. In contrast, however, both deaf and hearing signers showed greater accuracy in detecting motion in the right than the left visual field and enhanced N1 attention effects over the left temporal and parietal regions. Thus, rather than functional reallocation, these results seemed to indicate the influence of learning a visual-manual language on visual perception, irrespective of deafness.

This work sets the foundation for subsequent studies by Daphné Bavelier, who did her postdoctoral fellowship with Helen and continued a seminal line of studies on the influences of deafness and sign language on visual attention. Consistent with the previous findings of greater sensitivity to peripheral visual stimuli in deaf people, Proksch and Bavelier (2002) found that deaf people's performance on a visual attention task was reduced more by peripheral than central distractor stimuli. In contrast, hearing non-signers and signers both showed greater interference by centrally presented distractors, suggesting the cause of the effect was deafness and not sign language experience. This finding was replicated using a different task, the attentional network test, by Dye et al. (2007) who again found greater interference in deaf than hearing participants when peripheral distractor stimuli were presented. Dye et al. (2009) employed the useful field of view task, which requires simultaneous attention to a central target and localization of a peripheral one. Notably, this study included four groups, comprising deaf and hearing signers and non-signers. Deaf participants – irrespective of signing experience – outperformed hearing people (both signers and non-signers) on this task. Brozinsky and Bavelier (2004) examined sensitivity to visual motion in the central and peripheral visual fields and did not find overall differences between deaf signers and hearing non-signers. However, replicating Neville's previous studies, deaf signers showed a right visual field/left hemisphere advantage whereas hearing non-signers showed either the opposite trend of lateralization or no lateralization, depending on the measure.

Bavelier and colleagues also extended this line of work using functional magnetic resonance imaging (fMRI). Bavelier and colleagues (2000) found greater activation of medial temporal to medial superior temporal visual area 5 (MT/MST-V5; the region typically involved in visual motion processing) in deaf native signers than hearing non-signers, but only for motion in the peripheral visual field, not in the central field of view. They also found left-lateralized MT/MST-V5 activation in deaf signers, but right-lateralized activation in hearing participants, for all moving stimuli. Deaf participants showed stronger effective connectivity with parietal regions than hearing people, specifically during attention to peripheral motion. In a second study, Bavelier and colleagues (2001) included CODAs and observed a pattern of results that paralleled those of Neville and Lawson's (1987a, 1987b, 1987c) ERP studies. That is, both deaf and hearing native signers showed overall left-lateralized responses in MT/MST-V5 to moving stimuli, while only deaf signers showed greater MT/MST activation to peripheral than central moving stimuli. Deaf signers also showed greater activation in two other areas associated with spatial cognition and biological motion processing, the posterior parietal cortex and posterior superior temporal sulcus, respectively. Thus, the ERP and fMRI work converge to suggest that early exposure to a signed language drives enhanced sensitivity of left hemisphere brain regions to visual motion, while early and lifelong auditory deprivation leads to enhanced sensitivity to movement in the visual periphery, which is associated with greater responses in several brain regions, including MT-MST-V5, parietal, and posterior superior temporal cortices.

In addition to Bavelier's research, Helen's lab continued work in this vein in subsequent decades. Armstrong and colleagues (2002) replicated the earlier finding of enhanced N1 amplitudes to visual motion and further showed that this was not a general enhancement of visual sensitivity, as N1 amplitudes were similar between deaf and hearing people in response to changes in the color of stimuli. Stevens and Neville (2006) replicated the finding of enhanced sensitivity to visual motion in the periphery in deaf signers relative to hearing non-signers, using a perimetry task to test sensitivity to motion out to 60° of visual angle. Scott and colleagues (2014), using fMRI, replicated Bavelier and colleagues' findings of enhanced fMRI responses to peripheral visual stimuli in deaf signers, in MT/MST-V5, and posterior parietal cortex. This study also delineated Heschl's gyrus – the location of the primary auditory cortex – in individual participants and found greater fMRI activation for peripheral than central visual stimuli in deaf but not hearing participants within this area.

Overall, these studies – along with a number of other studies performed by other research groups (e.g., Bosworth & Dobkins, 1999, 2002a, 2002b; Bottari et al., 2010; Mohammed et al., 2005) – converge to show that lifelong deafness leads to a pattern of alteration in visual perception that is largely specific to attended stimuli in the peripheral visual field, particularly tasks involving moving stimuli or visual distractors. Correspondingly, deafness is associated with an enhanced neural response to attended, moving stimuli in the visual periphery. To a large extent, these effects appear to reflect compensatory hypertrophy (functionally if not anatomically), in that specific neural responses in deaf people are enhanced, but within the same brain areas typically used by hearing individuals. On the other hand, there is some evidence as well for functional reallocation (often called *neuroplastic reorganization* today), for example Scott and colleagues' (2014) finding of greater Heschl's gyrus activation for peripheral stimuli in deaf people. Similar findings have also been reported by other groups. For example, deaf signers showed right superior temporal gyrus activation (encompassing Heschl's gyrus) in response to peripheral visual motion, while hearing people did not (Fine et al., 2005; Finney et al., 2001), and Cardin and colleagues (2013, 2016) reported activation in and around Heschl's gyrus for moving sign language stimuli in both deaf signers and non-signers, but not hearing non-signers – suggesting that this was an effect of deafness and not sign language experience. With that said, the effects of sign language experience were also a major focus of Helen's research, and in the next section, we review her contributions to this body of knowledge and how they influenced future studies.

Neural bases of sign language processing

As noted earlier, Helen was fortunate to begin her career at the Salk Institute in affiliation with the University of California, San Diego; here, at that time, a number of seminal researchers in the fields of sign language psycholinguistics and neurolinguistics were working and training some of the most influential researchers of the next generation in this field. This included Ursual Bellugi, Howard Poizner, and Edward Klima, along with trainees such as David P. Corina (see Chapter 4, this volume), Karen Emmorey, and Greg Hickok. Klima and Bellugi's book, *The Signs of Language* (1979), was influential in summarizing psycholinguistic work on ASL processing, and extending Stokoe's (Stokoe et al., 1976) work to demonstrate that not only is ASL structured like spoken natural human languages but it is processed in similar ways, through the visual-manual modalities. Bellugi also led neuropsychological work showing similar patterns of left-lateralization for signed and spoken languages (Bellugi et al., 1989; Corina, Poizner, et al., 1992; Corina, Vaid, et al., 1992; Corina et al., 1999; Hickok et al., 1996; Poizner et al., 1987).

Helen's early work on sign language processing extended these studies by comparing ERPs elicited by ASL to those elicited by English. Kutas et al. (1987) published perhaps the first ERP study of ASL processing, focusing on the N400 component elicited by semantically anomalous sentences. First described by Kutas and Hillyard (1980), the N400 is a negative-going ERP component peaking around 400 ms after the onset of a word, and largest over the vertex of the scalp. Its amplitude is larger for semantically anomalous words in sentences (e.g., *I take my coffee with milk and dog*) than for felicitous words in comparable sentences (e.g., *I take my coffee with milk and sugar*) – a phenomenon referred to as the N400 effect. Kutas, Neville, and Holcomb (1987) compared native English speakers with deaf native ASL signers, in a study where English speakers read or heard English sentences (in two separate conditions), while signers saw sequences of images depicting ASL sentences. Both English conditions, and the ASL condition, showed similar N400 effects, in terms of their timing, scalp distribution, and amplitude. The authors used the results to make the point that the N400 effect could not be attributable to either spoken language phonology or to orthography since it was comparable in ASL and English.

Helen's next ERP study of ASL was more extensive and systematic in its careful delineation of the effects of sign language experience and deafness (Neville et al., 1997). Four groups of participants were recruited, including both deaf and hearing native signers, along with hearing people who learned ASL as young adults (to become sign language interpreters), and hearing people with no knowledge of sign language. Again Helen took a pioneering technical approach to time-locking fluid human movement to event-related brain activity: ASL sentences were presented as a series of still images capturing the key positions and movement patterns of signs. Data analysis focused on two contrasts: one was between semantically anomalous and felicitous completions of sentences (as in Kutas et al., 1987), and the other was between signs conveying semantic content (*open class*; nouns, verbs, and adjectives) and those serving grammatical functions (*closed class*; pronouns, conjunctions, auxiliaries). The former contrast was expected to yield an N400 effect, while in spoken languages Helen's work had previously shown that open-class words typically elicit an N400-like component in contrast to an earlier and more left anterior negativity for closed-class words and associated with grammatical processing, labeled the N280 (Neville et al., 1992).

All three groups who were fluent in sign language showed the N400 effect for semantic violations, although the deaf native signers showed a somewhat earlier effect than either hearing group; hearing non-signers showed no N400 effect as expected. Replicating the earlier study, this result reinforced the contention that semantic information is processed similarly in signed and spoken languages – an effect that was later replicated again in Helen's lab using ASL movies rather than static stimuli (Capek et al., 2009). As well, the comparison between groups suggested that semantic information could be processed similarly in native signers and those who became fluent in ASL later in life. This finding is consistent with other work conducted by Helen's postdoctoral fellow, Christine Weber-Fox, in hearing people who learned a second spoken language at varying ages, which also showed minimal differences in N400 violation effects in later learners (Weber-Fox & Neville, 1996).

A markedly different pattern of results across groups was found, however, in the contrast between open- and closed-class signs. Relative to open-class signs, at left anterior electrodes both deaf and hearing native signers showed the N280 effect previously observed for spoken language users. Hearing late learners of sign language, however, did not show this N280. In contrast – and consistent with the

N400 violation effect – the N400 elicited by open-class relative to closed-class words was comparable across the three groups of signers. These results suggested an effect of AoA of sign language that was specific to grammatical processing. This was again consistent with Weber-Fox and Neville's (1996) findings in spoken language bilinguals, in which the ERP effects of grammatical violations were much more sensitive to AoA than the effects of semantic violations.

Helen was also among the first researchers in the world to compare the neural organization of signed and spoken languages using fMRI – which indeed was the primary reason one of the present authors (A.J.N.) chose to pursue his graduate studies in Helen's lab and why the other author (M.Mac.S) chose to visit. Initial work compared deaf native signers, CODAs (hearing native signers), and hearing non-signers while viewing sentences in ASL and written English (Bavelier et al., 1998a, 1998b; Neville et al., 1998). The results showed a similar network of left hemisphere regions was engaged when each group viewed sentences in their native language. Importantly, while hearing native English speakers (both monolinguals and CODAs) showed exclusively left hemisphere activation when reading English, the deaf native signers showed extensive activation in the left hemisphere in the areas typically associated with language processing – but in addition extensive activation in right hemisphere homolog regions, which were not activated in the hearing participants reading English. These regions are however engaged in hearing people perceiving audio–visual speech (MacSweeney et al., 2002), thus underlying similarity in the neural systems supporting sign and speech processing (see Emmorey, 2021 and MacSweeney et al., 2008 for reviews). Helen's research also examined the impact of delayed acquisition of sign language patterns on brain organization and processing. For example, her research showed altered neural patterns in late learners of sign language, including the lack of a typical ERP response to grammatical function words (the N280 for closed-class relative to open-class words; Neville et al., 1997), and a failure to engage brain regions activated in native signers (Newman et al., 2002).

These findings have been further extended in later work that built on Helen's legacy. For example, MacSweeney and colleagues (2008) compared deaf signers who had learned BSL from birth with those who had learned later, between the ages of 4 and 21. When performing phonological judgments, non-native signers showed greater activation of the left inferior frontal gyrus than native signers – both for BSL and for English. The latter finding is of critical interest because both groups had similar experience with English, and had also shown equal levels of English proficiency. Since increased fMRI signal is often interpreted as reflecting greater cognitive effort, these data are consistent with the assertion that having a robust first language (here a signed language) provides a solid basis on which to learn a second language (here English). These data support behavioral data underlining the critical importance of early language experience, in any modality, for later language development. For example, Mayberry and colleagues (2002, 2003) compared the English abilities of native English speakers, deaf native signers, deaf people who had no early language input and learned sign language in school, and native speakers of spoken languages other than English who learned English as a second language (ESL) later in life. Thus, the two latter groups learned English at similar ages, but the deaf individuals lacked any natural language input in the first ~9 years of life, while the ESL learners received normal spoken language input. The deaf people exposed to sign language from birth showed comparable English abilities to ESL learners, whereas the deaf people who lacked early natural language input performed significantly worse, particularly on more complex grammatical structures (see Mayberry, 2007, for a review).

Mayberry and colleagues also examined the impact of age of sign language acquisition on neural organization, across a group of adults who first learned ASL as their L1 between the ages of 0–14. There was a linear decline in activation of left hemisphere frontal and temporal language areas with increasing AoA, along with increased activation in occipital regions (Mayberry et al., 2011). This increased occipital cortex activation in non-native compared to native signers was also observed by Twomey and colleagues (2020). These findings suggest greater effort may be required in non-native signers for processing the low-level (visual) features of signs at the expense of fluent linguistic processing.

Mayberry and colleagues have also had the opportunity to examine ASL processing in two deaf adolescents who moved to the United States from Central America and who are described as having no first language (spoken language) before encountering ASL at the age of 14 years (Ramirez et al., 2014). Again, such cases represent unique opportunities to study language acquisition, since arguably only in cases of extreme deprivation could such instances be found in the hearing population. Using magnetoencephalography (MEG), Ferjan Ramirez and colleagues showed that even after 3 years of exposure to ASL, the teenager's responses to single signs were highly atypical, engaging right dorsal frontoparietal regions, rather than the typical left-lateralized frontotemporal network (Ferjan Ramirez et al., 2014). When followed up just over a year later, these cases still showed atypical neural processing for less familiar signs, although for more familiar signs they started to show activation in the typical left perisylvian network (Ferjan Ramirez et al., 2016). Ferjan Ramirez and colleagues (2016) argued that even though the timing of language experience inevitably affects the organization of neural language processing, language representation in the human brain can continue to develop with experience, even into adolescence.

To summarize, research involving people who are born deaf consistently indicates that early language exposure is critical to normal language development. People exposed to sign language from birth showed fluent command of sign language, and abilities to learn spoken languages such as English at later ages that are comparable to hearing second language learners. There does not seem to be a cost to learning sign language early on, in terms of deaf people's ability to later learn a spoken language or to read. On the other hand, delays in sign language exposure of only a few years lead to lifelong deficits in deaf children's ability to learn both signed and spoken language.

These findings are consistent with Helen Neville's long-standing contention (shared by many colleagues) that there are critical – or at least sensitive – periods early in human development during which exposure to a natural language is necessary for native-like language fluency, normal brain organization for language, and later L2 learning abilities. Moreover, it does not seem to matter whether one's first language is spoken or signed, as long as natural language input is provided. We next turn to considering the consequences of this research on deafness and sign language for children with CIs – after briefly reviewing the literature on CIs and language outcomes.

Language outcomes for children with CIs

While the aim of CIs is to provide auditory input to deaf people, the input CIs provide to the auditory system is not as rich as natural hearing. While the human cochlea represents frequencies using a place code – whereby different frequencies stimulate different locations along the surface of the cochlea in a continuous manner – CIs only stimulate the cochlea at between 8 and 32 locations ("channels"), although the auditory system adapts over time in such a way that experienced CI users are able to resolve a much finer-grained range of frequencies. Nonetheless, congenitally deaf CI users face dual challenges of both having to adapt to auditory input at a later stage of development than those born hearing, and having to learn to decode speech from a degraded stimulus. It is thus perhaps not surprising that the spoken language outcomes of people who received CIs as children are more variable, and on average, poorer, than those of hearing individuals. For example, one sample of children who received CIs before age 2 and tested between 2 and 4 years showed on average a 12-month delay in receptive spoken language skills compared to their hearing peers (Ceh et al., 2013). Other studies have found that approximately half of children who receive CIs early in life show spoken language abilities in the normal range when tested at ages ranging from 5 to 18 years (Boons et al., 2013; Geers et al., 2011b) – meaning both that CIs can be effective in supporting spoken language development, but that at the same time a disproportionate number of CI users show persistent deficits relative to their hearing peers. Indeed, Geers and colleagues (2011) noted significant gaps between verbal and non-verbal IQ scores in CI users, suggesting that CI users' spoken language outcomes were below what would be expected, given their non-verbal IQ level.

The factors that are predictive of CI outcomes have been a topic of intensive investigation. The strongest predictor of spoken language outcomes in children receiving CIs is age of implantation, with earlier implantation yielding better outcomes, and the best outcomes for children implanted before 1 year of age (Colletti et al., 2011; Cuda et al., 2014; Dettman et al., 2007, 2016; Leigh et al., 2013; Tobey et al., 2013; Walker & Bass-Ringdahl, 2008). There are two likely related reasons why earlier implantation is better than late: one related to the experience-dependent development of the auditory system, and the other to the development of spoken language abilities.

Neuroplastic reorganization

In the course of typical auditory development, neurons within the primary auditory cortex become tuned to particular acoustic features through experience. However, even in the absence of auditory input, a very rudimentary organization around these features still exists. This suggests that coarse genetic coding guides the organization of the auditory system, but that experience is critical to refine the general "outline" provided by genetics and to properly tune cells (Kral & Sharma, 2012). Studies of congenitally deaf cats have shown that the auditory cortex is subject to sensitive periods: cats receiving CIs prior to 4 months of age show normal, or nearly normal, patterns of electrophysiological responses to sound, whereas cats implanted later show much weaker and less organized responses – even after the same total duration of acoustic stimulation (Kral & Lomber, 2015; Kral & Sharma, 2012; Lomber et al., 2010). The lack of typical responses in later-implanted cats is likely caused by a combination of factors, including maturational changes in neurotransmitter receptor density, the duration of postsynaptic potentials, dendritic branching, synaptogenesis, and cortical inhibition. The extended absence of auditory input also seems to reduce neuroplastic sensitivity to external input (Kral & Sharma, 2012). While the developmental timeline in humans is longer, a similar pattern seems to exist. For example, studies of congenitally deaf people who received CIs at different ages have shown that children implanted before 3.5 years showed typical ERP responses to sounds, whereas those implanted between 3.5 and 7 years showed variable outcomes and those implanted after age 7 showed consistently and apparently permanently altered responses (Eggermont & Ponton, 2003; Sharma et al., 2002, 2005, 2015). Sharma et al. (2009) have suggested that prolonged deafness in early development leads to a "decoupling" between the primary auditory cortex and higher-order auditory processing regions that can in turn allow neuroplastic reorganization of brain areas that would normally be involved in processes such as understanding speech.

This theory aligns with the findings from Helen's lab and subsequent work reviewed earlier, showing changes in visual attentional abilities and evidence of neuroplastic reorganization including visual responses in the auditory cortex. Neuroplastic reorganization of auditory cortices for visual processing may create challenges for restoring hearing after CI implantation, which could lead to poorer spoken language outcomes. Indeed, Doucet and colleagues (2006) compared visual motion processing between good and poor CI users and found that those with worse CI outcomes showed ERP responses that were smaller and focused more anteriorly on the scalp (similar to Neville and Lawson's seminal findings) relative to proficient CI users and hearing adults. CI users with poor auditory comprehension also showed greater interference during speech processing in the presence of moving visual distractors (but not other visual distractors), relative to more proficient CI users (Champoux et al., 2009). On the other hand, recent animal evidence calls this interpretation into question. Land and colleagues (2016) showed that cross-modal plasticity in the higher-order auditory cortex of congenitally deaf cats did not limit auditory responsiveness to CIs; in fact, they conclude that "These results indicate that cross-modal reorganization is less detrimental for neurosensory restoration than previously thought" (p. 6175). This suggests that previous interpretations of the negative impact of early visual input to auditory cortices are likely to have been overstated and over-interpreted.

Language and home environment

Common social determinants of health are also predictive of CI outcomes, in particular socioeconomic status and maternal education level (Convertino et al., 2009; Geers et al., 2003; Hodges et al., 1999; Niparko et al., 2010; Sarant et al., 2014, 2018; Tobey et al., 2011), as well as parenting behaviors typically associated with educational attainment, such as the amount of input, speech styles, maternal sensitivity, level of parental involvement, and cognitive stimulation (DesJardin & Eisenberg, 2007; Fagan et al., 2014; Moeller, 2000; Quittner et al., 2013; Sarant et al., 2008). Children born earlier than their siblings (birth order) and/or having fewer siblings show better-spoken language outcomes (Geers et al., 2003; Sarant et al., 2014), and girls often do better than boys (Geers, 2003; Sarant et al., 2014). Better cognitive abilities in some domains also predict better-spoken language outcomes in CI users, including non-verbal IQ, working memory abilities, and fine motor development (Geers et al., 2003; Geers, 2003; Geers & Sedey, 2011; Horn et al., 2005, 2007; Pisoni et al., 2011; Pyman et al., 2000; Sarant et al., 2008, 2014). While many of these factors cannot be controlled, evidence has shown that interventions aimed at fostering positive interaction styles in parents can improve CI spoken language outcomes (Moog et al., 2011).

One particularly contentious question is whether deaf children should be taught sign language prior to implantation. Studies of spoken language (English) outcomes of children with CIs have often reported evidence of poorer outcomes among children who were sign language users (Archbold et al., 2011; Geers et al., 2011a, 2011c; Hodges et al., 1999; Ruffin et al., 2013; Sarant et al., 2001; Svirsky et al., 2000). However, this is not always the case (Connor et al., 2000; Connor & Zwolan, 2004). Anecdotally, many deaf educators and audiologists are reported to discourage parents from using sign language with deaf children who have CIs, on the basis of the belief that this will discourage the children from using their CI and thus lead to poorer spoken language outcomes – speculating that oral-only communication will provide a vital constraint that forces them to use their CI, and therefore lead to better spoken language use (Robbins, 2001).

However, on closer examination, the picture is actually more complicated than such recommendations would make it seem (see Hall et al., 2019 for review). Critically, the studies that have shown poorer spoken language outcomes among children using sign language had a very broad definition of "sign language user." That is, they did not focus on children exposed to a natural sign language from birth. Rather, they involved children with a very wide range of experience. Many used an approach known as "total communication" (TC). TC is not a language, but rather an educational approach that encourages a combination of natural sign languages, signing systems, gestures, and speechreading – often simultaneously. An assumption driving this approach is that signing systems can help children understand oral language when their only access is visual (speechreading and sign), or even when they have a CI but are unable to fully understand spoken language via the CI. This assumption has not, however, been supported by empirical evidence (Scott & Henner, 2020) and it is critical to recognize the error of conflating exposure to TC with natural sign language. Indeed, such conflation is ultimately harmful since it has led to strong positions discouraging parents to use natural sign language with their deaf children, to the detriment of those children's language development (Humphries et al., 2012).

Furthermore, children who report relying more on TC may be doing so because at the time of testing – for any number of possible reasons – they are struggling to understand speech through their CI. In other words, it is impossible to know whether the greater reliance on signed communication in children with poorer outcomes is a cause of their problems, or merely a symptom and compensatory mechanism. Indeed, Sarant and colleagues noted that "… deaf children of hearing parents in Australia tend to be placed in an oral stream first, and are moved into a signing environment only if they are making poor progress relative to other deaf children in the oral stream" (Sarant et al., 2001, p. 23). Naturally, children who cannot make sense of the incoming auditory stream will look to other sources of information such as manual communication and speechreading. It also appears that there may be qualitative differences in the home environments and parenting approaches of children who rely more on TC after implantation. Robbins (2001) notes, based on structured interviews, that parents of implanted children who preferred TC over oral communication reported having lower expectations of their children's communicative abilities with hearing people. These parents further reported often intervening on behalf of their children in conversational settings with other people, rather than letting their children attempt to communicate. Thus, continued use of sign language, to some extent, may well be a result of, rather than a cause of poor functional CI spoken language outcomes.

The consideration of what language input to provide to deaf children, both before and after receiving a CI, should be informed by the research reviewed earlier on sign language acquisition. The data clearly and consistently indicate that as adults, deaf native signers – who learned a *natural* sign language, such as ASL or BSL, from birth – show far better English skills than prelingually deaf people who did not learn sign language until they were school-aged or later (Chamberlain & Mayberry, 2008; Freel et al., 2011; Giezen et al., 2014; Guldenoglu et al., 2014; Mayberry et al., 2002; Mayberry & Lock, 2003). As the work from Helen's lab and others have shown, this is also reflected in brain organization (e.g., Twomey et al., 2020) – deaf native signers show patterns of brain activity during sign language processing that are highly comparable to what is seen in hearing people processing spoken language (see Emmorey, 2021 for a recent review). On the other hand, deaf people who did not learn a signed language until starting school, or later, show lifelong differences in neural responses to language, as well as weaker skills in both spoken and signed languages (see Mayberry & Kluender, 2018 for review).

Evidence-based recommendations

As Helen and others' research has shown, exposure to a natural language from birth, or as early as possible, is essential for normal language development and neural organization of the language system. Sign languages are equally as capable of providing these fundamental benefits as spoken languages. Even when CIs are readily available (which is not the case in many places for reasons such as cost and access to services), there will inevitably be a waiting period prior to the CI surgery and an additional period is required post-surgery before the CI is activated and the child begins receiving auditory input – followed by additional time adapting to the CI before speech is perceived at all clearly. Although hearing aids may be provided during the interval before CI activation, for children whose deafness is so profound as to warrant a CI, these aids likely provide little support for language development. The period between diagnosis and a level of restored hearing capable of supporting spoken language development is thus likely to be months or even years.

Given our understanding of the sensitive periods for language development in the first year of life, it is clear that parents should not simply wait for a CI before their children begin receiving language input. Sign language is the only natural human language that deaf children are able to perceive, and the evidence suggests that this should be provided, as much as possible and as early as possible. Even though parents who are starting to learn a sign language at the same time as their child cannot provide fluent, native-like input, there is strong evidence that young children pick up on linguistic structure and regularities even in imperfect, inconsistent input from non-fluent models, and end up producing more linguistically regular output (Brentari et al., 2011; Goldin-Meadow, 2005; Morford & Goldin-Meadow, 1997; Mylander & Goldin-Meadow, 1991) – a testament to the readiness of infant's brains to learn from language input. Parents do not need to become fluent signers in order to provide their deaf children with constructive language input. It has not yet been established "how good is good enough," and this is in itself an interesting current research question – indeed, in recent years many parents of children with hearing have taken it upon themselves to learn "baby sign" (sign language vocabulary) to facilitate communication and bonding with their infants. It has been suggested that this leads to positive language development and stronger parent–child interactions in hearing infants (Goodwyn et al., 2000; Goodwyn & Acredolo, 1993, 1998; Kirk et al., 2012; Mueller et al., 2013). Thus, in some countries, we have the paradoxical situation in which hearing infants are often taken to baby sign classes, while deaf infants are sometimes discouraged from being exposed to a sign language.

Providing deaf infants with sign language input prior to their receiving a CI – and continuing afterward – should simply be viewed as a form of bilingualism. A vast proportion of children in the world are raised in multilingual households, without negative consequences to their development (and possibly even benefits; Bialystok, 1999; Bialystok et al., 2008). The work reviewed earlier from Helen's lab and others has demonstrated that bilinguals with earlier exposure to their second language do better, and show more typical brain responses during language processing, than those who learn a second language late. For parents who worry that their child's deafness is a disability and that bilingualism will be an additional burden, we can point to the behavioral and brain imaging data showing that children exposed to sign language from birth show normal language development, regardless of whether they are deaf and learn only sign language as an L1 (Mayberry et al., 2002; Mayberry & Lock, 2003), or whether they are hearing, native sign-speech bilinguals (Davidson et al., 2014). Even children with severe intellectual disabilities such as Down's syndrome and autism spectrum disorder do not show any costs to being raised bilingually (e.g., English–French) as opposed to monolingually (Bird et al., 2005; Feltmate & Bird, 2008; Ohashi et al., 2012).

Conclusions

Stevens and Neville (2006) published a paper with the compelling, and highly apt, title "Neuroplasticity as a double-edged sword." Neuroplasticity can, on the one hand, allow an organism to adapt to experience, but, on the other hand, may create situations that are ultimately problematic for the organism. For example, evidence from Neville's lab and others, reviewed earlier, suggests selective enhancements of visual attention abilities – including the ability to detect motion in the periphery. However, both adults and children who are deaf also show greater distraction or interference by stimuli presented in the visual periphery (Bavelier et al., 2006; Dye et al., 2007, 2009; Proksch & Bavelier, 2002). Thus, enhanced sensitivity to motion in the visual periphery may be adaptive in helping deaf people detect events that others might detect through their hearing. However, this enhancement comes at the cost of greater distractibility and challenges in attending to information in the central visual field.

While these findings underscore the value of providing hearing with a CI as early as possible in life, Helen's work on sign language processing – and the research that has built on it subsequently – strongly emphasizes the importance of early natural language input. Early exposure to a natural sign language has immense long-term benefits to deaf children in properly establishing the neural networks for language processing, and ensuring the best opportunities for language development. Even if hearing is provided via a CI, a critical review of the literature suggests that there is no downside to early natural sign language exposure for deaf children. On the contrary, the evidence suggests clear and uncontroversial benefits of such exposure. As we have laid out in this chapter, this conclusion is strongly influenced by Helen's research legacy. She would be delighted with the impact and application of her research in this way. We are ever grateful to Helen for her foundational contributions to the study of deafness, sign language, and neural plasticity, and the skills and passion she passed on to us in pursuing our own endeavors in this field.

References

Archbold, S. M., Nikolopoulos, T. P., Tait, M., O'Donoghue, G. M., Lutman, M. E., & Gregory, S. (2011). Approach to communication, speech perception and intelligibility after paediatric cochlear implantation. *British Journal of Audiology*, *34*(4), 257–264.

Armstrong, B. A., Neville, H. J., Hillyard, S. A., & Mitchell, T. V. (2002). Auditory deprivation affects processing of motion, but not color. *Cognitive Brain Research*, *14*(3), 422–434.

Bavelier, D., Brozinsky, C., Tomann, A., Mitchell, T., Neville, H., & Liu, G. (2001). Impact of early deafness and early exposure to sign language on the cerebral organization for motion processing. *The Journal of Neuroscience*, *21*(22), 8931–8942.

Bavelier, D., Corina, D., Jezzard, P., Clark, V., Karni, A., Lalwani, A., Rauschecker, J. P., Braun, A., Turner, R., & Neville, H. J. (1998a). Hemispheric specialization for English and ASL. *NeuroReport*, *9*(7), 1537–1542.

Bavelier, D., Corina, D. P., & Neville, H. J. (1998b). Brain and language: A perspective from sign language. *Neuron*, *21*(2), 275 278.

Bavelier, D., Dye, M. W. G., & Hauser, P. C. (2006). Do deaf individuals see better? *Trends in Cognitive Sciences*, *10*(11), 512–518.

Bavelier, D., Tomann, A., Hutton, C., Mitchell, T., Corina, D., Liu, G., & Neville, H. (2000). Visual attention to the periphery is enhanced in congenitally deaf individuals. *The Journal of Neuroscience*, 20(17), RC93.

Bellugi, U., Poizner, H., & Klima, E. S. (1989). Language, modality and the brain. *Trends in Neurosciences*, *12*(10), 380–388.

Bialystok, E. (1999). Cognitive complexity and attentional control in the bilingual mind. *Child Development*, *70*(3), 636 644.

Bialystok, E., Craik, F., & Luk, G. (2008). Cognitive control and lexical access in younger and older bilinguals. *Journal of Experimental Psychology: Learning, Memory, and Cognition*, *34*(4), 859–873.

Bird, E. K.-R., Cleave, P., Trudeau, N., Thordardottir, E., Sutton, A., & Thorpe, A. (2005). The language abilities of bilingual children with Down syndrome. *American Journal of Speech-Language Pathology*, *14*(3), 187–199.

Boons, T., Raeve, L. D., Langereis, M., Peeraer, L., Wouters, J., & van Wieringen, A. (2013). Expressive vocabulary, morphology, syntax and narrative skills in profoundly deaf children after early cochlear implantation. *Research in Developmental Disabilities, 34*(6), 2008–2022.

Bosworth, R. G., & Dobkins, K. R. (1999). Left-hemisphere dominance for motion processing in deaf signers. *Psychological Science, 10*(3), 256–262.

Bosworth, R. G., & Dobkins, K. R. (2002a). The effects of spatial attention on motion processing in deaf signers, hearing signers, and hearing nonsigners. *Brain and Cognition, 49*(1), 152–169.

Bosworth, R. G., & Dobkins, K. R. (2002b). Visual field asymmetries for motion processing in deaf and hearing signers. *Brain and Cognition, 19*(1), 170 181.

Bottari, D., Nava, E., Ley, P., & Pavani, F. (2010). Enhanced reactivity to visual stimuli in deaf individuals. *Restorative Neurology and Neuroscience, 28*(2), 167–179.

Brentari, D., Coppola, M., Mazzoni, L., & Goldin-Meadow, S. (2011). When does a system become phonological? Handshape production in gesturers, signers, and homesigners. *Natural Language & Linguistic Theory, 30*(1), 1–31.

Brozinsky, C. J., & Bavelier, D. (2004). Motion velocity thresholds in deaf signers: Changes in lateralization but not in overall sensitivity. *Brain Research. Cognitive Brain Research, 21*(1), 1–10.

Capek, C. M., Grossi, G., Newman, A. J., McBurney, S. L., Corina, D., Roeder, B., & Neville, H. J. (2009). Brain systems mediating semantic and syntactic processing in deaf native signers: Biological invariance and modality specificity. *Proceedings of the National Academy of Sciences, 106*(21), 8784–8789.

Cardin, V., Orfanidou, E., Rönnberg, J., Capek, C. M., Rudner, M., & Woll, B. (2013). Dissociating cognitive and sensory neural plasticity in human superior temporal cortex. *Nature Communications, 4*(1), 1473–1475.

Cardin, V., Smittenaar, R. C., Orfanidou, E., Rönnberg, J., Capek, C. M., Rudner, M., & Woll, B. (2016). Differential activity in Heschl's gyrus between deaf and hearing individuals is due to auditory deprivation rather than language modality. *NeuroImage, 124*(Part A), 96–106.

Ceh, K. M., Bervinchak, D. M., & Francis, H. W. (2013). Early literacy gains in children with cochlear implants. *Otology and Neurotology, 34*, 416–421.

Chamberlain, C., & Mayberry, R. I. (2008). American Sign Language syntactic and narrative comprehension in skilled and less skilled readers: Bilingual and bimodal evidence for the linguistic basis of reading. *Applied Psycholinguistics, 29*(3), 367–388.

Champoux, F., Lepore, F., Gagné, J.-P., & Théoret, H. (2009). Visual stimuli can impair auditory processing in cochlear implant users. *Neuropsychologia, 47*(1), 17–22.

Colletti, L., Mandalà, M., Zoccante, L., Shannon, R. V., & Colletti, V. (2011). Infants versus older children fitted with cochlear implants: Performance over 10 years. *International Journal of Pediatric Otorhinolaryngology, 75*(4), 504–509.

Connor, C. M., Hieber, S., Arts, H. A., & Zwolan, T. A. (2000). Speech, vocabulary, and the education of children using cochlear implants oral or total communication? *Journal of Speech, Language, and Hearing Research, 43*(5), 1185–1204.

Connor, C. M., & Zwolan, T. A. (2004). Examining multiple sources of influence on the reading comprehension skills of children who use cochlear implants. *Journal of Speech, Language, and Hearing Research, 47*(3), 509–526.

Convertino, C. M., Marschark, M., Sapere, P., Sarchet, T., & Zupan, M. (2009). Predicting academic success among deaf college students. *The Journal of Deaf Studies and Deaf Education, 14*(3), 324–343.

Corina, D. P., Bellugi, U., & Reilly, J. (1999). Neuropsychological studies of linguistic and affective facial expressions in deaf signers. *Language and Speech, 42*(2–3), 307–331.

Corina, D. P., Poizner, H., Bellugi, U., Feinberg, T., Dowd, D., & O'Grady-Batch, L. (1992). Dissociation between linguistic and nonlinguistic gestural systems: A case for compositionality. *Brain and Language, 43*(3), 414–447.

Corina, D. P., Vaid, J., & Bellugi, U. (1992). The linguistic basis of left hemisphere specialization. *Science, 255*(5049), 1258–1260.

Cuda, D., Murri, A., Guerzoni, L., Fabrizi, E., & Mariani, V. (2014). Pre-school children have better spoken language when early implanted. *International Journal of Pediatric Otorhinolaryngology, 78*(8), 1327–1331.

Davidson, K., Lillo-Martin, D., & Pichler, D. C. (2014). Spoken English language development among native signing children with cochlear implants. *The Journal of Deaf Studies and Deaf Education, 19*(2), 238–250.

DesJardin, J. L., & Eisenberg, L. S. (2007). Maternal contributions: Supporting language development in young children with cochlear implants. *Ear and Hearing, 28*(4), 456.

Dettman, S. J., Dowell, R. C., Choo, D., Arnott, W., Abrahams, Y., Davis, A., Dornan, D., Leigh, J., Constantinescu, G., Cowan, R., & Briggs, R. J. (2016). Long-term communication outcomes for children receiving cochlear implants younger than 12 months: A multicenter study. *Otology & Neurotology, 37*(2), e82.

Dettman, S. J., Pinder, D., Briggs, R. J. S., Dowell, R. C., & Leigh, J. R. (2007). Communication development in children who receive the cochlear implant younger than 12 months: Risks versus benefits. *Ear and Hearing, 28*(2), 11S.

Doucet, M. E., Bergeron, F., Lassonde, M., Ferron, P., & Lepore, F. (2006). Cross-modal reorganization and speech perception in cochlear implant users. *Brain, 129*(12), 3376–3383.

Dye, M. W. G., Baril, D. E., & Bavelier, D. (2007). Which aspects of visual attention are changed by deafness? The case of the Attentional Network Test. *Neuropsychologia, 45*(8), 1801–1811.

Dye, M. W. G., Hauser, P. C., & Bavelier, D. (2009). Is visual selective attention in deaf individuals enhanced or deficient? The case of the useful field of view. *PLoS One, 4*(5), e5640.

Eggermont, J. J., & Ponton, C. W. (2003). Auditory-evoked potential studies of cortical maturation in normal hearing and implanted children: Correlations with changes in structure and speech perception. *Acta Oto-Laryngologica, 123*(2), 249–252.

Emmorey, K. (2021). New perspectives on the neurobiology of sign languages. *Frontiers in Communication, 6*, 748430.

Fagan, M. K., Bergeson, T. R., & Morris, K. J. (2014). Synchrony, complexity and directiveness in mothers' interactions with infants pre- and post-cochlear implantation. *Infant Behavior and Development, 37*(3), 249–257.

Feltmate, K., & Bird, E. (2008). Language learning in four bilingual children with down syndrome: A detailed analysis of vocabulary and morphosyntax. *Canadian Journal of Speech-Language Pathology and Audiology, 32*(1), 6–20.

Ferjan Ramirez, N., Leonard, M. K., Davenport, T. S., Torres, C., Halgren, E., & Mayberry, R. I. (2016). Neural language processing in adolescent first-language learners: Longitudinal Case studies in American Sign Language. *Cerebral Cortex, 26*(3), 1015–1026.

Ferjan Ramirez, N., Leonard, M. K., Torres, C., Hatrak, M., Halgren, E., & Mayberry, R. I. (2014). Neural language processing in adolescent first-language learners. *Cerebral Cortex, 1*(10), 2772–2783.

Fine, I., Finney, E. M., Boynton, G. M., & Dobkins, K. R. (2005). Comparing the effects of auditory deprivation and sign language within the auditory and visual cortex. *Journal of Cognitive Neuroscience, 17*(10), 1621–1637.

Finney, E. M., Fine, I., & Dobkins, K. R. (2001). Visual stimuli activate auditory cortex in the deaf. *Nature Neuroscience, 4*(12), 1171–1173.

Freel, B. L., Clark, M. D., Anderson, M. L., Gilbert, G. L., Musyoka, M. M., & Hauser, P. C. (2011). Deaf individuals' bilingual abilities: American sign language proficiency, reading skills, and family characteristics. *Psychology, 2*(1), 18–23.

Geers, A. E., Brenner, C. A., & Davidson, L. (2003). Factors associated with development of speech perception skills in children implanted by age five. *Ear and Hearing, 24*(1), 24S.

Geers, A. E., Brenner, C. A., & Tobey, E. A. (2011a). Long-term outcomes of cochlear implantation in early childhood: Sample characteristics and data collection methods. *Ear and Hearing, 32*(1), 2S.

Geers, A. E., & Sedey, A. L. (2011). Language and verbal reasoning skills in adolescents with 10 or more years of cochlear implant experience. *Ear and Hearing, 32*(1), 39S.

Geers, A. E., Strube, M. J., Tobey, E. A., Pisoni, D. B., & Moog, J. S. (2011b). Epilogue: Factors contributing to long-term outcomes of cochlear implantation in early childhood. *Ear and Hearing, 32*(1), 84S–92S.

Geers, A. E., Tobey, E. A., & Moog, J. S. (2011c). Editorial: Long-term outcomes of cochlear implantation in early childhood. *Ear and Hearing, 32*(Ci), 1S.

Giezen, M. R., Baker, A. E., & Escudero, P. (2014). Relationships between spoken word and sign processing in children with cochlear implants. *The Journal of Deaf Studies and Deaf Education, 19*(1), 107–125.

Global Burden of Disease Study 2013 Collaborators. (2015). Global, regional, and national incidence, prevalence, and years lived with disability for 301 acute and chronic diseases and injuries in 188 countries, 1990–2013: A systematic analysis for the Global Burden of Disease Study 2013. *The Lancet, 386*(9995), 743–800.

Goldin-Meadow, S. (2005). What language creation in the manual modality tells us about the foundations of language. *The Linguistic Review, 22*(2–4), 199–225.

Goodwyn, S. W., & Acredolo, L. P. (1993). Symbolic gesture versus word: Is there a modality advantage for onset of symbol use? *Child Development, 64*(3), 688–701.

Goodwyn, S. W., & Acredolo, L. P. (1998). Encouraging symbolic gestures: A new perspective on the relationship between gesture and speech. *New Directions for Child and Adolescent Development, 1998*(79), 61–73.

Goodwyn, S. W., Acredolo, L. P., & Brown, C. A. (2000). Impact of symbolic gesturing on early language development. *Journal of Nonverbal Behavior, 24*(2), 81–103.

Guldenoglu, B., Miller, P., Kargin, T., Hauser, P., Rathmann, C., & Kubus, O. (2014). A comparison of the letter-processing skills of hearing and deaf readers: Evidence from five orthographies. *The Journal of Deaf Studies and Deaf Education, 19*(2), 220–237.

Hall, M. L., Hall, W. C., & Caselli, N. K. (2019). Deaf children need language, not (just) speech. *First Language, 39*(4), 367–395.

Hickok, G., Bellugi, U., & Klima, E. S. (1996). The neurobiology of sign language and its implications for the neural basis of language. *Nature, 381*(6584), 699–702.

Hillyard, S. A., & Anllo-Vento, L. (1998). Event-related brain potentials in the study of visual selective attention. *Proceedings of the National Academy of Sciences of the United States of America, 95*(3), 781–787.

Hodges, A. V., Ash, M. D., Balkany, T. J., Schloffman, J. J., & Butts, S. L. (1999). Speech perception results in children with cochlear implants: Contributing factors. *Otolaryngology – Head and Neck Surgery, 121*(1), 31–34.

Horn, D. L., Fagan, M. K., Dillon, C. M., Pisoni, D. B., & Miyamoto, R. T. (2007). Visual-motor integration skills of prelingually deaf children: Implications for pediatric cochlear implantation. *The Laryngoscope, 117*(11), 2017–2025.

Horn, D. L., Pisoni, D. B., Sanders, M., & Miyamoto, R. T. (2005). Behavioral assessment of prelingually deaf children before cochlear implantation. *The Laryngoscope, 115*(9), 1603–1611.

Humphries, T., Kushalnagar, P., Mathur, G., Napoli, D. J., Padden, C., Rathmann, C., & Smith, S. R. (2012). Language acquisition for deaf children: Reducing the harms of zero tolerance to the use of alternative approaches. *Harm Reduction Journal, 9*(1), 16–16.

Kirk, E., Howlett, N., Pine, K. J., & Fletcher, B. C. (2012). To sign or not to sign? The impact of encouraging infants to gesture on infant language and maternal mind-mindedness. *Child Development, 84*(2), 574–590.

Klima, E. S., & Bellugi, U. (1979). *The signs of language*. Cambridge, MA: Harvard University Press.

Kral, A., & Lomber, S. G. (2015). Deaf white cats. *Current Biology, 25*(9), R351–R353.

Kral, A., & Sharma, A. (2012). Developmental neuroplasticity after cochlear implantation. *Trends in Neurosciences, 35*(2), 111–122.

Kuhl, P. K. (2004). Early language acquisition: Cracking the speech code. *Nature Reviews Neuroscience, 5*(11), 831–843.

Kutas, M., & Hillyard, S. A. (1980). Reading senseless sentences: Brain potentials reflect semantic incongruity. *Science, 207*(4427), 203–205.

Kutas, M., Neville, H. J., & Holcomb, P. J. (1987). A preliminary comparison of the N400 response to semantic anomalies during reading, listening and signing. *Electroencephalography and Clinical Neurophysiology. Supplement, 39*, 325–330. Scopus.

Land, R., Baumhoff, P., Tillein, J., Lomber, S. G., Hubka, P., & Kral, A. (2016). Cross-modal plasticity in higher-order auditory cortex of congenitally deaf cats does not limit auditory responsiveness to cochlear implants. *The Journal of Neuroscience, 36*(23), 6175–6185.

Leigh, J., Dettman, S., Dowell, R., & Briggs, R. (2013). Communication development in children who receive a cochlear implant by 12 months of age. *Otology & Neurotology, 34*(3), 443.

Lomber, S. G., Meredith, M. A., & Kral, A. (2010). Cross-modal plasticity in specific auditory cortices underlies visual compensations in the deaf. *Nature Neuroscience, 13*(11), 1421–1427.

MacSweeney, M., Calvert, G. A., Campbell, R., McGuire, P. K., David, A. S., Williams, S. C. R., Woll, B., & Brammer, M. J. (2002). Speechreading circuits in people born deaf. *Neuropsychologia, 40*(7), 801–807.

MacSweeney, M., Waters, D., Brammer, M. J., Woll, B., & Goswami, U. (2008). Phonological processing in deaf signers and the impact of age of first language acquisition. *NeuroImage, 40*(3), 1369–1379.

Mayberry, R. I. (2007). When timing is everything: Age of first-language acquisition effects on second-language learning. *Applied Psycholinguistics, 28*(3), 537–549.

Mayberry, R. I., Chen, J.-K., Witcher, P., & Klein, D. (2011). Age of acquisition effects on the functional organization of language in the adult brain. *Brain and Language, 119*(1), 16–29.

Mayberry, R. I., & Kluender, R. (2018). Rethinking the critical period for language: New insights into an old question from American Sign Language. *Bilingualism: Language and Cognition, 21*(5), 886–905.

Mayberry, R. I., & Lock, E. (2003). Age constraints on first versus second language acquisition: Evidence for linguistic plasticity and epigenesis. *Brain and Language, 87*(3), 369–384.

Mayberry, R. I., Lock, E., & Kazmi, H. (2002). Development: Linguistic ability and early language exposure. *Nature, 417*(6884), 38.

Mitchell, R. R., & Karchmer, M. A. (2004). Chasing the mythical ten percent: Parental hearing status of deaf and hard of hearing students in the United States. *Sign Language Studies, 4*(2), 138–163.

Moeller, M. P. (2000). Early intervention and language development in children who are deaf and hard of hearing. *Pediatrics, 106*(3), e43.

Mohammed, T., Campbell, R., MacSweeney, M., Milne, E., Hansen, P., & Coleman, M. (2005). Speechreading skill and visual movement sensitivity are related in deaf speech readers. *Perception, 34*(2), 205–216.

Moog, J. S., Geers, A. E., Gustus, C. H., & Brenner, C. A. (2011). Psychosocial adjustment in adolescents who have used cochlear implants since preschool. *Ear and Hearing, 32*(1), 75S.

Morford, J. P., & Goldin-Meadow, S. (1997). From here and now to there and then: The development of displaced reference in homesign and English. *Child Development, 68*(3), 420–435.

Mueller, V., Sepulveda, A., & Rodriguez, S. (2013). The effects of baby sign training on child development. *Early Child Development and Care, 184*(8), 1178–1191.

Mylander, C., & Goldin-Meadow, S. (1991). Home sign systems in deaf children: The development of morphology without a conventional language model. *Theoretical Issues in Sign Language Research, 2*, 41–63.

Neville, H. J. (1990). Intermodal competition and compensation in development. *Annals of the New York Academy of Sciences, 608*(1), 71–91.

Neville, H. J., Bavelier, D., Corina, D., Rauschecker, J., Karni, A., Lalwani, A., Braun, A., Clark, V., Jezzard, P., & Turner, R. (1998). Cerebral organization for language in deaf and hearing subjects: Biological constraints and effects of experience. *Proceedings of the National Academy of Sciences, 95*(3), 922–929.

Neville, H. J., Coffey, S. A., Lawson, D. S., Fischer, A., Emmorey, K., & Bellugi, U. (1997). Neural systems mediating American sign language: effects of sensory experience and age of acquisition. *Brain and Language, 57*(3), 285–308.

Neville, H. J., Kutas, M., & Schmidt, A. (1982a). Event-related potential studies of cerebral specialization during reading I. Studies of normal adults. *Brain and Language, 16*(2), 300–315.

Neville, H. J., Kutas, M., & Schmidt, A. (1982b). Event-related potential studies of cerebral specialization during reading II. Studies of congenitally deaf adults. *Brain and Language, 16*(2), 316–337.

Neville, H. J., Kutas, M., & Schmidt, A. (1984). Event-related potential studies of cerebral specialization during reading. *Annals of the New York Academy of Sciences, 425*(1), 370–376.

Neville, H. J., & Lawson, D. (1987a). Attention to central and peripheral visual space in a movement detection task: An event-related potential and behavioral study. I. Normal hearing adults. *Brain Research, 405*(2), 253–267.

Neville, H. J., & Lawson, D. (1987b). Attention to central and peripheral visual space in a movement detection task: An event-related potential and behavioral study: II. Congenitally deaf adults. *Brain Research, 405*(2), 268–283.

Neville, H. J., & Lawson, D. (1987c). Attention to central and peripheral visual space in a movement detection task. III. Separate effects of auditory deprivation and acquisition of a visual language. *Brain Research, 405*(2), 284–294.

Neville, H. J., Mills, D. L., & Lawson, D. S. (1992). Fractionating language: Different neural subsystems with different sensitive periods. *Cerebral Cortex*, *2*(3), 244–258.

Neville, H. J., Schmidt, A., & Kutas, M. (1983). Altered visual evoked potentials in congenitally deaf adults. *Brain Research*, *266*(1), 127–132.

Newman, A. J., Bavelier, D., Corina, D., Jezzard, P., & Neville, H. J. (2002). A critical period for right hemisphere recruitment in American Sign Language processing. *Nature Neuroscience*, *5*(1), 76–80.

Niparko, J. K., Tobey, E. A., Thal, D. J., & Eisenberg, L. S. (2010). Spoken language development in children following cochlear implantation. *Journal of the American Medical Association*, *303*(15), 1498.

Ohashi, J. K., Mirenda, P., Marinova-Todd, S., Hambly, C., Fombonne, E., Szatmari, P., Bryson, S., Roberts, W., Smith, I., Vaillancourt, T., Volden, J., Waddell, C., Zwaigenbaum, L., Georgiades, S., Duku, E., Thompson, A., & Team. (2012). Comparing early language development in monolingual- and bilingual- exposed young children with autism spectrum disorders. *Research in Autism Spectrum Disorders*, *6*(2), 890–897.

Pisoni, D. B., Kronenberger, W. G., Roman, A. S., & Geers, A. E. (2011). Measures of digit span and verbal rehearsal speed in deaf children after more than 10 years of cochlear implantation. *Ear and Hearing*, *32*(1), 60S.

Poizner, H., Bellugi, U., & Klima, E. S. (1987). *What the hands reveal about the brain*. Cambridge, MA: The MIT Press.

Proksch, J., & Bavelier, D. (2002). Changes in the spatial distribution of visual attention after early deafness. *Journal of Cognitive Neuroscience*, *14*(5), 687–701.

Pyman, B., Blamey, P., Lacy, P., Clark, G., & Dowell, R. (2000). The development of speech perception in children using cochlear implants: Effects of etiologic factors and delayed milestones. *The American Journal of Otology*, *21*(1), 57–61.

Quittner, A. L., Cruz, I., Barker, D. H., Tobey, E., Eisenberg, L. S., & Niparko, J. K. (2013). Effects of maternal sensitivity and cognitive and linguistic stimulation on cochlear implant users' language development over four years. *The Journal of Pediatrics*, *162*(2), 343–351.

Robbins, A. M. (2001). A sign of the times. *Advanced Bionics Corp*. Retrieved from www. advancedbionics.com/content/dam/ab/Global/en_ce/documents/libraries/SupportLibrary/Newsletters/Loud%20and%20Clear/A%20Sign%20of%20the%20Times.pdf

Ruffin, C. V., Kronenberger, W. G., Colson, B. G., Henning, S. C., & Pisoni, D. B. (2013). Long-term speech and language outcomes in prelingually deaf children, adolescents and young adults who received cochlear implants in childhood. *Audiology and Neurotology*, *18*(5), 289–296.

Sarant, J. Z., Blamey, P. J., Dowell, R. C., Clark, G. M., & Gibson, W. P. R. (2001). Variation in speech perception scores among children with cochlear implants. *Ear and Hearing*, *22*(1), 18.

Sarant, J. Z., Harris, D. C., Bennet, L., & Bant, S. (2014). Bilateral versus unilateral cochlear implants in children: A study of spoken language outcomes. *Ear and Hearing*, *35*(4), 396.

Sarant, J. Z., Harris, D. C., Galvin, K. L., Bennet, L. A., Canagasabey, M., & Busby, P. A. (2018). Social development in children with early cochlear implants. *Ear and Hearing*, *39*(4), 770–782.

Sarant, J. Z., Holt, C. M., Dowell, R. C., Rickards, F. W., & Blamey, P. J. (2008). Spoken language development in oral preschool children with permanent childhood deafness. *The Journal of Deaf Studies and Deaf Education*, *14*(2), 205–217.

Scott, G. D., Karns, C. M., Dow, M. W., Stevens, C., & Neville, H. J. (2014). Enhanced peripheral visual processing in congenitally deaf humans is supported by multiple brain regions, including primary auditory cortex. *Frontiers in Human Neuroscience, 8*, 177.

Scott, J. A., & Henner, J. (2020). Second verse, same as the first: On the use of signing systems in modern interventions for deaf and hard of hearing children in the USA. *Deafness & Education International, 23*(2), 1–19.

Sharma, A., Campbell, J., & Cardon, G. (2015). Developmental and cross-modal plasticity in deafness: Evidence from the P1 and N1 event related potentials in cochlear implanted children. *International Journal of Psychophysiology, 95*(2), 135–144.

Sharma, A., Dorman, M. F., & Kral, A. (2005). The influence of a sensitive period on central auditory development in children with unilateral and bilateral cochlear implants. *Hearing Research, 203*(1–2), 134 143.

Sharma, A., Dorman, M. F., & Spahr, A. J. (2002). A sensitive period for the development of the central auditory system in children with cochlear implants: Implications for age of implantation. *Ear and Hearing, 23*(6), 532–539.

Sharma, A., Nash, A. A., & Dorman, M. (2009). Cortical development, plasticity and re-organization in children with cochlear implants. *Journal of Communication Disorders, 42*(4), 272–279.

Stevens, C., & Neville, H. (2006). Neuroplasticity as a double-edged sword: Deaf enhancements and dyslexic deficits in motion processing. *Journal of Cognitive Neuroscience, 18*(5), 701–714.

Stokoe, W. C., Casterline, D. C., & Croneberg, C. G. (1976). *Dictionary of ASL on linguistic principles*. Silver Spring, MD: Linstok Press.

Svirsky, M. A., Robbins, A. M., Kirk, K. I., Pisoni, D. B., & Miyamoto, R. T. (2000). Language development in profoundly deaf children with cochlear implants. *Psychological Science, 11*(2), 153–158.

Tobey, E. A., Geers, A. E., Sundarrajan, M., & Shin, S. (2011). Factors influencing speech production in elementary and high school-aged cochlear implant users. *Ear and Hearing, 32*(1), 27S.

Tobey, E. A., Thal, D., Niparko, J. K., Eisenberg, L. S., Quittner, A. L., Wang, N.-Y., & Team, T. C. I. (2013). Influence of implantation age on school-age language performance in pediatric cochlear implant users. *International Journal of Audiology, 52*(4), 219–229.

Twomey, T., Price, C. J., Waters, D., & MacSweeney, M. (2020). The impact of early language exposure on the neural system supporting language in deaf and hearing adults. *NeuroImage*, 116411.

Vohr, B. (2003). Overview: Infants and children with hearing loss – Part I. *Mental Retardation and Developmental Disabilities Research Reviews, 9*(2), 62–64.

Walker, E. A., & Bass-Ringdahl, S. (2008). Babbling complexity and its relationship to speech and language outcomes in children with cochlear implants. *Otology & Neurotology, 29*(2), 225.

Weber-Fox, C. M., & Neville, H. J. (1996). Maturational constraints on functional specializations for language processing: ERP and behavioral evidence in bilingual speakers. *Journal of Cognitive Neuroscience, 8*(3), 231–256.

Interlude 5

SOUND OR SIGN?

Marta Kutas

Is it the mode of language or the auditory deprivation that accounts for
the observed differences in behavior or the ERP manifestation that
distinguishes someone congenitally deaf from another
who can hear just fine
on tests of visual perception, motion detection,
visuospatial attention, language comprehension or some like paradigm?

Flashing linguistic or nonlinguistic stimuli
at the fovea or in the visual periphery
Neville adjudicated between these alternative hypotheses, rather cleverly,
With a comparison group, called HOD,
of individuals whose hearing was normal and
grew up in a household where fingerspelling and visuo-manual sign,
pointing, handshapes, and movements of the hands in space
with accompanying facial expressions was the formal way
to explain, confess, and "verbally" opine.

Her experimental logic transparently clear:
when the results most closely adhere to those who can hear
group differences are ascribed to the fact that deaf individuals
are auditorily deprived
whereas when results are peer to those of deaf individuals
the responsible rulers
are from language experience derived.

DOI: 10.4324/9780429342356-14

8

MAKING MEMORIES LAST

How sleep promotes neuroplasticity

Randolph F. Helfrich and Robert T. Knight

Helen never seemed to sleep and had boundless energy. Her interests ranged far and wide and her trainees (like R.T.K.) were primed to have her sense of exploration. One of Helen's key interests was the plasticity of the human brain. In recent years, a multitude of research has revealed the pivotal role of sleep in mediating neuroplasticity in support of long-term memory formation. While sleep was not a topic that Helen studied herself, we are sure she would approve of its relevance for neuroplasticity. With that early career guidance, we dedicate this sleep chapter to Helen and review the most recent evidence of the role of sleep in forming lasting memories.

Sleep and memory formation

The systematic investigation of how sleep benefits memory formation started almost a century ago and since then it has mainly been governed by three key dogmas (Diekelmann & Born, 2010; Rasch & Born, 2013). First, it had been assumed that sleep's benefit on memory is the result of a passive process that guards new memories by reducing interference. Second, it had been thought that dreams during rapid eye movement (REM) sleep constitute a functional key substrate of memory consolidation; and third, a key emphasis had been on the role of the hippocampus in governing memory processes. In this chapter, we review the origins of these hypotheses and summarize a more contemporary model of sleep-dependent memory consolidation, which posits that memory consolidation is an active – and not a passive – process, which primarily takes place during non-REM (NREM) sleep (and not REM) and is dependent more on the neocortex than previously suspected.

In 1924, Jenkins and Dallenbach provided the first empirical evidence for sleep's role in memory formation (Jenkins & Dallenbach, 1924). Over the course

DOI: 10.4324/9780429342356-15

of almost two months, they repeatedly tested two participants who had to memorize nonsense syllables across different time intervals ranging from one to eight hours. Notably, they observed that recall performance was better when the participants slept during the retention interval. Initially, these exciting results were interpreted as "reduced interference" between the memorized and novel information (i.e., the time spent asleep shields new memories by reducing distractions that are abundant in the wake state). However, over time several lines of research questioned this passive theory and began to consider whether sleep itself might play a more active role in memory consolidation (Rasch & Born, 2013).

The interest in sleep-dependent memory formation was further fueled by the discovery of REM sleep by Aserinsky and Kleitman in 1953 (Aserinsky & Kleitman, 1953). The electroencephalogram (EEG) of REM sleep closely resembled electrical patterns as observed during wakefulness, while the participants were immobilized by muscle atonia and only their eye globes rapidly moved under the closed eyelids. An influential hypothesis suggested that since REM sleep is particularly associated with dreams, this might promote memory reactivation and consolidation during REM sleep (Rasch & Born, 2013). This idea was appealing because the EEG of REM sleep featured much richer spatiotemporal dynamics than non-REM sleep, which is characterized by highly synchronous bursts of slow wave (<2 Hz; Steriade et al., 1993) and spindle oscillations (11–16 Hz; De Gennaro & Ferrara, 2003). In particular, the presence of slow waves resembles other states of unconsciousness, such as coma or anesthesia, and, hence, was thought to index an unengaged cortex (Brown et al., 2010). However, in the 1980s several researchers, including Mircea Steriade (Steriade & Amzica, 1998; Steriade et al., 1987, 1993a, 1993b) and Gyorgy Buzsáki (Buzsáki, 1996, 1998), started to study the neurophysiological basis of sleep oscillations in more detail and soon came to realize that they might subserve information transfer and directed communication between different cortical and subcortical regions (Sirota & Buzsáki, 2005; Sirota et al., 2003; Steriade et al., 1993a). Since then, a wealth of evidence further substantiated these assertions, which now collectively indicates that NREM – not REM – sleep supports sleep-dependent memory formation (Diekelmann & Born, 2010; Rasch & Born, 2013; Walker & Stickgold, 2006).

Finally, the study of memory is inextricably linked to the hippocampus. Starting with patient H.M., a multitude of memory research has focused on hippocampal processing (Corkin, 2002; Squire, 2009). However, more recently several lines of research uncovered early cortical contributions to memory encoding and several reports studying sleep dynamics further suggested that cortical contributions might constitute a key element in organizing the hippocampal-neocortical dialogue in support of memory formation (Buzsáki, 1996; Sirota & Buzsáki, 2005).

In this chapter, we review the available evidence that supports the idea that NREM sleep oscillations constitute a functional substrate of memory reactivation, transfer, and consolidation during sleep.

The engram: sleep-dependent memory formation

The engram refers to the physical trace of a memory that is stored in the brain (Kitamura et al., 2017). However, there is no consensus about the level of observation that is needed to unequivocally establish the presence of an engram (Dudai, 2004). Therefore, depending on the chosen imaging modality, engrams have been observed at the level of single cells spiking, local field potentials, or even the functional magnetic resonance imaging signal (Rasch & Born, 2013). Hence, an engram can be found, for example, in the firing pattern of a cell ensemble (Eichenbaum, 2018), at the level of synaptic weights, which reflect short-term plasticity in support of memory maintenance (Stokes, 2015), or at the level of large-scale brain connectivity, where the precise spatiotemporal connectivity pattern could encode a distinct memory.

In particular, the investigations by Karl Lashley demonstrated that memories might not only be characterized by a single engram but are actually characterized by a brain-wide distributed pattern (Lashley, 1950). Contemporary imaging further supported this notion and it became increasingly clear that memory systems rely on the functional interaction of widely distributed, but functionally specialized, processing hubs (Buzsáki, 2015; Johnson & Knight, 2015). These networks span subcortical and cortical regions and typically include sensory cortices, the hippocampi, and prefrontal and parietal association areas. Furthermore, memory processes are often defined according to the mnemonic information, such as declarative and procedural memories, episodic or semantic memories, or explicit and implicit memories (Diekelmann & Born, 2010; Rasch & Born, 2013). However, it remains unclear if these different types of memories all rely on distinct neural mechanisms or if there is one common denominator that links seemingly different and abstract memory representations.

Taken together, the search for the engram is an overarching goal of contemporary cognitive neuroscience and there is currently little consensus on what level of observation and abstraction is necessary to detect an unequivocal memory representation in the brain (Dudai, 2004; Kitamura et al., 2017).

Systems memory consolidation theory

The systems memory consolidation theory proposes a framework that explains how newly acquired information, which is initially mainly hippocampus-dependent, undergoes a transformation and consolidation during sleep (Diekelmann & Born, 2010). In general, it is believed that newly acquired information is initially encoded in the hippocampus (Buzsáki, 2015). Over time, these newly acquired memories become less and less hippocampus-dependent, and become progressively more dependent on neocortical association areas (Maingret et al., 2016; Walker & Stickgold, 2006). In particular, the prefrontal cortex is thought to constitute a core structure for long-term memory instantiation (Stuss & Knight,

2013). This hypothesis strongly emphasizes the role of hippocampal-prefrontal pathways, which have been studied in great detail over the last three decades (Buzsáki, 1996; Maingret et al., 2016; Peyrache et al., 2009; Sirota et al., 2003). Critically, a large body of evidence stems from recordings in rodents, which poses a problem: Which areas constitute the prefrontal cortex in rodents (Carlén, 2017; Laubach et al., 2018)? Even within the field, there is currently only little consensus on whether rodents exhibit an equivalent to the human prefrontal cortex, the brain region that underwent the strongest development during evolution. The rodent prefrontal cortex may resemble human medial prefrontal regions, but most likely not portions of the dorsolateral or orbitofrontal cortex (Carlén, 2017).

The active systems memory consolidation theory suggests that spontaneous replay of mnemonic information initially strengthens the memory representations in the hippocampus (Antony & Schapiro, 2019; Foster, 2017). Replay refers to the fact that firing sequences that were first observed during the encoding of new information are now spontaneously "replayed" during rest or sleep (Foster, 2017; Peyrache et al., 2009). Notably, this replay can also occur in a time-compressed or reversed temporal order. This idea is in line with the idea of neuroplasticity as expressed by Hebb: "Cells that fire together wire together" (Hebb, 1949). The repeated joint firing of any coalition of neurons in a fixed sequence is thought to strengthen the weak representation of new memories. Critically, replay does not occur in isolation but is associated with a hippocampal sharp-wave-ripple oscillation (SWR; 100–200 Hz; Buzsáki, 2015). SWR is one of the most synchronized oscillations in the brain and likely reflects the joint firing of several hundred hippocampal cells in a synchronous manner. This high level of synchrony likely constitutes a temporal reference frame for cells to fire and helps to structure and strengthen the population firing code that is associated with the encoding of new information.

Evidence in support of this idea came from a recent human intracranial study that utilized direct hippocampal recordings to track both ripples and mnemonic representations (Zhang et al., 2018), which were quantified using representational similarity analysis (RSA; Kriegeskorte et al., 2008). RSA quantifies the similarity (or correlation) between an engram-like pattern during encoding, which can be either defined across time or across space and as a pattern that re-occurs at a later time point. Critically, Zhang et al. assessed the pattern during sleep, specifically in temporal proximity to the ripple event (Figure 8.1). They observed that ripples and replay of later remembered items were tightly coupled in time, which was less evident for items that were later forgotten. Hence, the authors established the behavioral relevance of ripple-mediated replay in the human hippocampus (Zhang et al., 2018).

These findings are in line with observations from rodent studies that demonstrated that cells fire preferentially during certain ripple phases (Buzsáki, 2015), hence supporting the notion that population oscillations and firing interact bi-directionally (Fröhlich & McCormick, 2010): The firing of thousands of cells gives rise to local field potentials, which in turn serve as a feedback mechanism to guide and structure neuronal firing. Taken together, multiple lines of research now converge on the notion that the hippocampal replay and ripple oscillations are hallmarks of memory consolidation.

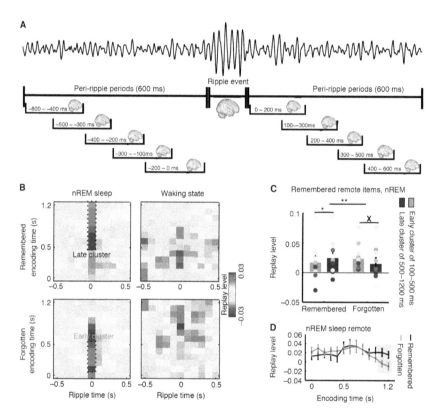

FIGURE 8.1   Hippocampal ripples and replay. (a) Empirical evidence for replay in humans was obtained from intracranial EEG recordings (dots reflect representative intracranial electrodes). *Top*: One exemplary ripple event and analysis strategy by means of a moving window approach. Evidence for replay (or reinstatement of mnemonic content) is quantified by the correlation of the spontaneous pattern with the pattern that was present during encoding. (b) Upper: Selective reinstatement of mnemonic representations during the ripple event ($t = 0$) during sleep (left) but not during wakefulness (right). *Lower*: Later forgotten items are characterized by a different pattern. (c) Interaction of encoding time and later remembered/forgotten items. (d) Replay is enhanced for later remembered items in a later time window.

Source: From Zhang et al. (2018). Figure reproduced with permission under the Creative Commons Attribution (CC BY) license.

Both replay and ripples are predominantly observed in the hippocampus but recently several groups have reported similar phenomena in the neocortex (Khodagholy et al., 2017; Norman et al., 2019; Peyrache et al., 2009; Vaz et al., 2019). In the classic systems memory consolidation theory, the transfer of mnemonic information from the hippocampus to the neocortex is organized by the two other cardinal sleep oscillations, namely slow waves (Steriade et al., 1993b) and spindles (De Gennaro & Ferrara, 2003; Steriade et al., 1993a).

Hippocampal ripples do not occur in isolation but are tightly nested in the trough of cortical sleep spindles (Clemens et al., 2007; Helfrich et al., 2019; Staresina et al., 2015), which in turn are nested in the peak of the slow wave, thus constituting a hierarchical triple coupling (Latchoumane et al., 2017) across three spatial (neocortex, thalamus, and hippocampus) and three temporal (~1, ~11–16, and 100–200 Hz) scales. It was assumed that the ripple triggered a cortical depolarization, which in turn triggered the expression of a spindle in thalamo-cortical loops (Mak-McCully et al., 2017; Steriade et al., 1987), which then arrived in the neocortex precisely during the "up-state" of the slow wave as recently demonstrated (Mak-McCully et al., 2017). A multitude of evidence suggested that slow waves and spindles promote the ideal neurophysiological milieu to mediate neuroplasticity to permanently store memories in neocortical circuits (Bergmann & Born, 2018; Niethard et al., 2018). Overall, this framework underscores a key role of the ripple in organizing large-scale networks in support of memory formation (Buzsáki, 2015). Critically, it also emphasized both the role of NREM sleep as well as the active role of sleep in mediating memory formation, hence contradicting the classic notion that sleep only passively guards new memories by reducing interference.

In recent years, several lines of investigation began to question the hippocampus-centric view of the systems memory consolidation theory. For instance, if replay and ripples occur spontaneously, which mechanisms ensure that the cortex is in a favorable state to utilize the supplied information (Sirota & Buzsáki, 2005)? An alternative account suggested that the directionality might be reversed: The cortical slow wave might trigger a thalamic spindle during its "down-state," which then arrives in the neocortex during the "up-state," that is, with a delay of half-a-cycle of the slow wave (Helfrich et al., 2019; Staresina et al., 2015). Jointly, these two might then shape the expression of the hippocampal ripple and replay of information. This process would ensure that information would be sent back to the neocortex when it is in a favorable state for further processing. This mechanism is discussed in more detail in the next paragraph.

NREM oscillations time information reactivation, transfer, and consolidation

Sleep oscillations are organized on multiple temporal scales. Most studies focus on the intrinsic or primary frequency of the oscillatory events (11–16 Hz activity) for spindles (De Gennaro & Ferrara, 2003; Steriade et al., 1987). However, upon closer inspection, sleep reveals a multitude of additional temporal scales. For instance, spindles do not occur in isolation but are tightly coupled to slow waves and ripples (Diekelmann & Born, 2010; Helfrich et al., 2019; Latchoumane et al., 2017), thus forming a cross-frequency dependency between different primary temporal scales. Furthermore, spindles periodically re-occur every 3–6 s (~0.3 Hz; Antony et al., 2018a; Helfrich et al., 2019), hence constituting a second-order temporal structure in the spindle amplitude. This fluctuation of the spindle amplitude is reminiscent of the infraslow oscillation (<0.1 Hz; Lecci et al., 2017; Watson, 2018) that has been shown to capture slow fluctuations during NREM sleep. Another extended temporal scale is that NREM and REM sleep cycle approximately every 90 min (Rasch & Born, 2013), while sleep and wakefulness are organized in blocks of ~8 h of sleep versus ~16 h of wakefulness. These examples are not exhaustive but are meant to illustrate the numerous temporal scales that govern sleep physiology.

Here we focus on the second-order rhythm of sleep spindles because recent evidence implied that the alternating of high-synchrony "spindle" and low-synchrony "no-spindle" states might actually reveal a fundamental property of the hippocampal-neocortical dialogue (Antony et al., 2018a, 2019; Hanslmayr et al., 2016; Helfrich et al., 2019). As reviewed earlier, it is reported that slow wave–spindle coupling shapes hippocampal ripples and replay (Latchoumane et al., 2017; Staresina et al., 2015). In this framework, spindles mainly serve as a messenger mechanism that conveys timing information from the neocortex to the hippocampus (Helfrich et al., 2019). However, spindles themselves have also been implicated in mediating neuroplasticity (De Gennaro & Ferrara, 2003) and might reflect a direct functional substrate that cements memories into long-term storage. Hence, spindles have been associated with at least two distinct functions (messenger versus plasticity mediator) in the brain.

However, this distinction overlooks the fact that comparable long episodes of NREM sleep are actually oscillation-free; that is, there is no apparent spindle or slow-wave activity in between two spindles, thus giving rise to a surprisingly desynchronized EEG during NREM sleep, which is characterized by a state of high entropy (Hanslmayr et al., 2016). In contrast, spindles are highly synchronized events that are accompanied by a state of reduced entropy. In the Shannon information theoretical framework (Quian Quiroga & Panzeri, 2009), high entropy is beneficial to imprint new information onto a circuit. Hence, it is conceivable that the inter-spindle interval subserves one function that has been previously associated with spindles, namely mediating plasticity (Antony et al., 2018a; Helfrich et al., 2019).

Here, spindles would trigger information reactivation and transfer from the hippocampus to the neocortex. Hippocampal-mediated information transfer peaks after the spindle has already subsided, that is, in a state of maximal cortical desynchronization during NREM sleep. In this state, the hippocampus supplies

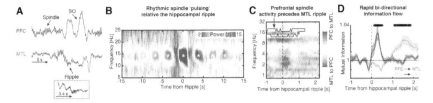

FIGURE 8.2   Bidirectional MTL–PFC interactions for inter-areal information transfer. (A) Oscillatory communication between the PFC and MTL. PFC activity is dominated by spindle and slow waves oscillations, while the ripple oscillations can be seen in the MTL. Simultaneous recordings reveal that spindle synchrony precedes ripple expression. (B) Rhythmic spindle pulsing relative to the hippocampal ripple (at *t* = 0). Note spindles (white asterisks) periodically re-occur every 3–6 s. (C) Directional information flow from the prefrontal cortex to the medial temporal lobe before the ripple (arrow, black outline highlights the statistically significant time–frequency pairs as determined by cluster-based permutation statistics) indicates that the prefrontal cortex is driving the ripple expression in the medial temporal lobe and that spindle (~16 Hz) serves as a key messenger mechanism to convey the directed influence. (D) Bidirectional information flow relative to the hippocampal ripple. Note that the flow from PFC to MTL is enhanced just after the ripple oscillations, while the expected MTL to PFC flow is only evident after 1 s.

newly encoded memories, which can efficiently be processed in the neocortex, which at that point is not engaged in a high-synchronous spindle state. Hence, information can efficiently be imprinted onto neocortical circuits in between two spindles (Figure 8.2). This hypothesis is in line with the observation that cue-trigger information reactivation was more efficient during the spindle than during the inter-spindle interval (Antony et al., 2018a; Cairney et al., 2018). Therefore, the two most prominent functions that have been associated with spindle activity might be the result of two different temporal scales that govern spindle expression and activity.

Coordinated neural rhythms and neuroplasticity

How can time-varying neural activity that rhythmically waxes and wanes support the formation of stable and continuous mnemonic representations (Helfrich & Knight, 2016)? A multitude of evidence on cross-frequency coupling implicated that coordinated neural activity might create a neurophysiological milieu that is ideal for information encoding, maintenance, and consolidation (Axmacher et al., 2010; Canolty & Knight, 2010; Canolty et al., 2006; Johnson & Knight, 2015).

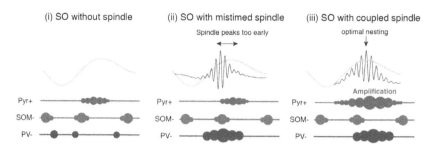

FIGURE 8.3 Relationship of cell firing and SO-spindle coupling. Schematics of cell-specific activity during a SO and SO-spindle coupling [adapted from (Niethard et al., 2018)]. (i) Excitatory activity in pyramidal neurons (Pyr+) is increased during the SO peak, while SOM interneuron activity is strongest during the state transitions from the down-to-up state and vice versa. (ii) The spindle peaks prematurely, hence is sub-optimally coupled to the SO. Note that spindle activity was associated with activity in PV neurons. (iii) When the spindle coincides with the SO peak then the Pyr+ activity was increased by more than 300%. This circuit is thought to optimize synaptic plasticity and support long-term memory retention.

One key assumption is that different neuronal rhythms are associated with different firing patterns of excitatory and inhibitory cells, which could mediate the storage of newly acquired information (Bergmann & Born, 2018; Canolty & Knight, 2010; Hyafil et al., 2015; Niethard et al., 2018). However, empirical evidence for this consideration remains surprisingly sparse.

One recent study that employed two-photon calcium imaging combined with electrophysiology during sleep in rodents provided an essential missing piece to the puzzle (Figure 8.3). Niethard and colleagues used wide-field two-photon calcium imaging to track the activity of excitatory (pyramidal cells; Pyr) as well inhibitory somatostatin (SOM) and parvalbumin-positive neurons over posterior cortical areas (Niethard et al., 2018). By recording simultaneous EEG, they were able to relate distinct firing patterns to oscillatory events, such as slow waves and spindles. Importantly, they also studied the interaction of slow waves and spindles. Their results jointly suggest that slow waves and spindles are characterized by a stereotypical firing pattern that consists of Pyr, SOM, and photovoltaic (PV)-cell activity. Critically, only when spindles were perfectly coupled to slow waves, did the authors observe an exponential increase in excitatory firing, which promotes the ideal neurophysiological milieu for neuroplasticity (Bergmann & Born, 2018). Hence, these findings reflect a milestone in explaining how neuronal rhythms interact with cell firing in support of memory formation.

It is very likely that similar considerations also apply to cross-frequency coupling as observed during encoding and wakefulness (Canolty & Knight, 2010; Hyafil et al., 2015; Johnson & Knight, 2015). During wakefulness, the two most prominent rhythms are the theta (4–8 Hz; Colgin, 2013) and the gamma (~40–80 Hz;

Fries, 2015) rhythms, which have been associated with a range of cognitive operations but have repeatedly been implicated with memory encoding, maintenance, and retrieval processes in the brain (Axmacher et al., 2010; Watrous et al., 2015). It would be an important advance to link these population oscillations to specific firing patterns in the human brain; however, current single-unit recording techniques in humans do not allow a clear differentiation into putative excitatory and inhibitory cells (Fried, Rutishauser et al., 2014; Rutishauser, 2019). Comparative work in non-human primates or rodents might provide the necessary means to bridge the explanatory gap between firing patterns, population oscillations, and behavior.

Boosting sleep-dependent memory consolidation through electrical brain stimulation to alleviate age- and disease-related decline

If neuronal oscillations are causally involved in forming new memories and mediating neuroplasticity, then one intriguing hypothesis is that modulation of these oscillatory patterns should impact memory formation (Hanslmayr et al., 2019). In a seminal experiment conducted approximately 15 years ago, researchers stimulated the prefrontal cortex in humans with slow (0.75 Hz) oscillating currents during sleep (Marshall et al., 2006). Marshall et al. reported that active stimulation improved memory recall performance the next day and critically, this was accompanied by an increase in the slow wave as well as spindle power. In particular, the latter finding was very encouraging, since it demonstrated that the oscillatory signatures do not occur in isolation, but are reciprocally coupled (Clemens et al., 2007; Staresina et al., 2015). Hence, if one modifies one of the cardinal sleep oscillations, then one will also impact coupled interactions. However, in the wake of these initially very promising results, several groups failed to observe similar effects and the evidence to date remains equivocal, as both successful and failed replications have been reported in the literature (Ladenbauer et al., 2017; Lafon et al., 2017; Lustenberger et al., 2016). Nevertheless, this line of research is actively being developed because it provides the unique opportunity to non-invasively modulate memory pathways that might be impaired in age- and disease-related cognitive decline (Wilckens et al., 2018). Two recent studies provided further support for this possibility.

In the first study employing whole-head scalp EEG recordings, it had been observed that older participants perform worse than younger participants on a declarative hippocampus-dependent overnight memory task, in which new associations between words and nonsense words are encoded (e.g., "bird" and "jubu"; Helfrich et al., 2018; Mander et al., 2013). Critically, both older and younger participants exhibited a comparable number of slow waves and spindles, and differences in their morphological features did not explain differences in task performance. However, it had been noticed that spindles peak prematurely in older participants – hence, indicating that the cardinal sleep oscillations in older participants were systematically mistimed, but not absent (Helfrich et al., 2018). Importantly, a difference that was as small as 50 ms predicted impaired memory formation in older participants (Figure 8.4). Furthermore, this functional deficit is directly correlated with the amount of grey matter (GM) atrophy in the medial prefrontal cortex.

In a second related study, the findings were recently replicated (Muehlroth et al., 2019). These results were encouraging because they implied that older participants exhibited all necessary substrates of successful overnight memory

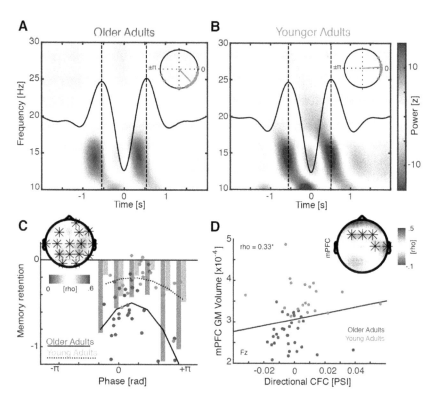

FIGURE 8.4   Impaired slow wave–spindle coupling predicts memory deficits. (A) SO trough-locked time–frequency representation (TFR) reveals elevated spindle power just before the SO peaks (dashed lines) in older adults. The inset highlights the average SO-spindle coupling phase across 32 older adults. (B) SO trough-locked TFR demonstrates that states of high spindle power coincide with SO peaks in younger adults. Same conventions as in panel A. (C) The precise SO-spindle coupling phase predicts overnight memory retention. In both groups, less forgetting was associated with more optimal coupling closer to the SO up-state (around 0°). (D) The strength of the directional influence of the SO phase on spindle power correlates with GM volume in the mPFC, suggesting that age-related atrophy impairs the temporal coordination of SOs and spindles, and hence impairs memory performance.

Source: The graphs are reproduced with permission from (Helfrich et al., 2018).

consolidation, such as slow waves and spindles, but these events were misaligned (Bergmann & Born, 2018; Helfrich et al., 2018; Muehlroth et al., 2019). This finding raises the question of whether it is possible to resynchronize these two events and alleviate memory disorders (Wilckens et al., 2018). Results that support this notion had recently been reported by another group in patients with mild cognitive impairment, where non-invasive brain stimulation was successfully used to increase both the coupling strength as well as to readjust the timing of the slow wave and spindle interaction (Ladenbauer et al., 2017). While this study is encouraging, the reviewed evidence is by no means conclusive and large trials are required to assess the efficacy of non-invasive stimulation protocols in alleviating age- and disease-related deficits in sleep oscillation coordination.

However, we speculate that this will be an emergent issue in future years since evidence is mounting that impaired slow wave–spindle coordination is also implicated in tau- and amyloid-pathologies in the medial MTL and PFC, respectively (Winer et al., 2019). For instance, Winer et al. reported that cortical slow wave–spindle coupling is reduced in patients with increased tau burden in the medial temporal lobe, which might signal a selective disruption of the hippocampal-neocortical dialogue during sleep. Given the societal burden of neurodegenerative diseases and the lack of treatment options, it is likely that the option of non-invasive electrical modulation will be further explored in the future to improve memory functions in patients with neurodegenerative diseases.

Conclusions

Taken together, we reviewed how cardinal sleep oscillations support active systems memory consolidation and discuss three main points. First, memory consolidation during sleep is a fundamentally active and not passive process. In other words, the sleeping brain generates prominent oscillatory patterns, which subserves the consolidation of new memories and their permanent storage in the neocortical association cortex (Diekelmann & Born, 2010; Helfrich et al., 2019; Rasch & Born, 2013). Second, the reviewed evidence emphasizes the key role of the neocortex in organizing information transfer from the hippocampus. In contrast to previous views, this framework posits that the hippocampal-neocortical dialogue is an "invited" dialogue, thus, forming cortico-hippocampal–cortical loops that ensure that mnemonic information arrives in the neocortex at favorable time points for subsequent processing (Antony et al., 2019; Buzsáki, 2015; Sirota & Buzsáki, 2005). Third, contemporary theories highlight the role of NREM sleep for memory formation, which is in stark contrast to previous considerations, which favored REM sleep. Currently, the role of REM sleep is not well understood (Boyce et al., 2017). In particular, REM sleep in humans is not characterized by prominent oscillation as REM sleep in rodents, where strong theta oscillations are evident (Gonzalez et al., 2018). It will be of great interest for future work to see what the role of REM sleep is in organizing the hippocampal-neocortical dialogue in support of memory consolidation.

Funding

This work was supported by the German Research Foundation (Emmy Noether Program, DFG HE8329/2–1; R.F.H.), the Hertie Foundation (Network for Excellence in Clinical Neuroscience; R.F.H.) and a NINDS grant R37NS21135 (R.T.K.).

References

Antony, J. W., Piloto, L., Wang, M., Pacheco, P., Norman, K. A., & Paller, K. A. (2018a). Sleep spindle refractoriness segregates periods of memory reactivation. *Current Biology: CB, 28*(11), 1736–1743.e4. https://doi.org/10.1016/j.cub.2018.04.020

Antony, J. W., & Schapiro, A. C. (2019). Active and effective replay: Systems consolidation reconsidered again. *Nature Reviews Neuroscience, 20*(8), 506–507. https://doi.org/10.1038/s41583-019-0191-8

Antony, J. W., Schönauer, M., Staresina, B. P., & Cairney, S. A. (2019). Sleep spindles and memory reprocessing. *Trends in Neurosciences, 42*(1), 1–3. https://doi.org/10.1016/j.tins.2018.09.012

Aserinsky, E., & Kleitman, N. (1953). Regularly occurring periods of eye motility, and concomitant phenomena, during sleep. *Science, 118*(3062), 273–274.

Axmacher, N., Henseler, M. M., Jensen, O., Weinreich, I., Elger, C. E., & Fell, J. (2010). Cross-frequency coupling supports multi-item working memory in the human hippocampus. *Proceedings of the National Academy of Sciences of the United States of America, 107*(7), 3228–3233. https://doi.org/10.1073/pnas.0911531107

Bergmann, T. O., & Born, J. (2018). Phase-amplitude coupling: A general mechanism for memory processing and synaptic plasticity? *Neuron, 97*(1), 10–13. https://doi.org/10.1016/j.neuron.2017.12.023

Boyce, R., Williams, S., & Adamantidis, A. (2017). REM sleep and memory. *Current Opinion in Neurobiology, 44*, 167–177. https://doi.org/10.1016/j.conb.2017.05.001

Brown, E. N., Lydic, R., & Schiff, N. D. (2010). General anesthesia, sleep, and coma. *The New England Journal of Medicine, 363*(27), 2638–2650. https://doi.org/10.1056/NEJMra0808281

Buzsáki, G. (1996). The hippocampo-neocortical dialogue. *Cerebral Cortex (New York, N.Y.: 1991), 6*(2), 81–92.

Buzsáki, G. (1998). Memory consolidation during sleep: A neurophysiological perspective. *Journal of Sleep Research, 7*(Suppl. 1), 17–23.

Buzsáki, G. (2015). Hippocampal sharp wave-ripple: A cognitive biomarker for episodic memory and planning. *Hippocampus, 25*(10), 1073–1188. https://doi.org/10.1002/hipo.22488

Cairney, S. A., Guttesen, A. Á. V., El Marj, N., & Staresina, B. P. (2018). Memory consolidation is linked to spindle-mediated information processing during sleep. *Current Biology: CB, 28*(6), 948–954.e4. https://doi.org/10.1016/j.cub.2018.01.087

Canolty, R. T., Edwards, E., Dalal, S. S., Soltani, M., Nagarajan, S. S., Kirsch, H. E., Berger, M. S., Barbaro, N. M., & Knight, R. T. (2006). High gamma power is phase-locked to theta oscillations in human neocortex. *Science (New York, N.Y.), 313*(5793), 1626–1628. https://doi.org/10.1126/science.1128115

Canolty, R. T., & Knight, R. T. (2010). The functional role of cross-frequency coupling. *Trends in Cognitive Sciences, 14*(11), 506–515. https://doi.org/10.1016/j.tics.2010.09.001

Carlén, M. (2017). What constitutes the prefrontal cortex? *Science (New York, N.Y.)*, *358*(6362), 478–482. https://doi.org/10.1126/science.aan8868

Clemens, Z., Mölle, M., Eross, L., Barsi, P., Halász, P., & Born, J. (2007). Temporal coupling of parahippocampal ripples, sleep spindles and slow oscillations in humans. *Brain: A Journal of Neurology*, *130*(11), 2868–2878. https://doi.org/10.1093/brain/awm146

Colgin, L. L. (2013). Mechanisms and functions of theta rhythms. *Annual Review of Neuroscience*, *36*, 295–312. https://doi.org/10.1146/annurev-neuro-062012-170330

Corkin, S. (2002). What's new with the amnesic patient H.M.? *Nature Reviews. Neuroscience*, *3*(2), 153. https://doi.org/10.1038/nrn726

De Gennaro, L., & Ferrara, M. (2003). Sleep spindles: An overview. *Sleep Medicine Reviews*, *7*(5), 423–440.

Diekelmann, S., & Born, J. (2010). The memory function of sleep. *Nature Reviews. Neuroscience*, *11*(2), 114–126. https://doi.org/10.1038/nrn2762

Dudai, Y. (2004). The neurobiology of consolidations, or, how stable is the engram? *Annual Review of Psychology*, *55*, 51–86. https://doi.org/10.1146/annurev.psych.55.090902.142050

Eichenbaum, H. (2018). Barlow versus Hebb: When is it time to abandon the notion of feature detectors and adopt the cell assembly as the unit of cognition? *Neuroscience Letters*, *680*, 88–93. https://doi.org/10.1016/j.neulet.2017.04.006

Foster, D. J. (2017). Replay comes of age. *Annual Review of Neuroscience*, *40*, 581–602. https://doi.org/10.1146/annurev-neuro-072116-031538

Fried, I., Rutishauser, U., Cerf, M., & Kreiman, G. (2014). *Single neuron studies of the human brain: Probing cognition*. Cambridge, MA: The MIT Press.

Fries, P. (2015). Rhythms for cognition: Communication through coherence. *Neuron*, *88*(1), 220–235. https://doi.org/10.1016/j.neuron.2015.09.034

Fröhlich, F., & McCormick, D. A. (2010). Endogenous electric fields may guide neocortical network activity. *Neuron*, *67*(1), 129–143. https://doi.org/10.1016/j.neuron.2010.06.005

Gonzalez, C. E., Mak-McCully, R. A., Rosen, B. Q., Cash, S. S., Chauvel, P. Y., Bastuji, H., Rey, M., & Halgren, E. (2018). Theta bursts precede, and spindles follow, cortical and thalamic downstates in human NREM sleep. *The Journal of Neuroscience: The Official Journal of the Society for Neuroscience*, *38*(46), 9989–10001. https://doi.org/10.1523/JNEUROSCI.0476-18.2018

Hanslmayr, S., Axmacher, N., & Inman, C. S. (2019). Modulating human memory via entrainment of brain oscillations. *Trends in Neurosciences*, *42*(7), 485–499. https://doi.org/10.1016/j.tins.2019.04.004.

Hanslmayr, S., Staresina, B. P., & Bowman, H. (2016). Oscillations and episodic memory: Addressing the synchronization/desynchronization conundrum. *Trends in Neurosciences*, *39*(1), 16–25. https://doi.org/10.1016/j.tins.2015.11.004

Hebb, D. O. (1949). *The organization of behavior: A neuropsychological approach*. New York: John Wiley & Sons.

Helfrich, R. F., & Knight, R. T. (2016). Oscillatory dynamics of prefrontal cognitive control. *Trends in Cognitive Sciences*, *20*(12), 916–930. https://doi.org/10.1016/j.tics.2016.09.007

Helfrich, R. F., Lendner, J. D., Mander, B. A., Guillen, H., Paff, M., Mnatsakanyan, L., Vadera, S., Walker, M. P., Lin, J. J., & Knight, R. T. (2019). Bidirectional prefrontal-hippocampal dynamics organize information transfer during sleep in humans. *Nature Communications*, *10*(1), 3572. https://doi.org/10.1038/s41467-019-11444-x

Helfrich, R. F., Mander, B. A., Jagust, W. J., Knight, R. T., & Walker, M. P. (2018). Old brains come uncoupled in sleep: Slow wave-spindle synchrony, brain atrophy, and forgetting. *Neuron*, *97*(1), 221–230.e4. https://doi.org/10.1016/j.neuron.2017.11.020

Hyafil, A., Giraud, A.-L., Fontolan, L., & Gutkin, B. (2015). Neural cross-frequency coupling: Connecting architectures, mechanisms, and functions. *Trends in Neurosciences*, *38*(11), 725–740. https://doi.org/10.1016/j.tins.2015.09.001

Jenkins, J. G., & Dallenbach, K. M. (1924). Obliviscence during sleep and waking. *The American Journal of Psychology*, *35*(4), 605–612.

Johnson, E. L., & Knight, R. T. (2015). Intracranial recordings and human memory. *Current Opinion in Neurobiology*, *31*, 18–25. https://doi.org/10.1016/j.conb.2014.07.021

Khodagholy, D., Gelinas, J. N., & Buzsáki, G. (2017). Learning-enhanced coupling between ripple oscillations in association cortices and hippocampus. *Science (New York, N.Y.)*, *358*(6361), 369–372. https://doi.org/10.1126/science.aan6203

Kitamura, T., Ogawa, S. K., Roy, D. S., Okuyama, T., Morrissey, M. D., Smith, L. M., Redondo, R. L., & Tonegawa, S. (2017). Engrams and circuits crucial for systems consolidation of a memory. *Science (New York, N.Y.)*, *356*(6333), 73–78. https://doi.org/10.1126/science.aam6808

Kriegeskorte, N., Mur, M., & Bandettini, P. (2008). Representational similarity analysis – Connecting the branches of systems neuroscience. *Frontiers in Systems Neuroscience*, *2*, 4. https://doi.org/10.3389/neuro.06.004.2008

Ladenbauer, J., Ladenbauer, J., Külzow, N., de Boor, R., Avramova, E., Grittner, U., & Flöel, A. (2017). Promoting sleep oscillations and their functional coupling by transcranial stimulation enhances memory consolidation in mild cognitive impairment. *The Journal of Neuroscience: The Official Journal of the Society for Neuroscience*, *37*(30), 7111–7124. https://doi.org/10.1523/JNEUROSCI.0260-17.2017

Lafon, B., Henin, S., Huang, Y., Friedman, D., Melloni, L., Thesen, T., Doyle, W., Buzsáki, G., Devinsky, O., Parra, L. C., & Liu, A. (2017). Low frequency transcranial electrical stimulation does not entrain sleep rhythms measured by human intracranial recordings. *Nature Communications*, *8*(1), 1199. https://doi.org/10.1038/s41467-017-01045-x

Lashley, K. S. (1950). In search of the engram. In *Society for experimental biology, physiological mechanisms in animal behavior (Society's Symposium IV)*. (pp. 454–482). New York: Academic Press.

Latchoumane, C.-F. V., Ngo, H.-V. V., Born, J., & Shin, H.-S. (2017). Thalamic spindles promote memory formation during sleep through triple phase-locking of cortical, thalamic, and hippocampal rhythms. *Neuron*, *95*(2), 424–435.e6. https://doi.org/10.1016/j.neuron.2017.06.025

Laubach, M., Amarante, L. M., Swanson, K., & White, S. R. (2018). What, if anything, is rodent prefrontal cortex? *ENeuro*, *5*(5). https://doi.org/10.1523/ENEURO.0315-18.2018

Lecci, S., Fernandez, L. M. J., Weber, F. D., Cardis, R., Chatton, J.-Y., Born, J., & Lüthi, A. (2017). Coordinated infraslow neural and cardiac oscillations mark fragility and offline periods in mammalian sleep. *Science Advances*, *3*(2), e1602026. https://doi.org/10.1126/sciadv.1602026

Lustenberger, C., Boyle, M. R., Alagapan, S., Mellin, J. M., Vaughn, B. V., & Fröhlich, F. (2016). Feedback-controlled transcranial alternating current stimulation reveals a functional role of sleep spindles in motor memory consolidation. *Current Biology: CB*, *26*(16), 2127–2136. https://doi.org/10.1016/j.cub.2016.06.044

Maingret, N., Girardeau, G., Todorova, R., Goutierre, M., & Zugaro, M. (2016). Hippocampo-cortical coupling mediates memory consolidation during sleep. *Nature Neuroscience*, *19*(7), 959–964. https://doi.org/10.1038/nn.4304

Mak-McCully, R. A., Rolland, M., Sargsyan, A., Gonzalez, C., Magnin, M., Chauvel, P., Rey, M., Bastuji, H., & Halgren, E. (2017). Coordination of cortical and thalamic activity during non-REM sleep in humans. *Nature Communications*, *8*, 15499. https://doi.org/10.1038/ncomms15499

Mander, B. A., Rao, V., Lu, B., Saletin, J. M., Lindquist, J. R., Ancoli-Israel, S., Jagust, W., & Walker, M. P. (2013). Prefrontal atrophy, disrupted NREM slow waves and impaired hippocampal-dependent memory in aging. *Nature Neuroscience*, *16*(3), 357–364. https://doi.org/10.1038/nn.3324

Marshall, L., Helgadóttir, H., Mölle, M., & Born, J. (2006). Boosting slow oscillations during sleep potentiates memory. *Nature*, *444*(7119), 610–613. https://doi.org/10.1038/nature05278

Muehlroth, B. E., Sander, M. C., Fandakova, Y., Grandy, T. H., Rasch, B., Shing, Y. L., & Werkle-Bergner, M. (2019). Precise slow oscillation-spindle coupling promotes memory consolidation in younger and older adults. *Scientific Reports*, *9*(1), 1940. https://doi.org/10.1038/s41598-018-36557-z

Niethard, N., Ngo, H.-V. V., Ehrlich, I., & Born, J. (2018). Cortical circuit activity underlying sleep slow oscillations and spindles. *Proceedings of the National Academy of Sciences of the United States of America*, *115*(39), E9220–E9229. https://doi.org/10.1073/pnas.1805517115

Norman, Y., Yeagle, E. M., Khuvis, S., Harel, M., Mehta, A. D., & Malach, R. (2019). Hippocampal sharp-wave ripples linked to visual episodic recollection in humans. *Science (New York, N.Y.)*, *365*(6454). https://doi.org/10.1126/science.aax1030

Peyrache, A., Khamassi, M., Benchenane, K., Wiener, S. I., & Battaglia, F. P. (2009). Replay of rule-learning related neural patterns in the prefrontal cortex during sleep. *Nature Neuroscience*, *12*(7), 919–926. https://doi.org/10.1038/nn.2337

Quian Quiroga, R., & Panzeri, S. (2009). Extracting information from neuronal populations: Information theory and decoding approaches. *Nature Reviews. Neuroscience*, *10*(3), 173–185. https://doi.org/10.1038/nrn2578

Rasch, B., & Born, J. (2013). About sleep's role in memory. *Physiological Reviews*, *93*(2), 681–766. https://doi.org/10.1152/physrev.00032.2012

Rutishauser, U. (2019). Testing models of human declarative memory at the single-neuron level. *Trends in Cognitive Sciences*, *23*(6), 510–524. https://doi.org/10.1016/j.tics.2019.03.006

Sirota, A., & Buzsáki, G. (2005). Interaction between neocortical and hippocampal networks via slow oscillations. *Thalamus & Related Systems*, *3*(4), 245–259. https://doi.org/10.1017/S1472928807000258

Sirota, A., Csicsvari, J., Buhl, D., & Buzsáki, G. (2003). Communication between neocortex and hippocampus during sleep in rodents. *Proceedings of the National Academy of Sciences of the United States of America*, *100*(4), 2065–2069. https://doi.org/10.1073/pnas.0437938100

Squire, L. R. (2009). The legacy of patient H.M. for neuroscience. *Neuron*, *61*(1), 6–9. https://doi.org/10.1016/j.neuron.2008.12.023

Staresina, B. P., Bergmann, T. O., Bonnefond, M., van der Meij, R., Jensen, O., Deuker, L., Elger, C. E., Axmacher, N., & Fell, J. (2015). Hierarchical nesting of slow oscillations, spindles and ripples in the human hippocampus during sleep. *Nature Neuroscience*, *18*(11), 1679–1686. https://doi.org/10.1038/nn.4119

Steriade, M., & Amzica, F. (1998). Coalescence of sleep rhythms and their chronology in corticothalamic networks. *Sleep Research Online: SRO*, *1*(1), 1–10.

Steriade, M., Domich, L., Oakson, G., & Deschênes, M. (1987). The deafferented reticular thalamic nucleus generates spindle rhythmicity. *Journal of Neurophysiology*, *57*(1), 260–273.

Steriade, M., McCormick, D. A., & Sejnowski, T. J. (1993a). Thalamocortical oscillations in the sleeping and aroused brain. *Science, 262*(5134), 679–685. https://doi.org/10.1126/science.8235588

Steriade, M., Nuñez, A., & Amzica, F. (1993b). A novel slow (< 1 Hz) oscillation of neocortical neurons in vivo: Depolarizing and hyperpolarizing components. *The Journal of Neuroscience: The Official Journal of the Society for Neuroscience, 13*(8), 3252–3265.

Stokes, M. G. (2015). "Activity-silent" working memory in prefrontal cortex: A dynamic coding framework. *Trends in Cognitive Sciences, 19*(7), 394–405. https://doi.org/10.1016/j.tics.2015.05.004

Stuss, D. T., & Knight, R. T. (2013). *Principles of frontal lobe function.* Oxford: Oxford University Press.

Vaz, A. P., Inati, S. K., Brunel, N., & Zaghloul, K. A. (2019). Coupled ripple oscillations between the medial temporal lobe and neocortex retrieve human memory. *Science (New York, N.Y.), 363*(6430), 975–978. https://doi.org/10.1126/science.aau8956

Walker, M. P., & Stickgold, R. (2006). Sleep, memory, and plasticity. *Annual Review of Psychology, 57,* 139–166. https://doi.org/10.1146/annurev.psych.56.091103.070307

Watrous, A. J., Deuker, L., Fell, J., & Axmacher, N. (2015). Phase-amplitude coupling supports phase coding in human ECoG. *ELife, 4.* https://doi.org/10.7554/eLife.07886

Watson, B. O. (2018). Cognitive and physiologic impacts of the infraslow oscillation. *Frontiers in Systems Neuroscience, 12,* 44. https://doi.org/10.3389/fnsys.2018.00044

Wilckens, K. A., Ferrarelli, F., Walker, M. P., & Buysse, D. J. (2018). Slow-wave activity enhancement to improve cognition. *Trends in Neurosciences, 41*(7), 470–482. https://doi.org/10.1016/j.tins.2018.03.003

Winer, J. R., Mander, B. A., Helfrich, R. F., Maass, A., Harrison, T. M., Baker, S. L., Suzanne, L., Knight, R. T., Jagust, W. J., & Walker, M. P. (2019). Sleep as a potential biomarker of tau and β-amyloid burden in the human brain. *Journal of Neuroscience,* 0503–0519. https://doi.org/10.1523/JNEUROSCI.0503-19.2019

Zhang, H., Fell, J., & Axmacher, N. (2018). Electrophysiological mechanisms of human memory consolidation. *Nature Communications, 9*(1), 4103. https://doi.org/10.1038/s41467-018-06553-y

Interlude 6

THE IMPORTANCE OF PARENTING

Marta Kutas

Train the parent (or primary caretaker) and the child
separately as well as together
so they can both practice and learn the skills to weather chaotic
times that inherently circle poverty, lower resilience,
and void most guarantees of immunity
so they can learn the skills to better weather
family instability, unpredictability,
crowding, and environmental noise with some acquired poise
by routinizing daily activities (such as reading time, bedtime,
and other regularities), countering the inevitable negativities
stemming from adversity by understanding how to harness and
guide neuroplasticity to developmental success.

DOI: 10.4324/9780429342356-16

9

CHANGING BRAINS FOR SOCIAL JUSTICE

Eric Pakulak and Courtney Stevens

In the final years of her career, Helen Neville ended almost every talk she gave to a wide range of audiences with a quote from Bertrand Russell: "A habit of basing one's convictions upon evidence . . . would go a long way towards curing most of the ills from which the world suffers" (Russell & Edwards, 1967, pp. vi–vii). In this chapter, we illustrate how Helen took this quote to heart and gave it life via her relentless drive to address issues related to social justice via rigorous science. In particular, Helen's commitment to using critical, evidence-based thinking to address broader societal issues led to a line of research in which our group developed evidence-based approaches to improve outcomes for families from lower SES backgrounds. This work provides an example of research for the public good, and in particular the systematic process that allowed basic research to be translated to evidence-based interventions.

We situate the review of this program of research into a larger framework that interrogates the value – both real and potential – of applying cognitive neuroscience to the study of socioeconomic disparities. This program of research took as its starting point a robust literature linking socioeconomic status (SES) with a wide and disparate range of distal outcomes. These outcomes, which in many cases widen across development and extend into adulthood, include school grades, high school graduation rates, physical and mental morbidity, as well as mortality (e.g., Lipina & Posner, 2012; McEwen & Gianaros, 2010; Nusslock & Miller, 2016; Pakulak et al., 2018; Ursache & Noble, 2016). While these broad relationships have been well known for decades, models in cognitive neuroscience seek to elucidate the intermediate pathways and neurobiological mechanisms underlying these relationships. Rather than serving as an end goal of research, identifying specific pathways can then inform the design and evaluation of interventions designed to reduce SES-related disparities in outcomes.

DOI: 10.4324/9780429342356-17

Here, we focus on two pathways that have been characterized as primary mechanisms linking socioeconomic background to differences in later life outcomes. These are (1) the linguistic environment, which can impact language and literacy outcomes as well as brain function for language, and (2) chronic stress exposure, which can impact the development of attention and self-regulation skills as well as the brain network supporting these skills (e.g., Pakulak et al., 2018; Ursache & Noble, 2016). Evidence on the development and plasticity of these neural systems and related pathways, and in particular the neuroplasticity of selective attention, informed a series of studies moving from basic research on the effects of selective attention on neural processing to intervention research examining the malleability of these processes in young children from lower socioeconomic backgrounds.

In the following sections, we first review socioeconomic disparities related to these two key outcomes (language and attention/self-regulation). Second, we present an approach that moves beyond documenting differences to identifying malleable pathways linking socioeconomic background to the development of these neural systems, with an emphasis on the role of the caregiving environment. Next, we describe how this basic research informed the development of an intervention targeting these malleable pathways. The resulting two-generation intervention for families in poverty included work with both preschool children and their parents/caregivers and emphasized the role of the caregiving environment to influence both the linguistic environment as well as family stress and self-regulation in children. An initial study demonstrated the effectiveness of the program across a wide range of outcome measures, including a neural index of selective attention, as well as positive changes in parents. The final section examines how this program of research has now moved toward working at scale, including collaboration with partners across multiple fields. We end with a consideration of what questions should be prioritized as the field moves forward, as well as the professional value of interdisciplinary interactions among researchers examining these questions at different levels of analysis.

Pulling back the curtain: socioeconomic disparities in brain development

A key insight from Helen's research on neuroplasticity was that one way to "pull back the curtain" on a complex set of relationships is to examine which neurobiological systems are most sensitive to differences in experience during development. Our line of intervention research began with basic research that applied this insight to examine the systems that are sensitive to early adversity, as well as the environmental factors that influence their development. This is not meant to serve as a reductionist approach to understanding poverty. Instead, this approach can be used to identify specific pathways that could serve as individual levers within larger efforts to address poverty. By this view, such research has the potential to provide immediate and evidence-based approaches implementable at multiple levels of society, from the home environment to public policy.

Childhood socioeconomic disadvantage can have a lasting legacy, with early socioeconomic disadvantage linked to a strikingly wide range of later negative life outcomes, including academic and health outcomes (for more extensive reviews, see e.g., Hackman et al., 2010; Lipina & Posner, 2012; McEwen & Gianaros, 2010; Pakulak et al., 2018; Ursache & Noble, 2016). A number of factors that co-occur with early socioeconomic disadvantage – and that often interact with one another – are likely to contribute to these differences in life outcomes. For example, socioeconomic background is also associated with variation in school quality, neighborhood safety, nutrition, and health care access (e.g., McEwen & Gianaros, 2010; McEwen & McEwen, 2017). In this respect, multiple pathways may contribute to SES disparities in later academic, health, economic, and other life outcomes. At the same time, emerging theories point to a set of integrated biological systems that are affected by early adversity and might underlie many of the diverse outcomes associated with early socioeconomic disadvantage (e.g., Lipina & Posner, 2012; McEwen & Gianaros, 2010; Nusslock & Miller, 2016; Pakulak et al., 2018; Ursache & Noble, 2016). Here, we highlight two core systems, language and attention/self-regulation, that have been the focus of basic research in both cognitive neuroscience and studies specific to poverty and early disadvantage. Studies that have examined or reviewed multiple cognitive domains suggest that these systems show the greatest and/or most consistent relationships with SES (e.g., Hackman & Farah, 2008; Hackman et al., 2010; Noble et al., 2005; Ursache & Noble, 2016).

Differences in language and literacy skills have been hypothesized as one key cognitive disparity underlying overall SES-related achievement gaps, either as a result of limited language skills or a mismatch between the language skills of children from lower SES backgrounds and the skills required to succeed in school (e.g., Bradbury et al., 2015; Hoff, 2013). Early socioeconomic adversity has long been associated with poorer language outcomes (for more extensive reviews, see e.g., Perkins et al., 2013; Ursache & Noble, 2016). These differences emerge before the beginning of formal schooling and widen across the school years (Bradbury et al., 2015). SES has also been shown to account for variability in the structure and function of neural systems important for language in both children and adults (e.g., Krishnadas et al., 2013; Noble et al., 2012, 2015; Pakulak & Neville, 2010; Raizada et al., 2008).

Differences in aspects of attention and self-regulation have also been hypothesized to play a key role in SES-related achievement gaps (e.g., Hackman et al., 2010; Ursache & Noble, 2016). Attention and self-regulation are complex constructs that include a range of component processes. Attention includes basic arousal as well as focused selective attention, which involves both enhancing selected information (signal enhancement) and suppressing irrelevant information (distractor suppression; e.g., Stevens et al., 2009). Self-regulation is defined as primarily volitional regulation of attention, emotion, and executive function for the purposes of goal-directed actions (Blair & Raver, 2012, 2015). Executive functions subsume a diverse set of psychological processes, including inhibitory control, working memory, and cognitive flexibility (e.g., Diamond, 2006, 2013). Importantly, attention and self-regulation are foundational systems for learning across domains (Blair & Raver, 2015; Stevens & Bavelier, 2012) and also display relatively greater plasticity compared to other neural systems (Stevens & Neville, 2014).

Behavioral and neuroimaging measures of attention and self-regulation also consistently show differences as a function of socioeconomic background (Blair et al., 2011; Farah et al., 2006; Mezzacappa, 2004; Noble et al., 2005, 2007; Sarsour et al., 2011). Often these studies have examined specific subskills considered part of attention and self-regulation, such as inhibitory control, attention shifting, response inhibition, and working memory. These disparities are evident across the lifespan, emerging in infancy (Lipina et al., 2005) and also documented throughout childhood (Noble et al., 2005, 2007) and into adulthood (Evans & Schamberg, 2009). A growing body of evidence suggests that SES also accounts for differences in the structure and function of neural systems important for attention and self-regulation (Barch et al., 2016; for an extensive review, see Brito & Noble, 2014; Conejero et al., 2018; Hanson et al., 2011; Jenkins et al., 2011; Luby et al., 2013; Noble et al., 2012, 2015; Raizada et al., 2008; Sheridan et al., 2012).

Although we and others often discuss different pathways by which early experience affects language versus attention/self-regulation (Brito & Noble, 2014; Noble et al., 2012), it is important to note that there is some overlap in, and interaction between, pathways (e.g., Ursache & Noble, 2016), such that strategies that target one pathway may ultimately benefit multiple outcome domains (Stevens & Pakulak, in press). For example, shared book reading is an activity that can support language development but might also improve aspects of attention and self-regulation as it involves joint attention. Also, as discussed later, pathways targeting language and attention are particularly sensitive to the early caregiving environment, a potentially powerful buffer of the interaction between early adversity and these systems.

Just as the human brain and related systems display sensitivity to adversity that can have profound effects across the lifespan, the exquisite plasticity of the brain also confers opportunity for resilience in the face of early adversity. Indeed, a substantial proportion of children who experience early adversity avoid many of these poor outcomes. One way this resilience can come about is via experiences that buffer these vulnerable systems in the context of adverse environmental conditions. While this picture is undoubtedly complex, one aspect of the environment that is a potentially powerful buffer is the early caregiving environment.

The caregiving environment central to both pathways is in focus here. Adult caregivers play a central role in language acquisition, and evidence suggests that aspects of caregiving such as maternal sensitivity mediate relationships between SES and child language outcomes (e.g., Raviv et al., 2004). Consistent with a larger body of research with animal models, a growing body of research in humans also suggests that a relationship with a sensitive and nurturing caregiver can potentially buffer the effects of early adversity on systems supporting self-regulation (e.g., Stevens & Pakulak, in press). In particular, parental sensitivity and responsiveness are important for the development of a secure attachment relationship, which is in turn important for the development of neurobiological systems supporting regulatory function (e.g., Gunnar et al., 1996).

For example, a retrospective study found that high caregiver nurturance early in development provides a buffer against the long-term health problems associated with early adversity, such as mortality risk, cardiovascular disease, and autoimmune disease (Miller et al., 2011). Evidence also suggests that caregiving is associated with structural differences in the brain systems discussed earlier, as parental nurturance at age 4, measured by the Home Observation for Measurement of the Environment Inventory, predicts hippocampal volume in adolescents from lower SES backgrounds (Rao et al., 2010); in addition, caregiver support mediates the effects of early adversity on the structure of the hippocampus (Luby et al., 2013). However, multiple aspects of environments associated with socioeconomic adversity increase the amount of stress experienced by parents (e.g., financial hardship, housing instability, and neighborhood crime). Moreover, increased parental stress has been found to reduce the likelihood of sensitive maternal childcare and the development of secure attachments, which in turn increases the likelihood of stressful interactions with caregivers (e.g., Blair & Raver, 2012; Meaney, 2010).

Taken together, these data suggest that outcomes related to language, attention, and self-regulation show differences as a function of socioeconomic background, are sensitive to differences in caregiving, and have been hypothesized to serve as foundational skills, with the potential to influence processing across a range of domains and predictive of academic success (Blair & Raver, 2015; Stevens & Bavelier, 2012). While correlational evidence such as that described earlier should be interpreted with caution, taken together, these findings suggest that well-documented disparities in these outcomes associated with early adversity emerge early and may endure into adulthood. Given the importance of these skills for general academic achievement, this also suggests that language, attention, and self-regulation are skills that should be targeted early in development. Below, we describe work from Helen's Brain Development Lab at the University of Oregon that evolved from a focus on the plasticity of neural systems for selective attention, to intervention research examining the malleability of language and attention in children from lower socioeconomic backgrounds.

From basic to translational research: a rewarding prospect

As the work evolved to a more applied focus, Helen often ended her talks with the following statement: "In a society committed to equal opportunity for all many may find the prospect of reducing the economic gap rewarding."

An education par excellence

One of Helen's favorite quotations was from William James: "An education which should improve this faculty would be *the* education *par excellence*" (James, 1890, p. 424). The "faculty" referred to by William James is attention. While James went on to say "But it is easier to define this ideal than to give practical directions for bringing it about" (James, 1890, p. 424), this is the very challenge Helen's lab took on in the later years of her life. Our transition to translational research began with a line of basic research on the development and plasticity of selective attention (for reviews, see Isbell et al., 2017; Stevens & Neville, 2014). The term "selective attention" refers to the ability to select and preferentially process specific information in the environment while simultaneously suppressing the processing of irrelevant, competing distractors, and thus requires many subskills that are part of attention and self-regulation (e.g., inhibitory control, distractor suppression, signal enhancement). We have emphasized selective attention because it is a skill that has the potential to impact functioning across a range of domains. In this respect, we consider selective attention to act as a "force multiplier" that can have broad-reaching impacts on different aspects of cognition. In support of this, performance on selective attention tasks has been linked both to academic skills in general (e.g., Stevens & Bavelier, 2012) and to specific cognitive abilities, including speech segmentation, working memory, and non-verbal intelligence (e.g., Astheimer & Sanders, 2012; Giuliano et al., 2014; Isbell et al., 2016).

The basic neural mechanisms supporting selective attention seem to be in place early in development. Using event-related brain potentials (ERPs), we have found that in both adults and children as young as three, the amplitude of neural responses to auditory stimuli is enhanced with selective attention within 100 ms of stimulus presentation (Coch et al., 2005; Sanders et al., 2006). However, we later observed that some groups of children did not show the same effect of selective attention on neural processing, such as children with specific language impairments or with low pre-literacy skills (Stevens et al., 2006, 2013). Yet our most striking findings were differences in the effects of selective attention on neural processing as a function of children's socioeconomic backgrounds.

In both preschool (Giuliano et al., 2018; Hampton Wray et al., 2017) and early childhood (Stevens et al., 2009) samples, we found that lower SES was associated with reduced or absent effects of selective attention on early neural processing. Independently, a separate research group demonstrated similar SES disparities in an adolescent sample (D'Angiulli et al., 2008). Moreover, these ERP studies permitted a degree of specificity about mechanisms: in all cases, socioeconomic differences in selective attention were limited specifically to reduced suppression of distracting information in the environment, as opposed to differences in enhancing task-relevant information (D'Angiulli et al., 2008; Giuliano et al., 2018; Hampton Wray et al., 2017; Stevens et al., 2009). While reduced distractor suppression may be advantageous in environments that may be less predictable and present more potential threats, it may not be advantageous in environments such as school classrooms, where the ability to suppress surrounding noise and maintain attention on the teacher for increasingly longer periods of time is important.

At the same time, we had evidence suggesting that these neural mechanisms were modifiable, with enhancements of the effects of selective attention on neural processing possible in some circumstances. For example, individuals born congenitally deaf or blind exhibited larger effects of selective attention in the remaining modalities (Neville & Lawson, 1987; Röder et al., 1999). Likewise, when children received intensive language or literacy instruction that effectively improved the targeted skill, we also observed increases in the effects of selective attention on neural processing (Stevens et al., 2008, 2013). This raised the hypothesis that we might be able to develop interventions that targeted selective attention directly, rather than tangentially, and in ways that harnessed some of the pathways described earlier linking early adversity to language and attention/regulation outcomes. However, this work was undertaken to recognize that the goal was not necessarily to "remediate a deficient system" but rather to support children in deploying a skill that may be particularly important in classroom environments. Indeed, reduced suppression of environmental information might be adaptive in more chaotic environments associated with early adversity, but maladaptive in a classroom environment (Blair & Raver, 2012, 2015). As discussed later in the chapter, these observations led to hypotheses concerning the training of these foundational systems.

When the rubber meets the road

One of Helen's central tenets was to address questions using evidence and data. Rather than wondering about something and talking endlessly, Helen believed in taking the risk to do the experiment and "see what happens when the rubber meets the road." It was this spirit that pushed the lab to consider how our basic research on the plasticity of selective attention could be translated into interventions to improve attention and self-regulation in preschool children. Taking an experimental approach to these questions into the "real world" presented numerous challenges, and some of Helen's colleagues questioned her sanity for leaving the comfortable confines of a well-controlled lab setting. But Helen was determined to move beyond correlation to address important scientific questions and to develop programs that might help the most vulnerable in society. Helen also recognized the need for an interdisciplinary and collaborative approach and brought together a team that included educators and intervention scientists while initiating a collaboration with Head Start of Lane County (HSOLC).[1] Head Start is a federally funded program serving families with preschool-aged children living at or below the poverty line. Fortunately, HSOLC embraced the partnership, and this led to over 15 years of collaborative work that is still ongoing (O'Neill et al., 2018).

When we first began the partnership, we were motivated by lab discussions in which we had hypothesized that changes in attention and self-regulation could act as force multipliers, supporting gains across multiple domains. Given the evidence on the neuroplasticity of these systems early in development (e.g., Stevens et al., 2008, 2009, 2013), we decided to focus on preschool-aged children. We were also motivated by research on the importance of caregiving and the home environment, which suggested that working directly with parents would be a powerful way to target multiple key pathways related to the linguistic environment as well as family stress. This focus on caregiving was also informed by the seminal work of Phil Fisher and colleagues at the Oregon Social Learning Center (OSLC), who showed that a parenting intervention targeting family stress regulation in foster parents normalized diurnal cortisol patterns in foster children (Fisher et al., 2000, 2007; Fisher & Stoolmiller, 2008).

A series of pilot studies working with HSOLC resulted in the development of a two-generation intervention that involved simultaneously working with parents and children; detailed descriptions of the intervention can be found elsewhere (Neville et al., 2013). Briefly, children received small-group training in activities aimed at improving attention, self-regulation, and stress regulation. The parent component, adapted in part from OSLC work (Fanning, 2007; Reid et al., 1999), consisted of procedures encouraging family protective factors and strategies targeting family stress regulation, parental language use and interactive responsiveness, and facilitation of child attention, including explicit links to the child component. We were also able to directly compare two different delivery models of this two-generation approach, which differed in the relative balance of child- versus parent-focused training. While both models included both a parent and child component, we compared a model that included relatively more time working with parents (and thus likely influencing the caregiving environment) versus a model that involved more time with child-directed activities but less time working directly with parents. Given the role of the home environment on the pathways being targeted, we predicted that the more parent-focused model would yield the greatest gains.

The initial evaluation study included an eight-week delivery of these two models as well as a passive control group that received Head Start with no additional programming (Neville et al., 2013). We targeted typically developing, monolingual children ($N = 141$) and their parents/guardians/caregivers (hereafter "parents"), all of whom were participants in HSOLC. Families were randomly assigned to one of three groups: the more parent-focused model, the more child-focused model, or Head Start alone. Perhaps most strikingly, and consistent with our hypotheses, children randomly assigned to the more parent-focused model showed improvements in brain function for selective attention at 100 ms. After the eight-week program, their brain function for selective attention looked more like that of their higher SES peers, demonstrating that these neural systems were malleable and could be improved with training. This also provided the first evidence from a randomized controlled study to document positive changes in brain function in children from backgrounds of poverty.

In addition to greater changes in brain systems for attention, children in the more parent-focused intervention showed more positive changes than those in other groups in a range of other outcomes including standardized measures of language and non-verbal IQ, as well as parent ratings of children's social skills and problem behaviors. We also found changes in the caregiving environment related to both language and stress that were greater among parents assigned to the more parent-focused intervention. For example, parents showed improvements in verbal turn-taking with their children, an aspect of language behavior that predicts good language development. Parents also reported reductions in parenting stress, suggesting that two-generation interventions have the potential to change the caregiving environment in ways that may benefit children and also parents themselves. Thus, in this seminal study, we were able to document changes both in key pathways by which early adversity is hypothesized to affect the development of systems important for language and attention/self-regulation, as well as behavioral and neurophysiological improvements in these systems in preschool-aged children.

This initial intervention study also illustrated some of the ways neuroscience could be applied to the educational field. Research from cognitive neuroscience informed the focus on multiple aspects of language, parenting stress, and brain functions for selective attention, as neuroscience research had shown that these neurobiological systems are particularly sensitive to environmental differences associated with early adversity and mediated by key pathways associated with caregiving. Evidence from cognitive neuroscience also informed specific training approaches. For example, given the research described earlier on the mechanisms of selective attention, we collaborated with an experienced educator to develop engaging activities that would simultaneously train signal enhancement and distractor suppression. Finally, our direct assessment of brain function for selective attention allowed us to show that this neural system was both malleable with a family-based intervention and that this malleability was specific to the intervention model that involved more emphasis on caregiving broadly, and on key pathways associated with language and stress specifically.

Candles in the darkness

When beginning this research, we recognized that inequality was a complex "wicked problem," and also that it would be meaningful to conduct research that begins to address the problem at some level. The initial intervention research described earlier, although promising, was the first step. Once we had proof of concept, an important next candle to light involved steps to replicate the results while developing a model of the intervention that could be more widely implemented with broader populations and integrated into preschool contexts. This line of research involved expanding the work to consider different types of diversity represented in Head Start classrooms but not in the original study, such as students whose first language is not English and caregivers who do not speak English. In addition, this involved exploring what steps would be needed to generate a program that could be integrated into existing Head Start services and thus delivered by educators already in place at Head Start sites, rather than requiring trained research staff to deliver.

These next steps required interdisciplinary collaboration in order to conduct a rigorous adaptation of the intervention for different cultural contexts. We also recognized that, in order to develop a delivery model of the intervention that could be integrated into Head Start services, it was necessary to greatly increase the degree of collaboration with our Head Start partners.

Our first collaboration was with experts in the cultural adaptation of interventions (for more detail, see Pakulak et al., 2017). This work focused on adapting the program for Spanish-speaking Latino families, a large segment of the population in our region that had been excluded in our original study. To do this, we employed the Cultural Adaptation Process (CAP) model (Domenech Rodriguez & Wieling, 2004). The three-phase CAP model emphasizes working closely with community stakeholders in a systematic, iterative process. This work involved not only the translation of materials but also an extensive process of obtaining feedback in focus-group format from local Latino community members, including Head Start parents. This feedback resulted in adaptations to the curriculum that maintained fidelity to the core instructional components while addressing the concerns of focus-group members. For example, this collaborative process revealed concerns about our strategies in the initial version of the intervention for helping parents to use specific praise when working with their children. Most of the original examples focused on praising children for aspects of independence; however, work with the target community suggested that examples of praising actions more relevant to Latino values would be more culturally appropriate. Thus, we added examples that involved praising actions that show respect (i.e., *respeto*), promote family ties, and demonstrate loyalty to the family (i.e., *familismo*).

Our second collaboration provides an illustrative example of the value of a truly bidirectional collaboration between educators and researchers (for more details, see O'Neil et al., 2018). In order to develop a scalable delivery model of the intervention, it was necessary to greatly increase the degree of collaboration between HSOLC and our lab. While the working relationship between organizations provided a strong foundation for the project, to accomplish our goal of developing a delivery model that could be integrated into the existing HSOLC infrastructure we formed inter-organization working groups. By taking this approach, members of both organizations contributed meaningfully to the final product.

The resulting model, called *Creating Connections: Strong Families, Strong Brains* (CC), is designed to be deliverable by Head Start specialists independent of researcher support and replicable by other preschool programs. In contrast to our previous model, CC features full-year classroom implementation of the child component ("Brain Train;" BT), with the eight-week parent component delivered mid-year in small-group format to maintain the emphasis on discussion and role-playing. The development of this model also presented an opportunity to expand the emphasis on two of our targeted mechanisms, stress and self-regulation. To accomplish this, we adapted strategies from the parent component for use by teachers as classroom behavioral management strategies. These behavioral management strategies include those for using enhanced language with children, such as specific praise and noticing, clear statements, and specific metacognitive ("thinking") vocabulary, as well as strategies to improve consistency and predictability through schedules, routines, and calendars. We reasoned that increasing the degree of integration between child and parent components would then, as parents received the parent component in the middle of the school year, increase the level of consistency and predictability between the classroom and home environment. This would potentially reduce stress for children, given the predicted increase in consistency experienced by children between the two environments in which they spend most of their time.

Another important aspect of Helen's legacy with regard to social justice was her emphasis on the importance of educating non-scientists about demanding and critically evaluating evidence, as well as about the great potential of neuroplasticity. Our lab maintained a strong community outreach program, and thanks to Helen's vision countless thousands of children, parents, teachers, and community members have learned from interactive presentations featuring a bucket of brain specimens. These presentations took place in classrooms, visits to our lab, or at a wide range of community events and were often led by Helen herself, despite the rigors of her schedule; this commitment underscored her belief that increasing scientific literacy at all levels of society has the potential to address issues of social justice. In addition, and perhaps most revealing about Helen, she took great joy in these events and often related that teaching young children about the wonders of the brain was perhaps one of her favorite things to do.

Two specific examples illustrate ways in which Helen's community outreach legacy will endure. When colleagues in our university's Department of Economics started an unfunded program to encourage local at-risk students to pursue higher education, Helen contributed her time and her own money to maintain and expand the program. This program, the Summer Academy to Inspire Learning (http://sail.uoregon.edu/), has become a funded program involving numerous departments and serving thousands of local students, and the Psychology/ Neuroscience camp Helen founded remains an integral part of the academy.

Perhaps the most enduring example of Helen's passion for community outreach is a free video program about neuroplasticity produced by the lab. Despite numerous offers to write a book, Helen insisted that we instead create a user-friendly resource for parents, educators, and policymakers who care about children. She secured funding to partner with professional filmmakers to produce the film, *Changing Brains: Effects of experience on human brain development*, as well as a Spanish translation. The entire film was freely available, at Helen's insistence (its chapters can still be watched at http://tinyurl.com/youtube-braindvd), and has been integrated into teacher training programs, parenting programs, and used and enjoyed, nationally and internationally, by thousands.

Cause for optimism

It is easy to be disheartened by wicked problems, and in response Helen would often quote Antonio Gramsci, saying "I'm a pessimist because of intelligence, but an optimist because of will" (Gramsci, 1947/1994, p. 299). This quotation captures the spirit of her passion for using rigorous science to address questions of social justice. She emphasized the need for strong critical thinking and a skeptical evaluation of evidence, but at the same time, she embraced the optimism that such an approach can truly make a difference in the world. We close with a consideration of how we feel that a careful use of evidence from cognitive neuroscience in interdisciplinary collaborations has the potential to help Helen's legacy endure and for her optimism to increasingly become reality.

In line with Helen's vision, we believe that cognitive neuroscience represents a valuable and unique tool for understanding the complex interaction between socioeconomic experience, neuroplasticity, and outcomes across development, particularly in the context of interdisciplinary and cross-cultural studies. Research that embraces this vision has the potential to address issues related to social justice via rigorous science. The careful use of evidence from cognitive neuroscience can provide valuable insight into the mechanisms whereby inequality becomes biologically embedded and associated with a wide and disparate range of life outcomes (e.g., McEwen & Gianaros, 2010; Nusslock & Miller, 2016; Pakulak et al., 2018; Ursache & Noble, 2016), with the potential to guide the development and evaluation of programs designed to improve outcomes for those in poverty. The interdisciplinary line of research described in this chapter provides one example of such efforts.

In the coming decades, we believe that priority should be placed on *communication, sharing, and collaboration* between disciplines, more than on specific new research findings or directions. While different disciplines generally use different methodologies and tools to investigate research questions, there is often striking convergence in conclusions across levels and approaches. Neuroscience models that elucidate the biological embedding of social status also provide empirical data that can shift away from narratives that characterize poverty as an individual failure and move toward those that recognize the complex interactions between social structures and biological characteristics that shape outcomes early in development and across the life span (e.g., McEwen & McEwen, 2017).

More concretely, increasing communication among disciplines will need to involve greater reliance on interdisciplinary teams of researchers. When we talk only to those researchers who have a similar theoretical lens and analytic approach, our work may be well received, but it is also likely to have a more limited impact. To the extent that studies involve collaboration across disciplines (e.g., neuroscience, cognitive neuroscience, social and developmental psychology, genetics, epidemiology, prevention and intervention science, education, sociology, economics, and public policy), and integrate multiple methodologies (e.g., stress, physiology, health), there is more potential for important crosstalk. To these ends, interdisciplinary discussions and collaborations are critical to progress in the field. The real game changers in science – especially science for the public good that has the potential to address issues related to social justice – will be the recommendations that emerge from converging evidence.

The contributions from Helen's vision outlined in this chapter helped lay the foundation for the field of educational neuroscience, which continues to expand, thanks in part to this increase in interdisciplinary collaboration. While appropriate intellectual pessimism is warranted, research that embraces this vision provides ample cause for optimism that the numerous candles lighted by Helen, and by those inspired to follow her vision, will continue to illuminate the darkness.

Note

1 All royalties from the sale of this book will go to Head Start of Lane County.

References

Astheimer, L. B., & Sanders, L. D. (2012). Temporally selective attention supports speech processing in 3-to 5-year-old children. *Developmental Cognitive Neuroscience, 2*(1), 120–128.

Barch, D., Pagliaccio, D., Belden, A., Harms, M. P., Gaffrey, M., Sylvester, C. M., Tillman, R., & Luby, J. (2016). Effect of hippocampal and amygdala connectivity on the relationship between preschool poverty and school-age depression. *American Journal of Psychiatry, 173*, 625–634.

Blair, C., Granger, D. A., Willoughby, M., Mills-Koonce, R., Cox, M., Greenberg, M. T., Kivlighan, K. T., Fortunato, C. K., & the, F.L.P. Investigators (2011). Salivary cortisol mediates effects of poverty and parenting on executive functions in early childhood. *Child Development, 82*(6), 1970–1984. https://doi.org/10.1111/j.1467-8624.2011.01643.x

Blair, C., & Raver, C. C. (2012). Child development in the context of adversity: Experiential canalization of brain and behavior. *American Psychologist, 67*, 309–318.

Blair, C., & Raver, C. C. (2015). School readiness and self-regulation: A developmental psychobiological approach. *Annual Review of Psychology, 66*, 711–731.

Bradbury, B., Corak, M., Waldfogel, J., & Washbrook, E. (2015). *Too many children left behind: The US achievement gap in comparative perspective.* New York: Russell Sage Foundation.

Brito, N. H., & Noble, K. G. (2014). Socioeconomic status and structural brain development. *Frontiers in Neuroscience, 8.*

Coch, D., Sanders, L. D., & Neville, H. J. (2005). An event-related potential study of selective auditory attention in children and adults. *Journal of Cognitive Neuroscience, 17*(4), 605–622.

Conejero, Á., Guerra, S., Abundis-Guitiérrez, A., & Rueda, M. R. (2018). Frontal theta activation associated with error detection in toddlers: Influence of familial socioeconomic status. *Developmental Science, 21,* e12494.

D'Angiulli, A., Herdman, A., Stapells, D., & Hertzman, C. (2008). Children's event-related potentials of auditory selective attention vary with their socioeconomic status. *Neuropsychology, 22,* 293–300.

Diamond, A. (2006). The early development of executive functions. In E. Bialystok & F. Craik (Eds.), *Lifespan cognition: Mechanisms of change* (pp. 70–95). Oxford: Oxford University Press.

Diamond, A. (2013). Executive functions. *Annual Review of Psychology, 64,* 135–168.

Domenech Rodriguez, M. M., & Wieling, E. (2004). Developing culturally appropriate, evidence-based treatments for interventions with ethnic minority populations. In M. Rastogi & E. Wieling (Eds.), *Voices of color: First-person accounts of ethnic minority therapists* (pp. 313–331). Thousand Oaks, CA: SAGE.

Evans, G. W., & Schamberg, M. A. (2009). Childhood poverty, chronic stress, and adult working memory. *Proceedings of the National Academy of Sciences of the United States of America, 106*(16), 6545–6549.

Fanning, J. (2007). *Parent training for caregivers of typically developing, economically disadvantaged preschoolers: An initial study in enhancing language development, avoiding behavior problems, and regulating family stress.* PhD Dissertation, University of Oregon, Eugene, OR.

Farah, M. J., Shera, D. M., Savage, J. H., Betancourt, L., Giannetta, J. M., Brodsky, N. L., Malmud, E. K., & Hurt, H. (2006). Childhood poverty: Specific associations with neurocognitive development. *Brain Research, 1110,* 166–174.

Fisher, P. A., Gunnar, M. R., Chamberlain, P., & Reid, J. B. (2000). Preventive intervention for maltreated preschool children: Impact on children's behavior, neuroendocrine activity, and foster parent functioning. *Journal of the American Academy of Child & Adolescent Psychiatry, 39*(11), 1356–1364.

Fisher, P. A., & Stoolmiller, M. (2008). Intervention effects on foster parent stress: Associations with child cortisol levels. *Development and Psychopathology, 20*(3), 1003–1021.

Fisher, P. A., Stoolmiller, M., Gunnar, M. R., & Burraston, B. O. (2007). Effects of a therapeutic intervention for foster preschoolers on diurnal cortisol activity. *Psychoneuroendocrinology, 32*(8–10), 892–905.

Giuliano, R. J., Karns, C. M., Neville, H. J., & Hillyard, S. A. (2014). Early auditory evoked potential is modulated by selective attention and related to individual differences in visual working memory capacity. *Journal of Cognitive Neuroscience, 26*(12), 2682–2690.

Giuliano, R. J., Karns, C. M., Roos, L. E., Bell, T. A., Petersen, S., Skowron, E. A., Neville, H. J., & Pakulak, E. (2018). Effects of early adversity on neural mechanisms of distractor suppression are mediated by sympathetic nervous system activity in preschool-aged children. *Developmental Psychology, 54*(9), 1674.

Gramsci, A. (1994). *Letters from prison* (vol. 1, Ed. F. Rosengarten, Trans. R. Rosenthal). New York: Columbia University Press. (Original work published 1947)

Gunnar, M. R., Brodersen, L., Nachmias, M., Buss, K., & Rigatuso, J. (1996). Stress reactivity and attachment security. *Developmental Psychobiology, 29*(3), 191–204.

Hackman, D., & Farah, M. (2008). Socioeconomic status and the developing brain. *Trends in Cognitive Science, 13,* 65–73.

Hackman, D., Farah, M., & Meaney, M. (2010). Socioeconomic status and the brain: Mechanistic insights from human and animal research. *Nature Reviews Neuroscience, 11,* 651–659.

Hampton Wray, A., Stevens, C., Pakulak, E., Isbell, E., Bell, T., & Neville, H. (2017). Development of selective attention in preschool-age children from lower socioeconomic status background. *Developmental Cognitive Neuroscience, 26,* 101–111.

Hanson, J. L., Chandra, A., Wolfe, B. L., & Pollak, S. D. (2011). Association between income and the hippocampus. *PLoS One, 6*(5), e18712.

Hoff, E. (2013). Interpreting the early language trajectories of children from low-SES and language minority homes: Implications for closing achievement gaps. *Developmental Psychology, 49*(1), 4.

Isbell, E., Stevens, C., Pakulak, E., Wray, A. H., Bell, T. A., & Neville, H. J. (2017). Neuroplasticity of selective attention: Research foundations and preliminary evidence for a gene by intervention interaction. *Proceedings of the National Academy of Sciences, 114*, 9247–9254.

Isbell, E., Wray, A. H., & Neville, H. J. (2016). Individual differences in neural mechanisms of selective auditory attention in preschoolers from lower socioeconomic status backgrounds: An event-related potentials study. *Developmental Science, 19*(6), 865–880.

James, W. (1890). *The principles of psychology* (vol. 1). New York: Henry Holt & Co.

Jenkins, S. R., Belanger, A., Connally, M. L., Boals, A., & Durón, K. M. (2011). First-generation undergraduate students' social support, depression, and life satisfaction. *Journal of College Counseling, 16*, 129–142. https://doi.org/10.1002/j.2161-1882.2013.00032.x

Krishnadas, R., McLean, J., Batty, G. D., Burns, H., Deans, K. A., Ford, I., McConnachie, A., McLean, J. S., Millar, K., Sattar, N., & Shiels, P. G. (2013). Socioeconomic deprivation and cortical morphology: Psychological, social, and biological determinants of ill health study. *Psychosomatic Medicine, 75*(7), 616–623.

Lipina, S., Martelli, M., Vuelta, B., & Colombo, J. (2005). Performance on the a-not-b task of Argentinian infants from unsatisfied and unsatisfied basic needs homes. *Interamerican Journal of Psychology, 39*, 49–60.

Lipina, S. J., & Posner, M. I. (2012). The impact of poverty on the development of brain networks. *Frontiers in Human Neuroscience, 6*, 238.

Luby, J., Belden, A., Botteron, K., Marrus, N., Harms, M. P., Babb, C., Nishino, T., & Barch, D. (2013). The effects of poverty on childhood brain development: The mediating effect of caregiving and stressful life events. *JAMA Pediatrics, 167*(12), 1135–1142.

McEwen, B. S., & Gianaros, P. J. (2010). Central role of the brain in stress and adaptation: Links to socioeconomic status, health, and disease. *Annals of the New York Academy of Sciences, 1186*(1), 190–222. https://doi.org/10.1111/j.1749-6632.2009.05331.x

McEwen, C., & McEwen, B. (2017). Social structure, adversity, toxic stress, and intergenerational poverty: An early childhood model. *Annual Review of Sociology, 43*, 445–472.

Meaney, M. (2010). Epigenetics and the biological definition of gene x environment interactions. *Child Development, 81*, 41–79.

Mezzacappa, E. (2004). Alerting, orienting, and executive attention: Developmental properties and sociodemographic correlates in epidemiological sample of young, urban children. *Child Development, 75*(5), 1373–1386.

Miller, G., Chen, E., & Parker, K. (2011). Psychological stress in childhood and susceptibility to the chronic diseases of aging: Moving toward a model of behavioral and biological mechanisms. *Psychological Bulletin, 137*, 959–997.

Neville, H., & Lawson, D. (1987). Attention to central and peripheral visual space in a movement detection task: An event-related potential and behavioral study. III. Separate effects of auditory deprivation and acquisition of a visual language. *Brain Research, 405*(2), 284–294.

Neville, H., Stevens, C., Pakulak, E., Bell, T. A., Fanning, J., Klein, S., & Isbell, E. (2013). Family-based training program improves brain function, cognition, and behavior in lower socioeconomic status preschoolers. *Proceedings of the National Academy of Sciences, 110*(29), 12138–12143.

Noble, K. G., Houston, S. M., Brito, N. H., Bartsch, H., Kan, E., Kuperman, J. M., Akshoomoff, N., Amaral, D. G., Bloss, C. S., Libiger, O., & Schork, N. J. (2015). Family income, parental education and brain structure in children and adolescents. *Nature Neuroscience*, *18*(5), 773–778.

Noble, K. G., Houston, S. M., Kan, E., & Sowell, E. R. (2012). Neural correlates of socioeconomic status in the developing human brain. *Developmental Science*, *15*(4), 516–527.

Noble, K. G., McCandliss, B., & Farah, M. (2007). Socioeconomic gradients predict individual differences in neurocognitive abilities. *Developmental Science*, *10*, 464–480.

Noble, K. G., Norman, M. F., & Farah, M. J. (2005). Neurocognitive correlates of socioeconomic status in kindergarten children. *Developmental Science*, *8*(1), 74–87.

Nusslock, R., & Miller, G. E. (2016). Early-life adversity and physical and emotional health across the lifespan: A neuroimmune network hypothesis. *Biological Psychiatry*, *80*(1), 23–32.

O'Neil, L. V., Pakulak, E., Stevens, C., Bell, T. A., Fanning, J. L., Gaston, M., Gomsrud, M., Hampton Wray, A., Holmes, K., Klein, S., Longoria, Z., Reynolds, M., Snell, K., Soto, A., & Neville, H. J. (2018). Creating connections between researchers and educators. *Journal of Cognition and Development*, 1–24.

Pakulak, E., Hampton Wray, A., Longoria, Z., Garcia Isaza, A., Stevens, C., Bell, T., Burlingame, S., Klein, S., Berlinski, S., Attanasio, O., & Neville, H. J. (2017). Cultural adaptation of a neurobiologically informed intervention in local and international contexts. *New Directions for Child and Adolescent Development*, *2017*(158), 81–92.

Pakulak, E., & Neville, H. (2010). Proficiency differences in syntactic processing of monolingual native speakers indexed by event-related potentials. *Journal of Cognitive Neuroscience*, *22*(12), 2728–2744.

Pakulak, E., Stevens, C., & Neville, H. (2018). Neuro-, cardio-, and immunoplasticity: Effects of early adversity. *Annual Review of Psychology*, *69*.

Perkins, S. C., Finegood, E. D., & Swain, J. E. (2013). Poverty and language development: Roles of parenting and stress. *Innovations in Clinical Neuroscience*, *10*(4), 10–19.

Raizada, R. D. S., Richards, T. L., Meltzoff, A., & Kuhl, P. K. (2008). Socioeconomic status predicts hemispheric specialisation of the left inferior frontal gyrus in young children. *NeuroImage*, *40*, 1392–1401.

Rao, H., Betancourt, L., Giannetta, J., N, B., Korczykowski, M., Avants, B., Gee, J. C., Wang, J., Hurt, H., Detre, J. A., & Farah, M. (2010). Early prenatal care is important for hippocampal maturation: Evidence from brain morphology in humans. *NeuroImage*, *49*, 1144–1150.

Raviv, T., Kessenich, M., & Morrison, F. J. (2004). A mediational model of the association between socioeconomic status and three-year-old language abilities: The role of parenting factors. *Early Childhood Research Quarterly*, *19*, 528–547.

Reid, J. B., Eddy, J. M., Fetrow, R. A., & Stoolmiller, M. (1999). Description and immediate impacts of a preventive intervention for conduct problems. *American Journal of Community Psychology*, *27*(4), 483–517.

Röder, B., Teder-Sälejärvi, W., Sterr, A., Rösler, F., Hillyard, S. A., & Neville, H. J. (1999). Improved auditory spatial tuning in blind humans. *Nature*, *400*(6740), 162–166.

Russell, B., & Edwards, P. (1967). *Why I am not a Christian: And other essays on religion and related subjects*. New York: Simon & Schuster.

Sanders, L., Stevens, C., Coch, D., & Neville, H. J. (2006). Selective auditory attention in 3- to 5-year-old children: An event-related potential study. *Neuropsychologia*, *44*, 2126–2138.

Sarsour, K., Sheridan, M., Jutte, D., Nuru-Jeter, A., Hinshaw, S., & Boyce, W. (2011). Family socioeconomic status and child executive functions: The roles of language, home environment, and single parenthood. *Journal of the International Neuropsychological Society, 17*, 120–132.

Sheridan, M., Sarsour, K., Jutte, D., D'Esposito, M., & Boyce, W. (2012). The impact of social disparity on prefrontal function in childhood. *PLoS One, 7*, e35744.

Stevens, C., & Bavelier, D. (2012). The role of selective attention on academic foundations: A cognitive neuroscience perspective. *Developmental Cognitive Neuroscience, 2*(Suppl. 1), S30–S48.

Stevens, C., Fanning, J., Coch, D., Sanders, L., & Neville, H. (2008). Neural mechanisms of selective auditory attention are enhanced by computerized training: Electrophysiological evidence from language-impaired and typically developing children. *Brain Research, 1205*, 55–69.

Stevens, C., Harn, B., Chard, D. J., Currin, J., Parisi, D., & Neville, H. (2013). Examining the role of attention and instruction in at-risk kindergarteners: Electrophysiological measures of selective auditory attention before and after an early literacy intervention. *Journal of Learning Disabilities, 46*(1), 73–86.

Stevens, C., Lauinger, B., & Neville, H. (2009). Differences in the neural mechanisms of selective attention in children from different socioeconomic backgrounds: An event-related brain potential study. *Developmental Science, 12*(4), 634–646.

Stevens, C., & Neville, H. (2014). Specificity of experiential effects in neurocognitive development. In M. Gazzaniga (Ed.), *The cognitive neurosciences* (pp. 129–142). Cambridge, MA: The MIT Press.

Stevens, C., & Pakulak, E. (in press). The effects of socioeconomic adversity on the developing brain. In K. Cohen-Kadosh (Ed.), *The Oxford handbook of developmental cognitive neuroscience*. Oxford: Oxford University Press.

Stevens, C., Sanders, L., & Neville, H. (2006). Neurophysiological evidence for selective auditory attention deficits in children with specific language impairment. *Brain Research, 1111*, 143–152.

Ursache, A., & Noble, K. G. (2016). Neurocognitive development in socioeconomic context: Multiple mechanisms and implications for measuring socioeconomic status. *Psychophysiology, 53*(1), 71–82.

Interlude 7

A DOUBLE-EDGED SWORD

Marta Kutas

If the brain is plastic, and not fixed
then neither beneficial nor detrimental consequences are nixed
i.e., the viability of change via neuroplasticity by logical necessity
affords equal opportunity for increased vulnerability.

DOI: 10.4324/9780429342356-18

10

EXPLORING COMMON MECHANISMS OF BRAIN DEVELOPMENT AND ADULT PLASTICITY IN HUMANS AND RODENTS

Michael I. Posner and Mary K. Rothbart

Introduction

The idea that brain structure changes with experience took a long time to gain acceptance in neuroscience. It is now well established, however, thanks in part to the studies of Helen Neville of deaf persons and the primate studies of Michael Merzenich et al., (1984) on how experience shapes sensory systems. The combination of human and animal work convinced cellular neuroscientists of structural change and provided evidence that sensory alterations could shape important aspects of perceived experience in humans. In this essay, reviewing recent work, we explore the possibility of improving the function of brain networks underlying attention and their connections to memory. This chapter reviews studies showing that stimulation of the adult brain can change connectivity, perhaps using similar mechanisms to those found during early human development. In this work, we complement efforts made by Neville and her associates to integrate adult studies of attention (Neville, Schmidt & Kutas, 1983) with the development of attention in infants and children.

As humans, we have a remarkable ability to remember past events, a skill that, although sometimes diminished, continues for most of us until we die. It is obvious that new memories must be stored in the brain, but do they change the structure of the brain sufficiently to argue that the brain has been fundamentally altered? William James (1890) proposed that the brain remains open to change throughout life, and his idea was consonant with the strong emphasis on learning in psychology. Evidence that visual input was needed for the binocular cells of the kitten visual cortex to function introduced an emphasis on critical periods during development for experience to influence the brain (Hubel & Wiesel, 1964, 1970). Later, work by Michael Merzenich in primates showed that the size

DOI: 10.4324/9780429342356-19

of the primary somatosensory cortex could be altered even in adulthood. One method involved removing a digit (Merzenich et al., 1984); another method was an extensive practice in discriminating between tactile stimuli presented to that digit (Recanzone et al., 1992).

Human brain plasticity

Helen Neville began her investigation of plasticity in the human brain in the early 1980s. Her work showed that the processing of visual stimuli in the periphery, but not in the fovea, was enhanced in deaf people in comparison with typically hearing individuals (Neville et al., 1983). These and other results suggested that, in deaf people, the sensory systems of the brain were organized differently. Neville also tied changes in the dorsal parts of the visual system to development by finding that the brain that had been altered by auditory deprivation due to deafness was more vulnerable to disorders during development (Stevens & Neville, 2006). Moreover, Neville developed a theory (Bavelier & Neville, 2002) concerning which parts of sensory systems were most susceptible to changes and what function the change might serve.

In our view, there are three lessons to be learned from the history of plasticity research. First, evidence should apply both to humans and non-human animals; therefore, an appropriate animal model is needed to allow methods to illuminate the basic cellular and molecular mechanisms involved. Second, it is important to examine parallels between plasticity in adults and developmental processes in infants and children. A third lesson is that findings should have potential translational significance for those with cognitive/neurological deficits. In our work discussed in this chapter, we have attempted to apply all of these lessons.

Enhancing attention networks

Imaging results have provided support for the general idea of brain networks involving a number of areas widely distributed over the brain. Even very simple tasks like shifting attention between two locations or obtaining a single-word association have been shown to involve networks of cortical and subcortical brain areas (Posner & Raichle, 1994). The distance between areas of activity within these networks indicates the importance of accurate timing in orchestrating the action of these networks (Fields, 2015).

Anterior cingulate

The executive attention network provides control over voluntary thoughts and behaviors, allowing inhibition of competing actions. This network involves the anterior cingulate cortex (ACC). We have observed that as little as 5 days of meditation training enhanced the function of the executive network, as reflected by improved attention and control of stress (Tang et al., 2007). In addition, after one month of training, the white matter surrounding this network showed increased functional anisotropy (FA) in a study using diffusion tensor imaging (DTI) (Tang et al., 2010).

White matter

At the time, it was surprising that white matter should change in adults following meditation training. However, in the last few years many adult human and animal studies have shown changes in white matter with training (e.g., McKenzie et al., 2014; Wang & Young, 2014). We (Posner et al., 2014) hypothesized that a mechanism responsible for this increase in white matter involved frontal theta (4–8 Hz), which increases following two weeks of meditation training (Xue et al., 2014) and might activate previously dormant oligodendrocytes responsible for myelination.

To test this idea, we used a mouse model employing optogenetic methods (Fenno et al., 2011). We rhythmically increased or decreased the activity of output cells in the ACC using light pulses delivered at 1, 8, or 40 Hz for 20 sessions of half an hour each over a month (for a detailed description, see Weible et al., 2017). We found that low-frequency (1–8 Hz) stimulation of ACC output initiated oligodendrocyte proliferation (Piscopo et al., 2018). This effect did not occur with 40 Hz stimulation or suppression of output from the ACC at any frequency. Magnetic theta stimulation was also found to increase oligodendrocytes in the mouse brain (Cullen et al., 2019).

Because oligodendrocytes myelinate axons, we also created electron-micrographs at 16K magnification of tissue from the corpus callosum of mice that received rhythmic ACC stimulation and unstimulated controls (Piscopo et al., 2018). We compared the g-ratio (axonal diameter/axonal diameter + myelin) measured by electron microscopy from the two groups. We found that, for unstimulated control mice, the ratio was similar to those usually reported from the central nervous system of mice, but the g-ratio was significantly reduced in the stimulated mice over non-stimulated controls, suggesting an increase in myelin volume. This change may reflect improvements in connectivity between components of the distributed network.

We also found that a smaller g-ratio was correlated with reduced anxiety as measured by increased exploratory activity and time orienting to the outside environment (Weible et al., 2017). This evidence of reduced anxiety and increased orienting behavior indicated that the low-frequency stimulation in mice produced at least some of the behavioral effects found with meditation training.

Connecting attention to memory

Learning and network connectivity

Humans engage in many forms of learning. These include the learning of specific facts (explicit) and skills (implicit) as well as elaborate procedures for improving control of the body (physical training) and mind (e.g., meditation training). Research has not fully established the extent to which these different forms of learning rely on overlapping brain mechanisms.

The idea of synaptic plasticity began with the work of D.O. Hebb outlined in his 1949 book *The Organization of Behavior.* According to this idea, networks of neurons activated at a common time show an increased ability to connect functionally by changing their synaptic connections. The discovery of long-term potentiation (Bliss & Lømo, 1973) provided a neuronal mechanism for the Hebb synapse and has remained a principal model for plasticity in the human nervous system.

One of the major open questions in the field of neuroscience is how attention assists in storing and retrieving information in memory systems. It is well known that paying attention is important for storing and retrieving many forms of information (Chun & Turk-Browne, 2007). This can be shown by using a second task to divide attention during learning or retrieval of new items. There is considerable support for the role of the ACC in the retrieval of memories, summarized for a number of animals by Weible (2013). The circuitry involved in the interaction of attention and memory networks has been clarified by more recent rodent and human findings. These findings are discussed in the following paragraph and are summarized in Figure 10.1.

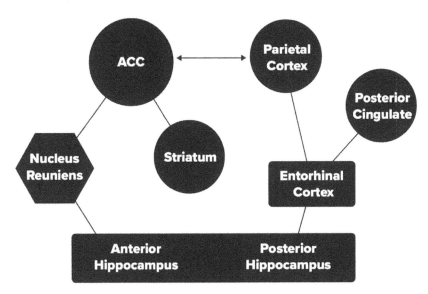

FIGURE 10.1   Interaction of brain areas involved in attention and memory networks as discussed in this chapter (adapted from Posner et al. 2022). Circles are primarily attention areas, while rectangles are primarily memory areas. A hexagon is used to show an important thalamic connection area between the two networks. The arrows indicate the direction of information flow. Pathways discussed in this chapter include two from the ACC/mid-prefrontal cortex to hippocampus, one through nucleus reuniens and the other through the entorhinal cortex.

Xu and Sudhoff (2013) used optogenetics in mice to explore the pathway leading from the mid-prefrontal cortex and ACC to the hippocampus. They found such a connection through the nucleus reuniens of the thalamus. Their work further suggested that this pathway was particularly important in the generalization of fear-related memory beyond the specific context in which fear was experienced. A similar conclusion was reached in research with humans (Bowman & Zeithamova, 2018). The authors used functional magnetic resonance imaging to explore generalization to a prototype figure after being exposed to a set of exemplars at varying remoteness from the prototype. They found that retrieval of the generalized prototype information involved the anterior hippocampus working in concert with the ACC and mid-prefrontal cortex.

A successful way of exploring the control of memory by attention is the Think, No-Think task, developed by Michael Anderson and associates (Anderson et al., 2004, 2015). In these studies, a person first learns to associate two words or pictures and is then cued when presented with the stimulus word either to think or not think about the response. Successful avoidance of conscious retrieval of the response involves down-regulation of the hippocampus via a network including the ACC (Anderson et al., 2004). Although participants are generally successful in avoiding thinking about the response, the suppressed word sometimes does break through into consciousness. In those trials, the parietal lobe shows strong activation, similar to the activation found when a person is cued to orient to a particular area in visual space to detect a target (Levy, 2008).

Thus, the anterior cingulate and posterior parietal lobe, both parts of the brain network known to be involved in different functions of attention, appear to play important roles in the memory functions of the hippocampus. The anterior cingulate/mid-prefrontal cortex is part of the executive network involved in the resolution of conflict. Lesions of the anterior cingulate produce a loss of voluntary control of behavior in disorders like akinetic mutism and the alien hand sign (Darby et al., 2018). The posterior parietal lobe is known to have a strong involvement in orienting to sensory stimuli (Corbetta & Shulman, 2002). Both areas appear to play similar roles in memory as they do in attention. In addition, memory for emotional material involves connections between the amygdala and the hippocampus (Yang & Wang, 2017) and is controlled by ventral subgenual parts of the ACC (Bush et al., 2000).

Enhancing memory

There is already some evidence that memory can be enhanced by theta stimulation. In one such study (Roberts et al., 2018), participants were presented with a set of words they classified as either animate or inanimate, and another set they classified as either manufactured or natural. After this phase, the experimental group was presented with auditory stimuli at 5.5 Hz (within the theta range) for

36 min and then given a memory test in which they were to recognize the words and the context in which the words were presented (i.e., the specific classification task). The participants exposed to theta stimulation did better than controls at remembering the classification task for the specific words but performed similarly to controls on recognition of whether the item was old or new. If this result is replicable, it shows that theta stimulation, even when not specifically targeted to any brain area, can improve the association between a stimulus and the context in which it was learned. However, the mechanism must be quite different than the one found in the mouse work (Piscopo et al., 2018; Cullen et al., 2019), since it occurs so quickly. We think that the increase in intrinsic theta found following the auditory stimulation might have helped to synchronize the information recalled in relation to the enhanced theta activity and thus improved participants' retrieval scores. Other synaptic mechanisms might be possible. It has been shown, for example, that a fast burst of stimulation can better induce a long-term improvement in activation (long-term potentiation) when it is synchronized with the theta rhythm (Larson & Mukacsy, 2015).

Another part of the brain's memory network is the entorhinal cortex (EC; see Figure 10.1). Neurons in this area become active when a monkey looks at a location (Meister, 2018) or orients to that location without any eye movement (Wilming et al., 2018). One pathway linking the ACC and hippocampus involves the EC (Anderson et al., 2015). The human and animal studies taken together suggest that suppression of memory during a task involves the thalamo-cortical pathway through nucleus reuniens, while suppression in anticipation of the task may involve an EC-to-hippocampus network. This EC-to-hippocampus connection may also underlie retrieval-induced forgetting which has been explored in both mice and humans (Bekinschtein et al., 2018). In support of the role of the EC, a rat study found that during associative learning, theta synchronization between the medial prefrontal cortex and the EC increased, while it decreased between EC and hippocampus (Takehara-Nishiuchi et al., 2012). It was later found that direct theta stimulation of the prefrontal cortex was related to improved executive control over hippocampal encoding of memory (Jerovi et al., 2018). While the function of each portion of this network is still unclear, it is clear that the general pathways shown in Figure 10.1 are important during both rodent and human learning.

Efforts are currently underway that might help determine what cellular processes are important in the connection between attention and memory. One study suggests that activation of hippocampal CA1 cells in mice is enhanced by a slow increase in excitability that could anticipate their cellular activity by hundreds of milliseconds (Bittner et al., 2017). We speculate that this slow cellular change might reflect attention to the critical information, as discussed earlier for monkeys. If this speculation is correct, it would provide a convenient target network for amplifying the contact between attention and memory.

Adult plasticity and development

We found that, after two weeks of meditation training for adults, the FA change seemed to involve primarily changes in axonal size or density (as indexed by axial diffusivity), while evidence of increased myelin (indexed by radial diffusivity) was also found after four weeks (Tang et al., 2012). This sequence appears to mimic what is found in development, where axons are laid down, followed by myelination (Stiles & Jernigan, 2010).

We are currently investigating whether we can directly induce changes in white matter in humans. This work involves constructing a head model for each participant (Luu et al., 2016) and defining a set of scalp electrodes to stimulate the anterior cingulate or any other chosen brain area. A small amount of electrical current at 6 Hz is then applied over the chosen electrodes in order to enhance theta rhythm in the ACC or other brain sites. In order to maximize the intrinsic theta rhythm, participants perform a task that activates the same brain area that is receiving stimulation. We have verified that this method can improve intrinsic theta in the anterior cingulate and motor cortex (Voelker et al., 2020). We are also conducting a long-term assessment of its effects on white matter using DTI. In one human study (Voelker et al. 2021) we were unsuccessful in modifying white matter as measured by FA.

Given the results of our meditation work, it is possible that changes in white matter induced by low-frequency electrical stimulation may be mediated through similar developmental mechanisms that produce changes in the fluency of processing from childhood to adulthood (Tucker & Luu, 2012; Voelker et al., 2017). If so, we might have a new way of determining links between physiological mechanisms such as myelination and behavioral change. The dramatic changes over the first dozen years of life are no doubt related to multiple brain changes in both grey and white matter. However, the slow development of humans makes it difficult to carry out the long-term longitudinal studies needed to associate the many potential brain mechanisms with behavioral changes in early life. DTI studies following meditation training show a sequence of adult white matter changes that occur in an order similar to what is found in development. In addition, our mouse studies (Piscopo et al., 2018; Weible et al., 2017) show that low-frequency stimulation can support similar mechanisms to those used in development and learning.

Applications

Given the successful change in white matter in mice and humans with stimulation and learning, it is now possible to test whether improving connections between memory and attention networks might enhance aspects of memory in those having difficulty because of normal aging or disorders that affect storage and retrieval of memories. Although the changes in white matter found with meditation and in our mouse studies are only about 10% of the pre-experimental values, they could be appropriate for improvement in some clinical cases and for improving normal function.

Clinical disorders

There are limited data favoring the idea that some clinical disorders might benefit from changes in connectivity. In one study, we compared smokers and non-smokers recruited to practice meditation with the goal of reducing stress. Smokers showed reduced connectivity between the ACC and striatum compared to non-smokers. The smokers did not necessarily have an intention to quit smoking. Nonetheless, two weeks of meditation training improved connectivity between the ACC and striatum and led to highly significant reductions in smoking (Tang et al., 2013). Neither of these effects occurred in a control group given relaxation training. Although further tests are needed, it was tempting to conclude that improved connectivity led to stopping or reducing smoking, even in those who had no intention to quit smoking and in some cases were not even aware that they had actually reduced their smoking.

Methylation and myelin

It is also possible that white matter improvement might influence normal learning and memory as suggested by the brief theta stimulation experiment cited earlier (Roberts et al., 2018). Gene methylation requires functioning of the folate metabolic pathway, and the gene encoding methylenetetrahydrofolate reductase (MTHFR) facilitates the production of a methyl precursor used in methylation reactions. Our research has shown improved learning by both children and adults with two copies of the 677C allele of the MTHFR gene (Voelker et al., 2016; Voelker et al 2017). The MTHFR gene has a number of influences on the brain, but one of these concerns is the speed of myelination. One speculation arising from this research is that some genes, such as MTHFR, might lead to an improved ability to alter white matter during learning. This might help us understand an important paradox in research related to individual differences in intelligence. Much research on expertise shows us the importance of domain-specific practice on the ability to carry out skills. This leads to the idea that skill depends upon experience. On the other hand, most studies of intelligence testing show correlations between the various domains tested suggesting a common factor called g (Spearman, 1904). If white matter change is an important mechanism of learning, genetic variation in the speed of such changes could underlie the correlation between domains, while the skill in any one domain would depend upon domain-specific practice (Posner & Barbey, 2020). Thus, people with faster learning skills might also have higher general intelligence.

More research is needed before we can determine whether there is a link between low-frequency stimulation in adult humans and the white matter change found during development. However, if this link is established, adult learning and stimulation studies may come to play a role in associating changes in behavior with specific brain changes found during development.

Applying Neville's lessons

This review has attempted to apply lessons learned from Helen Neville and her career in development, cognitive and clinical psychology. First, the work reviewed here connects human and mouse work, allowing for the exploration of detailed circuitry in the mouse while relating the mouse findings to important aspects of human performance. Second, the chapter examines whether learning and stimulation in adults take advantage of similar mechanisms found in child development. In the case of white matter change, cells known to be critical for myelination in children are reactivated by the use of low-frequency stimulation and perhaps also as a result of learning in adults. Finally, as Helen Neville did, the paper has examined efforts to use our current knowledge to improve the human condition.

Acknowledgments

The research related to this paper was supported in part by the Office of Naval Research through grants N00014-17-1-2824 and N00014-15-1-2148 to the University of Oregon. We appreciate the help of Aldis Weible and Pascale Voelker in reading this version.

References

Anderson, M. C., Bunce, J. G., & Barbas, H. (2015). Prefrontal – hippocampal pathways underlying inhibitory control over memory. *Neurobiology of Learning and Memory, 134*, 145–161. https://doi.org/10.1016/j.nlm.2015.11.008.

Anderson, M. C., Ochsner, K. N., Kuhl, B., Cooper, J., Robertson, E. Gabrieli, S. W., Glover, G. H., & Gabrieli, J. D. E. (2004). Neural systems underlying the suppression of unwanted memories. *Science, 303*, 232–235.

Bavelier, D., & Neville, H. J. (2002). Cross-modal plasticity: Where and how. *Nature Reviews Neuroscience, 3*, 443–452.

Bekinschtein, P., Weisstaub, N. V., Gallo, F., Renner, M., & Anderson, M. C. (2018). A retrieval-specific mechanism of adaptive forgetting in the mammalian brain. *Nature Communications, 9*, 4660. https://doi.org/10.1038/s41467-018-07128-7

Bittner, K. C., Milstein, A. D., Grienberger, C., Romani, S., & Magee, J. C. (2017). Behavioral time scale synaptic plasticity underlies CA1 place fields. *Science, 357*, 1033–1036.

Bliss, T., & Lømo, T. (1973). Long-lasting potentiation of synaptic transmission in the dentate area of the anaesthetized rabbit following stimulation of the perforant path. *Journal of Physiology, 232*, 331–356.

Bowman, C. R., & Zeithamova, D. (2018). Tracking the development of specific and generalized representations during concept learning. *Journal of Neuroscience, 38,* 2605–2614.

Chun, M. M., & Turk-Browne, N. B. (2007). Interactions between attention and memory. *Current Opinion in Neurobiology, 17,* 177–184.

Corbetta, M., & Shulman, G. L. (2002). Control of goal-directed and stimulus-driven attention in the brain. *Nature Reviews Neuroscience, 3,* 201–215.

Cullen, C. L., Sensi, M., Tang, A. D. Clutterbuck., M. T., Auderset, L., O'Rourke, M. E., Rodger, J., & Young, K. M. (2019). Low-intensity transcranial magnetic stimulation promotes the survival and maturation of newborn oligodendrocytes in the adult mouse brain. *Glia, 67,* 1462–1477. https://doi.org/10.1002/glia.23620.

Darby, R. R., Joutsa, J., Burke, M. J., & Fox, M. D. (2018). Lesion network localization of free will. *Proceedings of the National Academy of Science, 115*(42), 10792–10797.

Fenno, L., Yizhar, O., & Deisseroth, K. (2011). The development and application of optogenetics. *Annual Review of Neuroscience, 34,* 389–412. https://doi.org/10.1146/annurev-neuro-061010-113817.

Fields, R. D. (2015). A new mechanism of nervous system plasticity: Activity-dependent myelination. *Nature Reviews Neuroscience, 16*(12), 756–767. https://doi.org/10.1038/nrn4023.

Hebb, D. (1949). *Organization of Behavior.* New York: Wiley.

Hubel, D., & Wiesel, T. (1964). Effects of monocular deprivation in kittens. *Naunyn-Schmiedebergs Archiv for Experimentelle Pathologie und Pharmakologie, 248,* 492–497.

Hubel, D., & Wiesel, T. (1970). The period of susceptibility to the physiological effects of unilateral eye closure in kittens. *Journal of Physiology, 206,* 419–436.

James, W. (1890). *Principles of psychology.* New York: Holt.

Jerovi, J., Volle, J., Yu, X., Guan, L., & Takehara-Nishiuchi, K. (2018). Prefrontal theta oscillations promote selective encoding of behaviorally relevant events. *eNeuro, 5*(6). https://doi.org/10.1523/ENEURO.0407–18.2018.

Larson, J., & Mukacsy, E. (2015). Theta-burst LTP. *Brain Research, 1627,* 38–50. https://doi.org/10.1016/j.brainres.2014.10.034.

Levy, B. J. (2008). *Controlling intrusive memories: Behavioral and neural correlates of successful and failed memory suppression.* PhD Unpublished Thesis, University of Oregon, Oregon.

Luu, P., Arumugam, E. M. E., Anderson, E., Gunn, A., Rech, D., Turovets, S., & Tucker, D. M. (2016). Slow-frequency pulsed transcranial electrical stimulation for modulation of cortical plasticity based on reciprocity targeting with precision electrical head modeling. *Frontiers in Human Neuroscience, 10,* 377. https://doi.org/10.3339/fnhum.2016.00377.

McKenzie, I. A., Ohayon, D., Li, H., de Faria, J. P., Emery, B., Tohyama, K., & Richardson, W. D. (2014). Motor skill learning requires active central myelination. *Science, 346,* 318–322. https://doi.org/10.1126/science.1254960.

Meister, M. (2018). Memory system neurons represent gaze position and the visual world. *Journal of Experimental Neuroscience, 12,* 1–4. https://us.sagepub.com/en-us/nam/open-access-at-sage.

Merzenich, M. M., Nelson, R. J., Stryker, M. P., Cynader, M. S., Schoppmann, A., & Zook, J. M. (1984). Somatosensory cortical map changes following digit amputation in adult monkeys. *Journal of Comparative Neurology, 224*(4), 591–605. https://doi.org/10.1002/cne.902240408.

Neville, H. J., Schmidt, A., & Kutas, M. (1983). Altered visual evoked potentials in congenitally deaf adults. *Brain Research, 266,* 127–132.

Piscopo, D., Weible, A., Rothbart, M. K., Posner, M. I., & Niell, C. M. (2018). Changes in white matter in mice resulting from low frequency brain stimulation. *Proceedings of the National Academy of Sciences*, *115*(27), E6639–E6646. https://doi.org/10.1073/pnas.1802160115.

Posner, M. I., & Barbey, A. K. (2020). General intelligence in the age of neuroimaging. *Trends in Neuroscience and Education*, *18*, 10012.

Posner, M. I. & Raichle, M. E. (1994). *Images of Mind*. New York: Scientific American Library.

Posner, M. I., Tang, Y.-Y., & Lynch, G. (2014). Mechanisms of white matter change induced by meditation training. *Frontiers in Psychology*, *5*, 1220. https://doi.org/10.3389/fpsyg.2014.01220.

Posner, M. I., Weible, A. P., Voelker, P., Rothbart, M. K. & Niell, C. M. (2022). Decision Making as a Learned Skill in Mice and Humans *Frontiers in Neuroscience*, *16*, 834701. doi: 10.3389/fnins.2022.834701

Recanzone, G. H., Merzenich, M. M., Jenkins, W. M., Grajski, K. A., & Dinse, H. R. (1992). Topographic reorganization of the hand representation in cortical area 3b owl monkeys trained in a frequency-discrimination task. *Journal of Neurophysiology*, *67*, 1031–1056.

Roberts, B. M., Clarke, A., Addante, R. J., & Ranganath, C. (2018). Entrainment enhances theta oscillations and improves episodic memory. *Cognitive Neuroscience*, *9*(3–4), 181–193.

Spearman, C. (1904). General intelligence objectively determined and measured. *American Journal of Psychology*, *15*(2), 201–293.

Stiles, J., & Jernigan, T. L. (2010). The basics of brain development. *Neuropsychological Review*, *20*(4), 327–348.

Stevens, C., & Neville, H. (2006). Neuroplasticity as a double-edged sword: Deaf enhancements and dyslexic deficits in motion processing. *Journal of Cognitive Neuroscience*, *18*(5), 701–714.

Takehara-Nishiuchi, K., Maal-Bared, K., & Morrissey, M. D. (2012). Increased entorhinal-prefrontal theta synchronization parallels decreased entorhinal hippocampal theta synchronization during learning and consolidation of associative memory. *Frontiers in Behavioral Neuroscience*, *5*, 90. https://doi.org/10.3389/fnbeh.2011.00090.

Tang, Y.-Y., Lu, Q., Fan, M., Yang, Y., & Posner, M. I. (2012). Mechanisms of white matter changes induced by meditation. *Proceedings of the National Academy of Sciences*, *109*, 10570–10574.

Tang, Y.-Y., Lu, Q., Geng, X., Stein, E. A., Yang, Y., & Posner, M. I. (2010). Short-term meditation induces white matter changes in the anterior cingulate. *Proceedings of the National Academy of Science*, *107*, 15649–15652. https://doi.org/10.1073/pnas.1011043107.

Tang, Y.-Y., Ma, Y., Wang, J., Fan, Y., Feng, S., Lu, Q., Yu, Q., Sui, D., Rothbart, M. K., Fan, M., & Posner, M. I. (2007). Short-term meditation training improves attention and self-regulation. *Proceedings of the National Academy of Science*, *104*, 17152–17156. https://doi.org/10.1073 pnas.0707678104.

Tang, Y.-Y., Tang, R., & Posner, M. I. (2013). Brief meditation training induces smoking reduction. *Proceedings of the National Academy of Science*, *110*(34), 13971–13975.

Tucker, D. M., & Luu, P. (2012). *Cognition and neural development*. New York: Oxford University Press.

Voelker, P, Parker, A. N., Luu, P., Davey, C., Rothbart, M. K., & Posner, M. I. (2020). Increasing the amplitude of intrinsic theta in the human brain. *AIMS Neuroscience*, *7*(4), 418–437.

Voelker, P., Piscopo, D., Weible, A., Lynch G., Rothbart, M. K., Posner, M. I., & Niell, C. M. (2017). How changes in white matter might underlie improvement in reaction time with practice. *Cognitive Neuroscience, 8*(2), 112–118.

Voelker, P., Rothbart, M. K., & Posner, M. I. (2016). A polymorphism related to methylation influences attention during performance of speeded skills. *AIMS Neuroscience, 3*(1), 40–55.

Voelker, P., Sheese, B. E., Rothbart, M. K., & Posner, M. I. (2017). Methylation polymorphism influences practice effect in children during attention tasks. *Cognitive Neuroscience, 8*(2), 72–84.

Voelker, P., Weible A. P., Niell, C. M., Chavez R. S., Tovar, D. T., Rothbart, M. K. & Posner, M. I. (2021). Evaluating an Approach to Improving Attention Networks by Theta Stimulation. *Journal of Physical Medicine and Rehabilitation, 3/*1, 17–22.

Wang, S., & Young, K. M. (2014). White matter plasticity in adulthood. *Neuroscience, 276,* 148–160. https://doi.org/10.1016/j.neuroscience.2013.10.018.

Weible, A. P. (2013). Remembering to attend: The anterior cingulate cortex and remote memory. *Behavioural Brain Research, 245,* 63–75.

Weible, A. P., Piscopo, D. M., Rothbart, M. K., Posner, M. I., & Niell, C. M. (2017). Rhythmic brain stimulation reduces anxiety-relate behavior in a mouse model based on meditation training. *Proceedings of the National Academy of Science, 114*(10), 2532–2537.

Wilming, N., Konig, P., Konig, S., & Buffalo, E. A. (2018). Entorhinal cortex receptive fields are modulated by spatial attention, even without movement. *eLife, 7,* e31745. https://doi.org/10.7554/eLife.31745.

Xu, W., & Sudhof, T. C. (2013). A neural circuit for memory specificity and generalization. *Science, 339*(6125), 1290–1295.

Xue, S.-W., Tang, Y.-Y., Tang, R., & Posner, M. I. (2014). Short-term meditation induces changes in resting EEG theta networks. *Brain and Cognition, 87,* 1–6. https://doi.org/10.1016/j.bandc.2014.02.008.

Yang, Y., & Wang, J.-Z. (2017). From structure to behavior in basolateral amygdala-hippocampus circuits. *Frontiers in Neural Circuits, 11,* 86. https://doi.org/10.3389/fncir.2017.00086.

INDEX

www.ingramcontent.com/pod-product-compliance
Ingram Content Group UK Ltd.
Pitfield, Milton Keynes, MK11 3LW, UK
UKHW020006090125
453291UK00012B/87